MEASURING

MOTHER

EARTH

ALSO BY HEATHER ROBERTSON

NON-FICTION

Reservations Are for Indians
Grass Roots
Salt of the Earth
A Terrible Beauty: The Art of Canada at War
The Flying Bandit
More Than a Rose: Prime Ministers, Wives and Other Women
On the Hill: A People's Guide to Canada's Parliament
Driving Force: The McLaughlin Family and the Age of the Car
Writing from Life: A Guide for Writing True Stories
Meeting Death: In Hospice, Hospital, and at Home

FICTION

Willie: A Romance
Lily: A Rhapsody in Red
Igor: A Novel of Intrigue

ANTHOLOGIES

Her Own Woman
Canada's Newspapers: The Inside Story
From the Country

MEASURING

MOTHER

EARTH

How Joe the Kid Became Tyrrell of the North

HEATHER ROBERTSON

McCLELLAND & STEWART

Library and Archives Canada Cataloguing in Publication

Robertson, Heather, 1942-
Measuring mother earth : how Joe the Kid became Tyrrell of the North / Heather Robertson.

ISBN 978–0-7710–7539–1

1. Tyrrell, J. B. (Joseph Burr), 1858-1957.   2. Geologists – Canada – Biography.
3. Prospectors – Canada – Biography.   4. Geological Survey of Canada –
Biography.   5. Explorers – Canada – Biography.   6. Northwest, Canadian –
Discovery and exploration.   I. Title.

QE22.T8R62 2007   551.092   C2007-901413-5

We acknowledge the financial support of the Government of Canada through the Book Publishing Industry Development Program and that of the Government of Ontario through the Ontario Media Development Corporation's Ontario Book Initiative. We further acknowledge the support of the Canada Council for the Arts and the Ontario Arts Council for our publishing program.

Photos and maps courtesy of:
Archives of Ontario (AO)
Community History Project (CHP)
Glenbow Archives (GA)
Library and Archives Canada (LAC)
Thomas Fisher Rare Books Library (TFRBL)
Yukon Archives (YA)

Typeset in Janson by M&S, Toronto
Printed and bound in Canada

This book is printed on acid-free paper that is 100% recycled,
ancient-forest friendly (100% post-consumer recycled).

McClelland & Stewart Ltd.
75 Sherbourne Street
Toronto, Ontario
M5A 2P9
www.mcclelland.com

1 2 3 4 5   11 10 09 08 07

TABLE OF CONTENTS

ACKNOWLEDGEMENTS

I acknowledge with gratitude the support of the Canada Council for the Arts.

Among the many people who have assisted in my research, I wish to thank particularly the librarians of the University of Toronto's Thomas Fisher Rare Book Library, particularly manuscript librarian Jennifer Toews, and Katharine Martyn, who prepared the library's 1993 exhibition catalogue, "J.B. Tyrrell: Explorer and Adventurer." Jane Beecroft of Toronto's Community History Project was a helpful source of information about the Tyrrell family, George Luste about Barren Grounds travel, geologists Harvey Thorleifson and Andrew Breckenridge about glaciation and Lake Agassiz, and the Royal Tyrrell Museum of Palaeontology in Drumheller, Alberta, about dinosaurs. It was a pleasure to meet Joe Tyrrell's granddaughter, Katherine Tyrrell Stewart, and her family, and James Tyrrell's grandchildren, Helen Blythe and John Tyrrell, and John's wife, Ann. My thanks to my indefatigable editor, Dinah Forbes.

INTRODUCTION

Being therefore thus furnished with all necessaries, there were ready to depart upon the said voyage xv sayle of good shippes, whereof the whole number was to return agayne with their loadinge of gold ore in the end of the sommer, except those three ships, which should be left for the use of those captaynes which should inhabite there the whole yeare. And being in so good readynesse, the Generall, with all the captaynes came to the court, then lying at Greenewich, to take their leave of hir Majestie, at whose hands they all received greate encouragemente and gracious countenance. Hir Highnesse, besides other good giftes, and greater promises, bestowed on the Generall a fair cheyne of gold, and the rest of the captaines kissed hir hande, tooke their leave, and departed every man towardes their charge.

— from *The Thirde Voyage of Captaine Frobisher, Pretended for the Discoverie of Cataya, by Meta Incognita. Anno Do. 1578.*

The story of Canada's North, and Joe Tyrrell's role in it as scientist, explorer, miner, historian, and financier, begins in 1576 with a black rock that Captain Martin Frobisher brought back to England from *Meta Incognita*, a new land, now called Baffin Island, that he had discovered northwest of Newfoundland and Labrador. Frobisher, like Christopher Columbus and John Cabot before him, had been looking for Cathay, the Oriental paradise of fabulous treasure, but aside from an Inuit captive, a few strange plants, and a map of a northwestern strait (found later to be a

bay) Frobisher named for himself, the rock was his only interesting souvenir. Heavier than coal, it glistened golden when
heated. Three assayers dismissed it as common marcasite, but a
fourth claimed to have refined specks of gold from a fragment
of the rock.

This report was enough to persuade a group of merchant
adventurers, backed by Queen Elizabeth I and her courtiers, to
finance Frobisher's second voyage to *Meta Incognita* the following
summer. He was to locate the mines, and, if time permitted, reach
the Pacific Ocean. Frobisher returned to England with three more
Inuit captives, including a woman and her infant, and a shipload of
worthless rock. Undismayed, his financiers, the Cathay Company,
in 1578 appointed Frobisher admiral of a fleet of fifteen ships that
carried one hundred miners and sufficient supplies, including a
prefabricated house, to enable them to winter in the Arctic. The
planned habitation was abandoned when two ships bearing half of
the house were wrecked, and hungry sailors ate the winter's provisions, but in the autumn, the remains of the ice-battered fleet
straggled home with another two thousand tons of "fool's gold."

Denounced by his bankrupt investors as a simpleton or a
villain, Frobisher nevertheless acquired a fortune in genuine gold
bullion by plundering Spanish galleons in the West Indies, and in
1588, he was knighted by the Queen for contributing to the
defeat of the invading Spanish Armada. Like Homer's Odysseus,
Frobisher became a model for succeeding English explorers, an
audacious commander who triumphed over perils and disap-
pointments, and the earliest accounts of his three voyages to *Meta
Incognita* provided the dramatic script: storms and shipwreck,
snow, fog, icebergs, and frightening encounters with the Inuit
marked by mutual kidnappings and armed skirmishes. Five
English seamen captured by the Inuit were never seen again, and
all Frobisher's Inuit captives died soon after reaching England.
The English massacred a band of twenty Inuit, and on Frobisher's
third voyage, forty English seamen died of privation, exposure,
and drowning.

Captain George Best, who sailed with Frobisher on his last two voyages, transformed the ridiculed mining venture into a thrilling story of terror and heroism in his book, *A True Discourse of the Late Voyages of Discoverie for Finding of a Passage to Cathaya, by the North-Weast, Under the Conduct of Martin Frobisher General,* published in 1578. Best appealed to the imagination and emotions of the English people, among them a young, impressionable Will Shakespeare:

> How dangerous it is to attempt new discoveries, either for the length of the voyage or the ignorance of the language, the want of interpreters, newe and unaccustomed elements and ayres, straunge and unsavery meats, daunger of theeves and robbers, fiercenesse of wilde beasts and fishes, hugenesse of wooddes, daungerousnesse of seas, dreade of tempests, feare of hidden rockes, steepenesse of mountains, darknesse of sodaine falling fogges, continuall paines taking withoute anye reste, and infinite others.

Lest his readers become too frightened, Best continues: "How pleasant and profitable it is to attempt new discoveries, either for the sundry sights and shapes of strange beastes and fishes, the wonderful workes of nature, the different manners and fashions of diverse nations, the sundry sortes of gouernmente, the sight of straunge trees, fruite, foules, and beastes, the infinite treasure of pearle, gold and silver, the newes of new found landes, the sundry positions of the sphere, and many others."

For nearly three centuries, these themes inspired a failed, tragic quest for "a passage to Cathaya by the North-Weast." In 1611, Captain Henry Hudson and eight of his crew died in the attempt when they were set adrift by mutineers on the vast, frigid bay later named in Hudson's honour; Thomas Button, sent in search of Hudson the next year, named the Nelson River, which empties into bay on the west, for Robert Nelson, master of his ship *Resolution*, who, with many of Button's crew, died there during the winter of 1612–13; in 1620, Danish captain Jens Munck miraculously sailed home to Copenhagen from the mouth of the Churchill River with two survivors from his crew of sixty-three. Some ships and seamen vanished forever into the icy fog, and survivors returned as crazed and hideous as Coleridge's Ancient Mariner. Still, exploration and mapping of the Arctic archipelago, with its tantalizing bays and straits, encouraged an irrational, obsessive determination to discover the Northwest Passage long after it was obviously unusable, if it existed at all.

This drama was reaching a ghastly climax when Joseph Burr Tyrrell was born in the hamlet of Weston, northwest of Toronto, on November 1, 1858. Thousands of miles to the north, near King William Island, Captain Leopold M'Clintock of the Royal Navy was preparing an overland search for Sir John Franklin and the crews of his two ships, the *Erebus* and *Terror* – 134 officers and men – not seen since they had sailed from England in 1845. In the spring of 1859, M'Clintock came across three skeletons, one in a steward's uniform, and two more seated in a lifeboat mounted on a sledge. The boat contained only a little tea and chocolate, but it was loaded to the gunwales with an amazing quantity of goods, including silk handkerchiefs, toothbrushes, scented soap, and books. A cairn, surrounded by mounds of discarded clothing and ships' stores, contained a scrawled note reporting that Franklin had died in 1847, and that on April 22, 1848, the 105 men still living had abandoned the ships.

News of the fate of the Franklin expedition reached England in the midst of an uproar over the 1859 publication of Charles Darwin's *Origin of Species*, the culmination of nearly thirty years of scientific research beginning with his 1831–36 around-the-world voyage aboard the *Beagle*. Darwin put forward the theory that all living things, from algae to human beings, evolved through a process of natural selection, popularly called "survival of the fittest," that had nothing to do with God, Creation, or the Bible.

Arguments over Darwin's theory of evolution were as violent and anguished as debates over evidence that Franklin's dying sailors had practised cannibalism.

Joe Tyrrell grew up in a climate of moral unease, scientific radicalism, and social uncertainty. God was not secure in His Heaven, and for an active, inquisitive boy who loved being outdoors, the natural sciences provided a scholarly dimension to hunting trips and rambles through the woods, a way of seeing the familiar world around him in its infinite, mysterious complexity. The eminent British geologist Sir Charles Lyell had written about the curious beaches, or escarpments, north of Toronto, a landscape Joe crossed often on his travels to and from the city and nearby villages, and the Humber River valley, where he spent every spare moment, was a lesson in limestone and erosion. Geology created an alternative universe to the vision of the Book of Genesis, an Earth so ancient it had no known beginning, and no conceivable end, an Earth not fixed and static but in perpetual motion, continents heaving, sinking, and shifting, ocean beds thrust up into mountains, mountains worn away to river deltas and sandy seas. Fossils in the rocks told the story of life and death on Earth for millions of years, and the rocks themselves had once been liquid, molten, or specks of dust and ash suspended in water.

Peering into Earth's crust was a controversial new field of exploration in the nineteenth century, and geologists created a common unruly language to describe what they saw. Terms such as *Devonian, Cambrian,* and *Jurassic* were clearly related to places – the Devon, Cambria, and the Jura mountains – while others were descriptive: *cretaceous* meant "chalky." Depending on the whim or nationality of the observer, the terminology included Latin, English, French, German, Scots, and Irish; as an example, the names *Ordovician* and *Silurian* for distinctive rock formations were derived from names given to ancient British peoples. Early Canadian geologists added *Laurentian* and *Huronian.* Geology's peculiar language and heretical world view gave it the aura of a cult or secret society, and it was a field where an obscure provincial lad of modest means like Joe Tyrrell could achieve international recognition.

Joe had the good fortune to be born on the edge of North America's last Great Unknown. The Tyrrells' house was only a stone's throw from the Carrying Place Trail, an ancient portage that aboriginal people, followed by the French, had used to travel from Lake Ontario to Lake Huron via the Humber River and Lake Simcoe. The footpath had been replaced by a railway from Toronto directly to Lake Huron, but beyond the Great Lakes lay the mysterious North-West, an arid, icy wilderness populated by beaver, buffalo, wild Indians, French-Canadian voyageurs, and fur traders employed by England's Hudson's Bay Company. When Canada bought the vast North-West territory called Rupert's Land from the company in 1869, the government had only the vaguest idea of what it had purchased, or how much, if anything, it was worth. When Joe Tyrrell joined the Geological Survey of Canada in 1881, it became his job to find out.

Canada was no longer seen as an obstruction on the route to Cathay, but as a Cathay of the future. In 1716, James Knight, commander of a Hudson's Bay Company trading post at the mouth of the Churchill River, had been visited by a group of strange Chipewyan, or Dene, adorned with rings, bracelets, and knives of gleaming native copper. When the Chipewyan told Knight that in the barren mountains far to the west "there is found great Quantitys of pure Virgin Copper lumps of it so bigg that three or 4 men cant lift it," he excitedly concluded that the company's financial future lay with metals, not beaver pelts. Moreover, the Chipewyan described "a Parcell of Indians as lyes upon the west Seas as had a Yellow Mettle as they make use of as these do Copper," and another tribe of mountain people who "garnish themselves with a White Mettle and hangs it in their noses and ears." One woman claimed to have picked up lumps of gold, washed down from the mountains, on the shore of the western sea.

The Chipewyan had been escorted to Knight's post from the area of Great Slave Lake and the Coppermine River by their courageous young countrywoman Thanadelthur, and a company employee, William Stuart, the first European to venture into *Terra Borealis* west of Hudson Bay. Yet rather than establish an overland trade route, Knight chose to reach the western sea by sailing the unknown Northwest Passage; in 1718, his ships were wrecked on Marble Island off the west coast of Hudson Bay.

Knight's fate, and an arduous, economically unproductive overland journey to the Coppermine River by Samuel Hearne between 1769 and 1772, persuaded the Hudson's Bay Company to stick to fur. Company traders acquired an invaluable storehouse of information about all the North-West's resources, but their journals were kept under lock and key in London. When prospectors from California found lumps of gold on the rivers and creeks in the interior of British Columbia in the mid-nineteenth century, the Chipewyan stories at last achieved credibility.

By the time Joe Tyrrell headed west to the foothills of the Rockies in 1883, the gold men desired had come to include "black gold," coal and oil, and golden fields of grain. His task was to run his eyes and hands over Earth's skin and bones, and to measure, probe, and describe, in maps, photographs, and words, what he found. His equipment was simple: watch, chronometer, thermometer and barometer, sextant, artificial horizon, a compass or two, hammer, field glass, pocket notebooks, and camera. For the next forty years, the first fifteen with the Geological Survey, Joe followed Canada's receding frontier. In Alberta, he discovered the Drumheller coal deposit and unearthed the first fossil of a meat-eating dinosaur found in Canada. North and west of Lake Winnipeg, he mapped the shores of a vanished glacial lake named Agassiz, and later located two Ice Age glaciers, the Keewatin, west of Hudson Bay, and the Patrician, south of James Bay. In 1893 and 1894, he paddled across the Barren Grounds, by two different routes, from Lake Athabasca and Reindeer Lake to Hudson Bay, then travelled on snowshoes and by dog team south to Winnipeg. In 1898, Joe quit the Survey to prospect for gold in the Klondike. Bankrupt by 1905, he made his fortune late in life by buying a gold mine in Kirkland Lake, Ontario. Along the way, Joe Tyrrell broke open the Hudson's Bay Company's two-hundred-year-old archive, edited explorers' journals, and rescued geographer David Thompson's maps, journals, and unpublished autobiography from oblivion.

Discoveries depended on the voyager's ability to return home to tell his news, or on eyewitness accounts provided by associates such as Frobisher's Captain Best, otherwise, his bleached bones became part of someone else's story. A myth to begin with – *Meta Incognita* was familiar territory to the Inuit – a discovery story was a literary narrative in the tradition of epic poetry: events were dramatized, personalities exaggerated, and the long, dull parts left out. In 1872, William Francis Butler, a British army scout, published a melancholy memoir of the Canadian North-West, *The Great Lone Land*, followed by a sequel, *The Wild North Land*. His portrait of a limitless silent solitude, peopled only by the dying Red Man, became as dominant a stereotype for northwestern Canada as the Wild West, with its outlaws and massacres, was for the American prairie. A generation later, Jack London and Robert Service were writing novels and ballads about the Call of the Wild and the Great White Silence, and adventure novels, from dime westerns to *Treasure Island* and *King Solomon's Mines*, blurred distinctions between fact and fantasy; the explorers in Jules Verne's *Journey to the Centre of the Earth* and *Twenty Thousand Leagues Under the Sea* were scientists. Scientific discovery was a principal motive in explorations driven by commercial, military, and religious imperatives; to become "the first white man" to set foot on a "new found land" was an act of personal glory and political triumph.

Joe Tyrrell, bookish, nearsighted, and pear-shaped, boldly cast himself in the role of gentleman adventurer: educated and intellectual, but egocentric, obsessive, and hot-tempered. He prided himself on his skill as a hunter, and his ability to endure the hardships of wilderness travel, but, like Frobisher, he was something of a fool and a buccaneer, saved from destruction by luck, willpower, and his ability to command the loyalty of smarter, stronger companions, including Metis and Inuit guides, and his loyal wife, Dollie. Joe told his own discovery story, never the same way twice, in field diaries, letters, scholarly articles, newspaper and magazine interviews, unpublished notes, and a self-published biography, *A Canadian Geologist*. During his ninety-eight years, he participated in an Age of Discovery that began in birchbark canoes and culminated in space exploration.

James Knight had been right: Canada's future was not in fur, and its treasure of gold, copper, nickel, uranium, and diamonds lay in the North. Today, the North is sprinkled with mines Joe Tyrrell only imagined, but it remains a sparsely populated wilderness of rock, muskeg, and water, and a romantic tourist destination. Much of the landscape he travelled has disappeared, flooded by hydroelectric dams, and oil extraction from the Athabasca tar sands has turned the area into a moonscape. Global warming is transforming the circumpolar regions into a scientific laboratory, and the Northwest Passage, successfully sailed in 1906 by Norwegian Roald Amundsen, remains a source of controversy: Canada claims sovereignty, while the United States insists it is an international waterway. For prosperous urban Canadians huddled along the United States border, Canada's "northern vision," invoked frequently by politicians, is a source of patriotic pride. Is it a myth, a delusion, a joke, or our national identity? Joe Tyrrell's travels are part of this story.

CHAPTER ONE

Imagine: June 21, 1883, somewhere north of the Milk River, North-West Territories.

Eight hundred and ten . . . eight hundred and eleven . . . eight hundred and twel— erk! Joe's left foot sinks beneath him. He peers through the bug netting that swaddles his face. Ahead, reeds glisten in the pale green buffalo grass. His boot makes a sucking noise as he pulls it up for the next step. Another miserable swamp! And this country is supposed to be desert. At least that's what Captain Palliser's old map says: "No water. High level plain." But it has poured rain almost every day of the two weeks Joe has been in this Canadian corner of the Great American Desert, and his map doesn't show this shallow gully that he has been following for hours because he's making a new map, measuring it step by step, one thousand Roman paces to the mile. You'd think the Geological Survey of Canada would use an odometer, but no, he's a lowly assistant on his first expedition, and his boss, Dr. George Mercer Dawson, says making a pace survey for twenty miles in the stifling heat is a rare educational opportunity.

Joe is sweating so hard his glasses are fogging up. He tugs impatiently at the cord fastening the netting around his neck and flings it back; a corner of the net catches on his glasses and sends them flying over his head. He wheels, but where he had seen tufts of new grass and slim reeds and earth stained white with alkali, he now sees a flat, fuzzy carpet of indeterminate ochres and greens.

He squints to catch a glint of sunlight on glass, but the sky is a dull, monochrome grey.

Joe kneels and crawls, groping with outstretched hands, until he has covered a circle within a twelve-foot radius. No glasses. Here he is, in the middle of nowhere, and he can't see! He gropes in his pocket for his compass. At least he can read it well enough to find his way to the expedition's new camp, if the camp is where it is supposed to be – but what if the tents are hidden away in a thicket down by a creek? The prairie here is said to be gouged by deep gullies, called coulees, that you almost tumble into before you see them. How can he walk through this strange country when he can't see where he's going? And if he leaves, he'll never find his glasses. A blind geologist.

Joe sits and waits. He's been in this predicament before. Someone is bound to come for him. The Survey can't simply leave him to rot on the prairie. He can visualize the headlines: BRILLIANT YOUNG ONTARIO SCIENTIST LOST IN NORTH-WEST. SURVEY DIRECTOR BLAMED. They won't want his skeletal remains to be found a year or two from now, gnawed by animals and bleached as white as the buffalo skulls he saw piled up at the end of the Canadian Pacific Railway tracks at Maple Creek. Joe has read about grizzlies, and wolves, but he'll likely die of hunger first. He has a few frogs and leeches for company, but they aren't any more edible than the blackbirds' eggs he has collected as specimens. The brackish water is drinkable, though he'll shit his guts out later.

It feels pleasant to rest his aching feet. He rummages in his inside pockets for his pipe and tobacco pouch. A smoke will calm his nerves and keep the mosquitoes at bay. It might even attract some Indians. They aren't far away. He saw a crowd of them at Maple Creek when he got off the CPR boxcar, cocooned in their bright striped blankets, feathers and quills and bits of fur sticking out of their long black hair, staring at the steam engine just like the folks did back home in Weston.

Joe ties his handkerchief to the end of his shotgun and props it up as a signal. A light rain is falling, and even on this bare plain he'll be hard to spot in the drizzle. He has dreamed of exploring the Great Lone Land since he was a kid at school staring at the blank space on a map of the North-West over which the cartographer had scrawled "Buffalo Run." Now here he is, but the Indians say Mother Earth has swallowed the buffalo. There are other explanations for the herds' disappearance – the railroads, mass slaughter – but still, it is an enigma.

To the west, above the sloping banks of the coulee, the prairie horizon is shrouded in mist. Joe feels submerged, as if he's sitting at the bottom of a pond. He is, in a way. Not a pond, but a sea, a dried-up tropical sea that covered this part of North America hundreds of millions of years ago. The land he is sitting on was lower then, and enough fossils have been found in the dry rocks to prove that this ancient sea teemed with shelled creatures unlike anything living in the world today. Joe finds fossils unbearably boring; he prefers to imagine these stony carapaces pulsating, brilliantly coloured, wriggling and burrowing and squirting, paddling along with their hairlike legs, antennae waving, eyes and mouths gaping, closing, tentacles probing among corals and sponges and seaweeds waving in the lazy current. Jellyfish too, giant worms, and translucent blobs, half plant, half animal. What a genius Darwin was to perceive that all life may have begun as a single primordial organism.

About eight miles to the southwest, in a blossoming chokecherry thicket on the bank of a nameless creek, Thompson, the expedition's cook, and Graydon, the wagon driver, are cleaning up after lunch. A few mouthfuls of salt pork and bannock simmer in the skillet. The kid should've been here long ago. It's time to move on.

They both look towards the creek, where Dr. Dawson is sitting on his camp stool under a canvas awning, writing in his pocket notebook. The little doctor seems unconcerned, and they both know better than to disturb him when he's scribbling.

Thompson goes off to scrub the kettle, Graydon gathers wood to take along for their supper fire. Can't depend on finding buffalo chips like they used to. The clouds clear off. Graydon stretches out in the shade of the wagon and pulls his hat over his eyes, cursing the fat kid for a tenderfoot. It's land fit for no man out there.

Little Doc at last comes up the riverbank, wet, and carrying his clothes. Naked, he looks like a spider: long hairy legs and arms, dark hair and beard, and a small, rounded, humpbacked torso. Doc fishes in his pants pocket for his tobacco and cigarette papers, rolls, lights, inhales, and blows a perfect smoke ring. As far as he's concerned, it won't hurt Mr. Tyrrell to sweat it out a bit. But Graydon offers to saddle up and take a look. It's Sun Dance season, an emotional religious festival for both the Blackfoot and the Cree. The North West Mounted Police are harassing the Indians to stick to their reserves, but Big Bear's rebellious Cree are on the move, no one knows exactly where. The warriors know a government man when they see one. Young Joe Tyrrell could make a valuable hostage.

Graydon and his pony follow their four-legged shadow away from the setting sun. Graydon has never been in this area before, and he's almost ready to turn back when his horse startles at the glint of light on . . . metal? Rock? It's to the south, near a pond. As he rides closer, a human shape uncurls itself from around a gun propped up with rocks. The kid jumps to his feet, waving him off and shouting.

Graydon dismounts and cups his ear to hear what the kid is croaking. Joe circles his eyes with crooked fingers, then waves towards the ground around him. Careful! Be careful! Graydon treads cautiously, feeling the earth with his toes. He spots the spectacles staring up at him from a reedy pool and pulls them out, unbroken.

The kid's thanks embarrass him. What a dumb thing to do. Graydon gestures towards the pony, she'll carry two. Joe shakes his head. Thanks anyway. He'll finish the survey. Joe starts walking with long strides, eight hundred and thirteen . . . fourteen . . . fifteen . . .

Joe expects a severe dressing-down, even dismissal, when he reaches camp, but Doc Dawson merely tells him, with a smile, that he'll have to pick up his speed. Joe's worst humiliation is having to wear his glasses on a thong around his neck, like mittens. Doc even pays him a compliment about the slough he had stumbled into: he calls it Tyrrell's Lake.

The next day, Joe stood on the top of the Milk River Ridge and watched the sun set behind a shining bank of grey, white-tipped clouds: the Rockies! The mountains were their destination for this season's exploration, but they seemed a very long way away. Would he have to walk? But walking, Joe soon discovered, was preferable to jolting for hours over the rough, stony prairie in the heavy wagon. Except for Doc and Thompson bouncing far ahead in the buckboard, he and Graydon were solitary wanderers in a sagebrush and cactus moonscape. Joe's face became so chapped and blistered that he let his beard grow. "The wind and rain are peeling me away quite rapidly," he writes in his field notes on June 27. "In two or three months probably there will be nothing of me left. . . . I am too becoming very brown and shaggy, so that it seems to me that the head of a broom dipped in Raw Sienna would resemble me very closely, especially if it had been pulled out a little at the bottom." His face and hands were swollen with insect bites: "The mosquitoes," he notes, "are like a band of Pythian horsemen determined to harass the enemy either advancing or retreating." His clothes were scratchy with dust, sweat, and lice. The men bathed and washed their shirts and underwear only on Sundays, or when it rained.

Joe shot at the inquisitive antelope that came teasingly close, then kicked up their heels and bounded away out of range. Potting prairie dogs was easier, but the *Sciurus richardsonii* was so common it was not worth collecting, even for its parasites. Fleas were at least of some scientific interest. As a student, Joe had made a special study of water mites and bird lice, and had corresponded with several German scientists until his professors at the University of Toronto cautioned him there was no work for entomologists in Canada. Still, he always picked off a few specimens alive and popped them into a vial of alcohol. Graydon said the Indians ate their lice. Joe could appreciate that, if the Indians were forced to live like he was on bacon, beans, grease bread, and tea. It seemed Doc Dawson had never heard of scurvy.

Little Doc set a relentless pace. At first light, about 4:30 a.m., Thompson kindled the fire and Graydon and Joe rounded up the horses. Pasture was so poor that the horses sometimes strayed for miles, and it was often 6:00 a.m. or later before the expedition started off. They rarely camped for the night before 7:00 p.m., and the men took turns standing watch. Joe kept himself awake on watch trying to detect in the chorus of frogs and the hollow boom of the bitterns the human note of an Indian signalling an attack. The Blackfoot and Cree were notorious horse thieves, and the mounted police at Maple Creek had told frightening tales of scalp raids and massacres. Little Doc had stocked up with enough rifles and revolvers to equip a geological cavalry, as they jokingly called themselves, but so far their only encounter with the Cree had been hospitable. Not far from Maple Creek, they had driven up to Big Bear's band, camped in a valley for their Sun Dance. The hairs on Joe's neck had bristled as naked, painted warriors brandishing spears galloped full tilt towards them, but at the last minute, with great whoops, they thundered past on either side.

As Joe explored the tributaries of the Milk River, he was puzzled that they were spending so much time in a sterile place Dawson had examined ten years earlier as part of the joint United States–Canadian boundary survey. Joe thought they were searching for coal, copper, and gold, yet the Milk River Ridge, a trove of Paleozoic fossil shells and fish fragments, showed only traces of coal. Perhaps Doc had something up his sleeve. He liked to go

"Big Bear's Camp, Maple Creek, June 6, 1883." Photo by G. M. Dawson. (LAC, PA-959746)

off alone, leaving Joe to scramble up and down the riverbanks by himself. Joe diligently scrutinized the layers of sediment, and pecked away with his hammer, but apart from a little soft coal, he found only clay, sand, gravel, and pebbles. Still, every evening, when Joe couldn't keep his eyes open, Doc grilled him on the exact colour, texture, and location of the rocks he had found. Identifying a pebble as Cretaceous was only a start: was it Pierre? Or Laramie? Edmontonian? Impatient with British and American terminology, Doc was working out a Canadian vocabulary, but Joe defined most of what he found as rubble, till, drift, or, in a word, dirt.

Exactly. Dawson was struggling to determine exactly how this thick layer of common rubble had come to be deposited on the ancient Paleozoic and Mesozoic bedrock. The old, conventional theory, ardently espoused by his father, William Dawson, principal of McGill College in Montreal and Canada's most esteemed geologist, argued that these landforms, once the sunken seabed of a long, deep arm of the Arctic Ocean, had been shaped by powerful tidal currents and floating ice from distant northern glaciers. Yet the soil contained no marine organisms, and Little Doc's own research along the forty-ninth parallel at Lake of the Woods and the Missouri Coteau had uncovered moraines, striations, and other incontrovertible proof of a glacier's presence this far south, evidence supported by American geologists working in New England and the northern states. Although it seemed incredible that any glacier would have been able to move millions of tons of heavy rock, clay, and debris hundreds of miles over flat ground, the best explanation Little Doc could find for Tyrrell's Lake and the Milk River area's other stagnant, dead-end coulees was that they were remnants of old glacial rivers that had dried up as the ice retreated and mountain streams gouged new channels.

Traces of gold had been found in the sand of the North Saskatchewan River near Fort Edmonton, so all the coulees and creek beds deserved close scrutiny. And if you examine boulder clay closely, Mr. Tyrrell, Doc said, you'll find it full of spores, algae, living organisms – a whole new field for inquiry! Doc was famous for his enthusiasms and his practical jokes, and Joe wondered if Doc was pulling his leg, or parroting another of his father William's crackpot theories. Years ago, William Dawson claimed to have discovered the world's oldest fossilized living organism in a chunk of volcanic rock. He named it *eozoon*, and convinced geology's godfather, Sir Charles Lyell, of its authenticity. However, metallurgists soon proved it to be a lifeless mineral.

Joe found plenty of clay, mixed with manure, when they hit the Macleod–Benton trail. He'd read avidly about the great Fort Benton mule trains, groaning along, the mules lashed by the curses of their whip-cracking skinners, and there they were, spread out before him, lines of prairie schooners, canvas billowing in the sharp wind. It was pouring rain, and the mules screamed as they sank in the muck. The weakest were shot and unhitched, and the train plodded ahead more easily over their carcasses. As soon as the land began to rise, Thompson signalled a halt at a low bluff: the mule train would pack a good trail for tomorrow. Joe writes:

"Belly River, Coal Banks, 1883." Joe is likely the figure in the distance. Photo by G.M. Dawson. (LAC, PA-037554)

"June 27, 1883

"Rose early, four o'clock. Breakfast. Baked dough, pork, tea. Off by twenty to six. Travelled over a grassy plain which, at first, was cool and refreshing: but, as the sun rose, became hot and glaring, the air very oppressive, almost stifling us; and, as we drove along in the wagons, we'd fall asleep for a few minutes: then came a rude wakening, as the wheels bumped into some gigantic rut cut out by the prairie schooners. . . .

"About half past ten we arrived at Coal Banks, in the bottom of the valley of Belly River, the sides of which are about five hundred feet high at this point. The valley looked very beautiful to us as the trees which cover the flats are the first we have seen for about three weeks. The town consists of three houses and half a dozen tents. Here there is a good ferry across the river. We tried to purchase some provisions but only secured some sugar, dried apples and baking powder. . . . The river here flows rapidly, and beside us is a thicket of poplar, green grass, and altogether it is a pretty spot. They are building a steamer here now but it will have to do well to make headway against this current."

Joe felt a little deflated to find a coal mine in active operation on the west bank of the river. He was supposed to be discovering coal out here. Yet an ordinary Yankee prospector, Nick Sheran, had beaten the Geological Survey to it ten years before. The mine was a crude affair, an open pit dug into the bank, and a dozen men were hacking at the coal with shovels and pickaxes. The lumps were dumped into wagons, the wagons loaded on to the ferry and then pulled more than a hundred miles across the open prairie to the new Canadian Pacific Railway depot at Medicine Hat. The CPR needed enormous supplies of coal to fuel its engines, and one of the railroad's financiers, Alexander Galt, had already bought the mine.

It was disillusioning, to be sent out here to find coal to run the CPR. The big money men in Toronto and Montreal seemed to be using the Survey to line their pockets. It was a lesson in scientific research Joe hadn't expected to learn, and his dismay grew the next day when they reached Fort Macleod.

Nine years earlier, when he was just a boy, Joe had followed every step of the North West Mounted Police's great march across the prairie to defend Canada and protect the Indians from the American whisky smugglers at Fort Whoop-Up. From the sketches in the Toronto newspapers, he'd imagined Fort Macleod to be a huge fortress, high on a hill, and he'd dreamed about galloping after desperadoes in his scarlet tunic, chasing buffalo, and powwowing with Blackfoot chiefs. But the real Fort Macleod was a simple, homely square of log stables and bunkhouses surrounded by a rough palisade, and the mounted police lounged about in their shirtsleeves. A scabby little settlement had sprung up on the surrounding flats and bluffs, a litter of shacks and tents, all helter-skelter, the crooked paths deep in garbage and noisy with men, mules, and cattle. Most of the hand-lettered signs seemed to advertise saloons. Whisky was perfectly legal here, as

Main Street, Fort Macleod. (GA, NA-967-41)

long as it wasn't sold to Indians. Graydon said most of Fort Macleod's saloons were owned by John Jerome Healy, the same American whisky smuggler the mounted police had marched west to destroy; Sheriff Healy, as he now called himself, had quietly closed Fort Whoop-Up before the police arrived.

Fort Macleod was the Canadian terminus for the I.G. Baker Company's mule trains from Fort Benton, Montana. Joe waited around the crowded warehouse, hoping for mail, while Doc Dawson haggled for pack horses to take them into the mountains. It seemed strange that letters from eastern Canada would come all the way across the United States by train, then north from Fort Benton by pony express, but the CPR would be at Fort Calgary any day now, it was said. Joe had mixed feelings about the railway. The Grand Trunk Railway ran right past their house in Weston – his father had thought the location a good investment – and while Joe was used to the cacophony of clacking, grinding, and tooting, he preferred the music of the wind, and the yipping of coyotes at night. Only weeks ago, he had ridden the CPR from Winnipeg to the end of steel at Maple Creek, and he'd watched an army of navvies throw down ties and hammer in steel rails, making a monstrous centipede that crawled towards the horizon. It was hard to blame the Indians for pulling up the survey stakes and camping in the creature's path. Unless they scalped the surveyors.

July 1, Dominion Day, was a Sunday, so Thompson and Graydon got Saturday night off to do the town. Joe and Doc stayed in camp. It was a clear, cool evening, the air heavy with the scent of prairie roses (*Rosa suffulta*, Joe noted). Joe was happy to have purchased a jar of jam at the I.G. Baker store, and Doc, a charming bon vivant in Ottawa, may have broken out a bottle of Scotch to toast the Queen, Canada, science, the Survey, the sun, and the stars. Joe fell asleep looking at the night sky.

On July 3, they rode up the south fork of Old Man River towards Crow's Nest Mountain and the pass across the Rockies. Lush meadows, broken by dense stands of spruce, sloped upward towards the jagged, snow-capped peaks. Joe was on horseback at last, a scrawny nag to be sure, but quiet. The Tyrrells didn't own a saddle horse, and Joe had to rent a neighbour's for two weeks to practise. They crossed to the south side of the river, swimming the horses and poling the loaded wagon like a scow, then headed for the Garnett brothers' ranch in the valley. The ranch, a plain log house, was mostly a trading post, and it would be their jumping-off place for three trips through the mountains.

It was late, almost suppertime, the next afternoon before all the baggage was tightly bundled and strapped across the horses' backs. Everything but the bare necessities had to be left behind at the ranch; Joe was allowed one blanket and a single change of clothes, but at the last minute he tied a prospector's pan across his pack. Thunder boomed through the valley, and black clouds, rent with lightning, rolled in from the west. An icy rain pelted down. Yet Little Doc gave the signal to start, and the caravan, lit up by lightning, straggled off. Joe walked ahead, soon outdistancing the skittish horses. An hour or two later, soaked to the skin and fearful of losing his way, he took shelter in a cabin, welcomed by a man named Lee, a whisky trader who had been in the country for

"Garnett's valley, south fork of Oldman River, July 6, 1883." Photo by G.M. Dawson. (LAC, PA-050759)

fifteen years. Together they watched the storm, "the most brilliant lightning I had ever seen," Joe later noted, "lightning like fire."

After some time, the wet, bedraggled caravan straggled up. Little Doc, sheltered from the downpour by his floppy sombrero, looked dazed and unsteady. Not long after they had started, an explosion of blinding light had seemed to hit him on the head, like the blow from an open hand. The lightning had struck the others too, but no one was injured, and after resting to catch their breaths, they had clambered back into their saddles and ridden on. Moments later, the sky brightened and the storm rumbled off.

Snow-capped Crow's Nest Mountain was gleaming in the setting sun when they all camped for the night and built a blazing fire to dry their clothes.

Joe was up before sunrise packing his saddlebags, eager to be off. Doc, chipper as always, called out: Good to see you getting an early start, Mr. Tyrrell! Today you'll be making a pace survey of the Crow's Nest Pass. You'll be measuring for longitude and collecting botanical specimens along the way. Joe writes:

"July 6

"After dinner I set out on foot into the foothills. . . . It will be on the whole the surest way to see the mountains; but I think I will have the disadvantage of being separated from the rest of the party and so will not be able to converse with those who are old mountaineers, except at meal time."

Joe was fearful that he would get lost in a chasm, and never find his way out. He needn't have worried: he met no one, but the path through the pass was well-trodden. Still, it was so steep and stony he had to struggle to keep his paces even. He stopped often to rest, take his bearings, and admire the breathtaking view. It was astonishing to realize that he was looking at an old, flat ocean bottom, thrust up, twisted, folded, and eroded, but he could clearly see the layers of sandstone, limestone, and shale on the mountains' sheer sides.

Nine hundred and five, and six, and seven . . . Day after day, he plodded on. Late in the morning, the pack train would trot past him, Doc riding ahead, eyes forward. The first day, Joe waved and called hello, but Doc gave no sign of recognition. Joe would catch up with them at lunch camp, but he'd barely have time to bolt his cold, greasy grub before they'd ride off again, leaving him to tramp behind as best he could. Two hundred and fourteen, and fifteen, and sixteen . . . As badly as his legs ached when he made it into camp for the night, his heart burned more hotly with resentment.

The country became rougher. As Joe clambered over the deadfall that blocked the trail, he had to invent a formula to calculate the variations in the length of his stride. He was so slow he often had to stop at twilight, mark his place, rush ahead to the camp, and then return at daybreak to finish his survey before starting on the next leg. No matter how tired he was, Doc insisted that he write up his observations each night:

"July 10, Crow's Nest Lake

"For a couple of miles the trail runs along the steep edge of the Lake, and here I collected a number of interesting fossils.

Lunch in a little valley where I sorted out and changed the papers on some plants; then started off up a little valley with mountains to the right and left of me, then turned South and entered British Columbia in the midst of a beautiful wooded country where I shot a blue grouse with my revolver, which we afterward had for supper. Mosquitoes bad here, air has grown warm. The bush is the finest I have seen on the trail; pine, spruce and poplar. My hands are swollen twice their natural size from the stings of insects. Tried the rifles to-night and turned in under my blankets to sleep for the first time on British Columbian soil.

"July 12, Michel Camp, B.C.

"In the morning we investigated the coal seams here. I found one about three feet thick near the forks, a fine bituminous coal, evidently first quality gas coal. I collected flowers also in the swamps and pressed them in camp. After dinner two parties passed us on the way to Kootenay and a little later we started after them. We went up Michel Creek and over a height of land, about a thousand feet high, into the valley of Coal Creek where we camped for the night, a dreary place. Graydon shot a woodchuck which we had for supper; not bad in flavour but exceedingly tough.

"July 13, Coal Creek

"I got off on my walk about eight, ahead of the rest, giving me a good start. They were late in catching up, as the way had been rough and stony and the packs kept slipping off the horses, so that they did not reach me until nearly two. I myself had stumbled on, stopping to take a bearing here and there or climbing mountains to get a better view of the trail, until my boots were almost torn off my feet. It was the shortest but hardest morning I had yet. After lunch the horses refused to be caught, and it was between four and five that we got again on the trail. Crossed to Elk River and camped for the night. A most gorgeous view from here. Fires are burning in the distance and it is beginning to get smoky. But there is not much danger from the fire, as the country all around has been burned over dozens of times. It is frightful to see so much fine timber gone, rampikes standing in millions

all over the country. . . . We have so far travelled whole days
through forests almost entirely destroyed by fire.

"July 14

"To-day we got into the middle of the fire, which is burning on both sides of the river, trees falling constantly with a
noise like thunder. We camped in the valley of a creek running
into the valley of the Elk, in the midst of desolation, every green
thing destroyed. The thermometer fell one degree below freezing last night."

Thunderstorms and showers of cold rain cleared the suffo-
cating smoke, but the rough path became slippery. On July 16,
Joe found himself alone at the bottom of a steep, overgrown
canyon: the trail he had been following, apparently made by a
mountain sheep, petered out at a rock face. He gingerly retraced
his steps over the slimy boulders, and was glad to find the rest of
the men waiting anxiously where he had veered off. He expected
Doc to send him away again in the right direction, but Doc was
seated on his camp stool, bending over maps and mathematical
tables, occasionally glancing at his watch or squinting at the sky.
It's supposed to be here, he muttered. We should hit the bridge
to the Kootenay trail *right here*. But there was no bridge across
the foaming creek, and no Kootenay trail.

We're lost, Joe thought. It was one thing to locate their
position precisely on a flat sheet of drawing paper, quite another
to navigate in the rain a precipitous labyrinth of smouldering
deadfall and icy torrents. Thompson and Graydon scratched
their heads and spat tobacco juice; neither had been in the
Rockies before.

We'll need an Indian guide, Doc said.

Trails through the valleys had been made by the local
Kootenay Indians during their hunting and trading expeditions
to the south and east, but the Kootenays lived on the other side
of the torrent. As Joe scouted along the creek for a crossing, he
was stopped short by the faint sound of a man's shout coming
from the bank above. Hallooo? Hallooo? Joe called. A call came

in reply, then a sound like banging on a tin pan. When Joe clambered up, he found a ragged, shivering fellow, soaked to the skin, his bloody, swollen feet stretched out in front of him. He wore a white man's clothes and spoke English, but he'd only say that he'd lost his horse, and had come up lame trying to walk. He had no clear idea where he was going, but he had crossed the bridge not long before, and if he could borrow a horse he would happily return that way with them. Bandaged, fed, and revived with a shot of Doc's whisky, their pilgrim soon led them over the rickety bridge and up the trail towards the settlement of Kootenay on Wild Horse Creek.

Kootenay – a log cabin, two empty wigwams, and a ferry – was the fiefdom of an old settler named Galbraith. He had a farm on a broad, dry plain several miles away, with a good house, a herd of cattle, and a vegetable garden. No Indians were around, Galbraith said, but he gave Joe directions for the expedition's return across the Rockies through the North Kootenay Pass.

For the next week, they followed an Indian trail south through spruce groves broken by alpine meadows of wildflowers. The weather was warm, and the sun shone through the haze of smoke that obscured the mountaintops. Joe stopped often to pick plants and shoot at the grouse that scattered in his path; he could almost catch them with his bare hands. Graydon dourly praised his marksmanship, and Joe took being called "The Kid" as a compliment. He had found his stride, his wind, and his muscles. He was perfectly content walking alone, with the mountains and his thoughts for company.

The Survey's speed was determined by their horses' need for water and pasture, and by Doc's passions for fly-fishing and photography. Thompson had a knack for choosing campsites beside trout streams, and while he started the fire, Doc would disappear up the creek, rod dangling over his shoulder, flies stuck in his hatband. With luck, he'd be back with a string of trout before the kettle boiled. At lunch, Doc and Joe would go off to take photographs, a scientific pursuit that often lasted the rest of the day, and the next. It rankled with Joe that Doc had scrimped on flour and sugar in order to pack along his cumbersome oak camera, hood, tripod, and at least a hundred heavy boxes of glass photographic plates. Doc liked scenic views, preferably from a mountaintop, and it was Joe's job to assist in transporting the plates and equipment. Once set up, they inevitably had to move the equipment a dozen times to find the right angle, then wait while the mist cleared, or the shadows lengthened. Still, Joe was curious to see if the photographs would turn out better than sketches, especially in the rain. He hated having his own portrait taken, and he sympathized with the Indians who, after hours of palaver and friendly pipe smoking, scattered into the bush as soon as Doc stuck his head under the hood.

Doc kept trying. A little more than four feet tall, Dawson was stronger than many full-grown men, and more stubborn too. His nickname came not from his many academic honours, but from Thompson's laconic response to all his requests: "You're the doctor!" Doc could sit for hours on a rock, sketching, but fly into a fit of temper over a strayed horse or the slightest delay in breaking camp at daylight. No matter how miserable the weather, how chilled and hungry and tired the men, or lame the horses, the expedition pressed on.

On July 29, they reached the summit of the North Kootenay Pass. It had been a hard climb through a steep gorge in bitter cold; fresh snow covered the ground, and the surrounding peaks were shrouded in smoke. Doc decided to wait until the smoke cleared so that he could take a photograph. They built a fire in the lee of a rock, but as darkness fell they could find no saplings long enough to make tent poles. Doc rolled himself in his blanket by the fire and fell asleep.

Joe couldn't believe it. The temperature was −8 Fahrenheit! He sat up by the fire as long as he could stay awake; when he opened his eyes at daybreak, he was stiff and cold and surprised to be alive. He washed in snow and dried himself with a frozen towel while Doc bustled about with his glass plates. At noon the air was as smoky as ever, and Doc reluctantly led the caravan down the valley towards the Garnetts' ranch.

Stopping only long enough to unload their bags of specimens, pack fresh clothes, and write letters home, they set off on August 1 to explore the Livingston Range. After that, their route would lead south to Waterton Lake on the International Boundary, northwest through the Columbia River valley to the Kicking Horse Pass, across the pass and east to Fort Calgary. The distance would be about four hundred miles, not including side excursions, climbing mountains, and getting lost. However, they had about two months until snowfall. Joe wasn't concerned about walking that far now, but on the west flank of the Livingstons he had to survey narrow chasms so steep a mountain goat would flee in fear.

Take a look up there, Tyrrell! Doc would say, waving his hammer towards a stream roiling through a cleft in the dark, mossy rock. See how far you can go! Not far, was Joe's inevitable answer. Dead-end creeks and rivulets gushed out of hidden springs, and the rock was devoid of gold, copper, or coal. Joe was eager to make a discovery, something famous like the pass through the Selkirk Range near the Kicking Horse River that Major A.B. Rogers was rumoured to have found, but he had to be content with filling in a portion of his map as simply *"rough, wooded hills."*

Then, in mid-August, as Joe was tramping south on the east side of the Livingston Range, heading for the Garnetts' ranch, he found himself following a scattering of rounded, lichen-covered boulders partially sunk in the earth, like giant, misshapen eggs. The boulders looked so incongruous that their placement at first seemed man-made, like Stonehenge in England, or the Great Wall of China, but Joe had heard no stories of an ancient temple or fortification here, and he could make no engineering sense out of them. Smoothed and scratched as they were, they didn't seem to be sculpted, yet they did not resemble the angular slabs of limestone and sandstone that fell at random off the mountainsides. When Joe scraped away the lichen, the stone was the same speckled granite he'd found in the Gatineau Hills north of Ottawa. Joe climbed higher up the slope to get a better view: the boulders seemed to form a wavy line, like toes on a foot. How did they get here? Doc, surprisingly, had no quick and confident explanation. In fact, the question made him testy and ill at ease. Certainly, the boulders, some as large as houses, had been transported hundreds, perhaps thousands of miles from the north and east – but had they been carried by a massive Ice Age glacier, or by floating icebergs? Swiss Alpine geologist Louis Agassiz had shown some forty years earlier that glaciers might deposit rocks in improbable, or erratic, locations, and that millennia of glacial abrasion could round, scratch, and polish hard granite, but Dawson, having rather hastily advocated his father's iceberg theory in his 1875 "Report on the geology and resources of the region in the vicinity of the 49th parallel," was too loyal, or embarrassed, to admit he might have made an error. Unwittingly, Joe Tyrrell had walked into an unsolved geological conundrum, a repressed family argument, and a religious controversy.

The iceberg theory, discredited everywhere but in Canada, had been put forward by British geologists in order to bring Ice Age evidence into awkward conformity with Noah's Flood. Most Protestant Christians believed the Bible to be the revealed Word of God, and therefore true. Since the Book of Genesis did not mention an Ice Age, Agassiz was violently denounced and his ideas repudiated, but once the evidence of glaciation in Scandinavia and Great Britain seemed incontrovertible, biblical scholars attempted to incorporate it into the sacred text. The most passionate and influential of these Mosaic proselytizers was Doc's father.

William Dawson was a paradox. As a young man in Nova Scotia in the 1840s, his discoveries of fossilized trees and an early, extinct reptile had placed him among the world's leading natural scientists; even *eozoon* had not seriously undermined his reputation. But following the publication of Darwin's *Origin of Species* in 1859, Dawson, an elder in the Presbyterian Church, condemned natural selection in favour of a popular, fundamentalist Christian

belief in God's plan: the Creator designed and decided everything. Natural science, in this theology, was the sacred study of
God's works, and while the Book of Genesis required some interpretation – a day in God's time might mean eons in mortal time
– biblical revelation was the standard by which all science was
measured. Christians with inquiring minds preferred Dawson's
interpretation to consigning all scientists to Hell, and phenomena
that didn't fit into the procrustean bed of God's plan were sound
evidence that the Creator moved in mysterious ways.

By the summer of 1883, Elder Dawson's theological science
was embarrassingly antiquated, even in Canada, but he continued
to publish books and tracts, and his international reputation was
so great that no one dared challenge him. Joe Tyrrell was in a
ticklish spot. Should he go along with the theory of icebergs and
biblical deluge, in spite of his own contrary or skeptical opinions,
or risk the Dawsons' wrath and expulsion from the Survey? The
ghost of Joe's Quaker grandfather, Rowland Burr, told him: *Speak
the truth*. His Methodist mother admonished: *Pray to God*. Joe
decided to follow his father's Church of England counsel: *Keep
your mouth shut*. He had never explored, nor even seen, a glacier.
With good weather, and enough time, he might be able to investigate a vast icefield reported to lie northwest of the Kicking
Horse River.

September 21, 1883, Railway Surveyors' Camp, Kicking Horse Pass
Watch out! Rogers is coming! He's riding up the river! Look out!
As the warning buzzed from fire to fire, the surveyors scrambled
to hide their bottles and toss their garbage in the flames. Joe
stood up, keen to get a glimpse of the celebrated American army
officer, Indian fighter, and discoverer of the Rogers Pass. He had
no idea what to expect. To his men, Major "Hell's Bells" Rogers
was a foul-mouthed tyrant who worked them to death on a con-
vict's diet of baked beans. Joe understood: his own pet peeve

"Glacier Mountain, Kicking Horse Pass, September 25, 1883." Photo by G.M. Dawson. (LAC, PA-050768)

was porridge. All the same, Joe imagined a picturesque figure, a Buffalo Bill in white buckskins, but the hero who trotted into the firelight was a wizened gnome in blue overalls sporting filthy white side-whiskers.

Hell's Bells! exclaimed Rogers when he saw Little Doc. Rogers waved them both over to his tent and gestured to them to sit on the ground by the fire. Joe looked around for a kettle, frying pan, a dish or a cup, but Major Rogers's reputation for living on air seemed to be correct. Rogers was delighted to describe, with pantomime and dramatic gestures, how he and his Shuswap Indian guides had dangled over precipices and leaped yawning crevasses on their successful foray through the previously unpenetrated Selkirk Range, but he expressed himself in such a torrent of profanities, punctuated by streams of tobacco juice, that Joe barely caught a phrase here and there. Joe tried to find out if a track led from the Kicking Horse River to the bluish-white glacier he'd seen shining in the sun at the bend of the Columbia River, but he could only grasp that those mountains were inaccessible.

The next morning, Joe reluctantly turned his horse's head to the east: home. He could hear in the distance the din of the CPR track being laid towards the Kicking Horse Pass, and a single line of horse-drawn supply wagons was snaking gingerly along a narrow, winding trail cut into the sheer face of the mountain, hundreds of feet above the rapids. The wagons' outside wheels were so close to the edge they appeared about to slip over. Often, Joe was told, they did. Joe wanted to walk, but the straw boss, a hulking blackbeard the packers called simply Man, or The Man, refused. If a horse makes it across the pass with a load of dynamite, and back, it knows what it is doing, Man said.

Joe clung to the reins and stared fixedly at his horse's ears. His right leg brushed the stone wall of the canyon; his left leg swung in space. Showers of pebbles pattered on the path and rolled beneath his horse's hooves. Later Joe had no memory of how long the trip took. He dismounted on wobbly legs, his shirt and jacket soaked with sweat.

Forest fires burned on either side of the wagon trail, and the wind that swirled the smoke overhead carried squalls of sleet and snow. Jagged stones cut the horses' hooves, and miasmas of black flies rose from the swamps. They could find no grass, no game, not even a bird or a berry in what Doc called "this abomination of desolation." In the past three months, the noisy, greasy centipede they had left behind at Maple Creek had wriggled across the prairie to meet them here.

Joe had travelled many more miles than the railway, nearly three hundred of them on foot – but what did he have to show for it? Several bags of fossils, rocks, and pressed plants whose names he didn't know yet. They had located numerous rich seams of coal in the foothills, but in the process had largely confirmed discoveries made by others, and while Joe had assiduously panned every mountain trickle, he'd found not a fleck of gold. As for Noah's icebergs, how could Joe state in public that he didn't believe in God?

The mountains were covered with snow on October 5 when their cold and weary little caravan plodded up to the McDougalls' Methodist mission on the Bow River. Joe was curious. He'd grown up with stories in the *Christian Guardian* praising the McDougalls' selfless work among the heathen Stonies of the North-West, and he had pictured the family living in rags in a tipi piled high with Bibles. But what he saw was a sprawling log house, a general store, a post office, an inn, stables, corrals full of cattle and horses, and, to one side, a small church and a school for the Stonies. A spread, as they say out here in the west. Reverend John McDougall supervised the Stonies' souls and schooling, while his brother Dave ran the family's ranch and freighting company. Joe appreciated the McDougalls' hospitality, but he made a mental note to tell his mother not to give another penny to the Methodist Mission Society.

They waited for the snow to stop falling long enough to make a final short foray up the Bow and Kananaskis rivers. Snow'll melt in a day or two, Doc would say, and roll another cigarette. All of Joe's warm clothing, such as it was, had been left behind at Garnett's ranch.

Thompson and Graydon, itching to get home to their families, were paid off; Stoney guides would take Joe and Doc up the valleys. Snowbound for a second day, Joe lost patience. I think I'll head up the Bow Valley anyway, he told Doc. It's only fifty miles. Joe half expected Doc to call it quits for the year, but oh no, Doc jumped up and gave the order to start. Joe writes:

"October 7

"Almost all morning was occupied in getting our horses and getting our Indians. Dr. had a smart-looking man of about 25, dressed better than most Indians take the trouble to dress, in fact he was the best dressed man in the party. I had an old fellow of perfectly uncertain age except that he must have been more than forty, with but one eye, the defect being hidden by a bunch of hair which he drew over one half of his face. . . . We travelled together til evening and camped together on the Kananaskis. . . .

"October 8

"In the morning just as day began to dawn the snow began to fall, little by little, and by breakfast time it was falling quite heavily. . . . We travelled along an Indian trail til three, the snow falling heavier and heavier all the time. We stopped for an hour, built a fire and warmed ourselves. . . ."

Isaac, Joe's guide, searched in vain for a ford across the Bow River that would take them to an engineers' camp: "It got quite dark & we unsaddled & made a fire & had a bed under a spruce tree & determined to be as comfortable as possible for the night. I had taken the precaution to put a tin of corned beef in my pocket so we were not quite supperless. . . ."

Joe's equanimity was a far cry from the near panic he had felt at sleeping in the snow only three months earlier. The next morning, Isaac found the trail, and they arrived safely back at the McDougalls' two days later. On October 12, Joe and Doc packed their gear and boarded a train for Calgary. Joe writes:

"October 13

"At Calgary at the Calgary House, the hotel of the town. It is full of guests, but we put two beds in a tent close by and slept well. Went to the railway station with Dawson's baggage, and bade him good-bye. He is off to Ottawa. To-night I am going to have a real room, with solid walls, a door, and shall sleep between clean sheets. The town is full. I met W.F. King of Ottawa and Douglas Armour, and a lot of others. I am going to McLeod [*sic*] to get our stuff as soon as I can. There is no stage until the 19th: so I am going to ride down on horseback tomorrow, then return here with our stuff and take the train home."

Joe was astounded to run into fellows he knew from the University of Toronto and Upper Canada College, sons of lawyers and judges and bankers. What were these fine gentlemen doing in a dusty shack town, dolled up in cowboy gear like Deadwood

Tent Town of Calgary. (GA, NA-1315-9)

Dick? Looking for land, they said. Anyone could lease ranchland for a penny an acre per year, as much as you wanted. Senator Cochrane had already snaffled a hundred thousand acres not far from town, and millions were left. Town lots were harder to get, but on Calgary's rutted main street, an old schoolmate of Joe's from Weston, Jimmy Lougheed, had hung out a shingle advertising his services as a barrister and solicitor.

⌣

October 15, Calgary–Macleod Trail
A south wind blows wet snow in Joe's face. The flakes melt and smear his glasses. His horse trots on. Joe is grateful that she seems to know the way; there is no place to rest, not even a shrub for shelter. It will be ages yet before he reaches the next stopping place at Willow Creek. The snow becomes thicker, heavier; Joe drifts along in a cold, white cloud.

The mare shakes her head, twitches her ears, snuffles, and picks up the pace. In a few moments, she swings to the left. Joe glimpses dark shapes, fence rails, and he hears, not too far away, the soft bellow of a steer. Tracks in the snow lead to a long log house, with firelight flickering through fancy glass windows, and a solid door with a horseshoe for a knocker.

A short, red-faced man opens the door. He wears a black silk vest over a starched white shirt and carries a riding crop.

Not hiring, boy. Full up here. Get on now. And he shuts the door in Joe's face.

Bloody Brits! Wild Bill Hickok'd smash the window in and blow the bugger's brains out.

Joe catches a whiff of a delicious supper cooking some-where in the back of the house: beef stew, turnips, potatoes, hot bread, butter – butter! – and apple pie, a pie that had to be made with Ontario apples, possibly even apples from the Tyrrells' own orchard. The kitchen! That's where the tramps go at home, to the cook!

The cook nods, room for one more, and slips Joe's twenty-five-cent piece into his apron pocket. Joe finds a corner in the stable and some feed for the mare, rubs her down, and slogs through the drifts to the bunkhouse. He squeezes in with the boys at a long trestle table, digs his tin plate, cup, and cutlery out of his packsack, and helps himself as the heavy, aromatic platters are passed from hand to hand. Apart from a grunt or two, no one gives him a word, or even a glance.

Joe's face and hands are leathery, scarred; his hair is long, his beard ragged, and his clothes stink of horse, sweat, and wood-smoke. A good smell. Funny, when he'd seen the cook's big Moffat stove, he'd almost blurted, *Moffat! We have a Moffat stove too, back home in Weston!*

Where is home? Joe smiles now as he remembers how angry he'd been last June, on the train out of Swift Current, when he'd had to sleep, along with Dawson and the others, on straw, in a boxcar, with their horses. *I am not a stable hand!* What a pompous, whiney little suck he'd been. *Mollycoddled,* that was Graydon's word. Among other words. Bumping into that bunch of Ontario greenhorns in Calgary, Joe realized that he'd come west to get away from them. As a boy, he'd been their target: egghead, book-worm, four-eyes, and, after he started collecting plants, pansy. Sure, out here, he could be a cowboy or a land speculator, but where would he find someone to talk to about Paleozoic seas, invertebrate fossils, glacial striations, or, God help him, variations in species of mountain lupins?

Joe misses his microscope, his books – his pocket Shakespeare turned to mush after the first week – and discussions with his colleagues at the Survey. This summer, he has learned to see Earth through both space and time, and he speaks an arcane language few others understand. Who will know of his adventures and discoveries unless he returns home to tell his stories? He'd like to be in Weston for his birthday, November 1. He'll be twenty-five. Not yet Sir Francis Drake, perhaps, but no longer a boy.

CHAPTER TWO

Winter 1883–84, Ottawa

What a luxury it was to be able to sleep in until seven, even eight o'clock, especially when the winter mornings were so dark and the deep snow on the streets muffled all sounds except the sleigh bells. Joe often missed breakfast, but his landlady, Mrs. Adams, gave him some bread and jam and a glass of milk. It suited Joe perfectly; after the past summer, the mere smell of bacon gave him heartburn, and while he had been boarding out for many years, he still pined for freshly laid eggs and vegetables straight from the garden. The Tyrrells kept livestock and chickens and grew all their own food, but their big, Georgian-style brick house with its formal rose garden resembled an Irish estate more than an Ontario homestead, and Joe hated being snubbed as a hayseed because he had grown up in a rural hamlet. Fortunately the Geological Survey offices were in the National Museum building at the corner of Sussex and George streets, beside the Byward Market, so he usually bought a good, cheap farmer's lunch and an apple or a sweet to eat at his desk.

His own desk! Joe had come up in the world, at least from the basement fossil storage room. Taken on at the Survey as an apprentice clerk in the summer of 1881, he had spent nearly two years helping the museum curator, J.F. Whiteaves, unpack, sort, clean, and identify thousands of invertebrate fossils to display in the Survey's new museum. Many of them were still partially encased in stone; most were incomplete, or broken. Trilobites,

Joseph Burr Tyrrell as a young man, date uncertain. (TFRBL, J.B.T papers, F3607)

ammonitcs, molluscs, corals . . . a bewildering number of species. The work was dusty, the old building's basement so dank and foul that Joe felt suffocated. He'd been on the point of quitting the Survey when the director, Dr. A.R.C. Selwyn, had promoted him to second-class clerk at $700 a year and sent him west with Dr. Dawson. This winter, Joe's task was to make a map based on his survey of the Bow River valley from Kicking Horse Pass to Calgary. He had been handicapped by forest fire smoke and heavy snow, but he had made the required observations as best he could.

He had never before made a map, and hadn't the faintest clue how to go about it. "Read this, Mr. Tyrrell," Dawson said coolly, and he tossed on Joe's desk Chauvenet's *Manual of Spherical and Practical Astronomy*.

Joe felt the thud as a slam at his science education. At Toronto's University College, he had specialized in geology, biology, chemistry, mineralogy, even meteorology, dropping everything else in his final year, but he had graduated with a Bachelor of Arts degree because the university did not offer a Bachelor of Science. Worse, while he had won prizes in his junior years, he had failed to win anything, especially the gold medal, on graduation. Dr. Dawson had been his examiner.

It was no secret that Joe had been hired on by the Survey through political patronage; so had all of his colleagues. Jobs in government service, whether federal or provincial, were awarded to friends and supporters of the party in power, and the Conservatives, led by Prime Minister Sir John A. Macdonald, had been in power in Ottawa since 1878. Joe's father, William, was a Conservative warhorse in York County, northwest of Toronto, and a frequent, albeit failed, candidate in parliamentary elections. William Tyrrell had known Sir John for forty years. William was not at all embarrassed to exploit his old friendship to wangle his son a job, and then meddle shamelessly to advance Joe's interests within the Survey.

William Tyrrell liked to get his way. A big, ruddy, blustery man, toughened from decades of outdoor work as a builder of mills and bridges on the Humber River, he had achieved local prominence as a justice of the peace, county councillor, and, recently, reeve of the village of Weston. Self-made, the immigrant descendant of ancient Norman–Irish gentry – a Tyrrell had invaded England with William the Conqueror – William affected formal dress, courtly manners, and an arrogant, authoritarian attitude, but when crossed, he was crude, hot-tempered, and vengeful. William wanted the best for his seven children, as long as they did what he wanted.

"William Tyrrell at sixty, 1876." (TFRBL, J.B T. papers, F3592)

William had decided that Joe would be a lawyer, and on Joe's graduation from university in 1880 he had been articled to the Toronto firm of Macdonald, Rose. Joe studied hard, because he had been offered no job in science, but he was bored by his menial, unpaid clerk's chores and in despair at the prospect of a lifetime of paperwork in an airless office. Joe had a history of pneumonia, and sickness became his escape; within months, his doctor diagnosed weak lungs and ordered him to find outdoor work.

Sickness was a soft spot with William Tyrrell. His first two sons had died in infancy, and Rob, the oldest boy, suffered from chronic chest congestion that the family euphemistically called "hay fever." A hint of tuberculosis was a virtual death sentence, as it was for most families. By a lucky coincidence (as Joe must have known), the Geological Survey of Canada was expanding. How could Sir John refuse William Tyrrell's sickly son a job that would save his life?

Sir John obliged, but Joe had barely settled in as an apprentice at the Survey before he complained about his lowly status and "miserable salary" of $500 a year. At that time, $500 a year was perfectly reasonable for a young man starting out; it was as much or more than Joe would earn as a schoolteacher, and junior university professors weren't paid much more. The problem was, Joe spent more than he earned, not on frivolities, unless you counted tobacco, but on books and subscriptions to scientific journals, a microscope, and lessons in drawing and watercolour to make geological illustrations. William, a spendthrift himself, shared his son's sense of grievance. When Dr. Selwyn had refused Joe's request for a raise and promotion in November 1882, William wrote to Sir John urging him to get Joe "a better position" that would allow him to work outdoors.

"I am sure he [Sir John] will take some steps in the matter," William writes to Joe. "He has always acted prompt and friendly and I expect him to do so now." Joe was not optimistic: "As to myself, perhaps Sir John will do something but it is not likely for he never speaks of any one interested in science in any better way than those d—n scientists, so you see I am in a bad line for his favour." In reply, William promised to "work on Sir John," but warned Joe not to be rash: "A lot of young men are looking for any sort of office."

William Tyrrell could ill afford to have his second son unemployed. At sixty-six, William had retired from business. Rob, a doctor, was struggling to set up his medical practice in Toronto, and the three youngest children were still in school. It would be inexcusable for Joe to throw away his expensive education, and unthinkable that a descendant of the Tyrrells of Grange Castle, County Kildare, might become a common labourer.

On December 19, 1882, Sir John A. Macdonald writes to William somewhat testily: "Dr. Selwyn informs me that your son is now in receipt of $700 per annum. This is a considerable advance. In the civil service, as you know, all salaries are progressive and no one can reach the top of the ladder without climbing it commencing at the lowest round."

Three months later, Joe confronted Selwyn with an audacious ultimatum: promote me to field geologist or I'll quit. Selwyn calmly accepted Joe's resignation; Joe had shown no aptitude for paleontology, he was chronically late for work, insubordinate, and hotheaded. New men quit the Survey all the time.

But Selwyn had reckoned without the prime minister. "Sir John has had a talk with Selwyn," William Tyrrell advises Joe on March 28, 1883. "Say nothing and keep your own council [sic]," then, on April 8, "Act with the greatest caution." Selwyn capitulated. Joe writes to his father on Monday, April 16, "On Saturday afternoon Dr. Selwyn called me into his room and asked me not to resign and that he would accede to my wishes and put me on the outside staff."

Joe didn't breathe a word to his colleagues about the prime minister's invisible hand in his promotion, but they were delighted: they all hoped and schemed for such good fortune! "Arse" Selwyn was cordially hated. He was English, to begin with, and hired other Englishmen as antique as himself; he was dictatorial, impatient, and unpredictable, and treated his geologists, no matter how experienced, as a headmaster would treat stupid, unruly schoolboys. In the summer, Joe and Dawson had been flabbergasted to meet Selwyn, in a buckboard, on the trail east of the Kicking Horse Pass. Looking for coal, he'd said. Weren't they doing that themselves, on his instructions?

Selwyn's haughtiness made him even less popular with those politicians who expected Canada's Geological Survey to promote the interests, however fraudulent, of land developers and mining speculators. By the early spring of 1884, anonymous letters in the newspapers were accusing Selwyn of incompetence, and the geologists were in open revolt. A parliamentary committee was debating Selwyn's dismissal, or the termination of the entire Survey.

The Survey's meagre annual budget was approved by a vote in the House of Commons every May, and the result was never certain. Geological expeditions to the remotest corners of Canada's *terra incognita*, lasting many months, had to be planned and outfitted long before it was known if their expenses would be covered, and those expenses had to be accounted for down to the last shoelace: Joe's friend Richard G. McConnell was refused a claim for clothes burned in a prairie fire that nearly killed him.

When Joe was in the North-West, there had been times when he'd thought that having to go hungry, sleep in the snow, and walk until his legs buckled beneath him had been deliberate efforts to punish or discourage him, but he understood now that while frugality was a necessity, self-denial was the monastic mystique of the Survey. Aside from their instruments, which had to be the best, any comfort, not to mention indulgence, was an insult to the memory of the Survey's revered, austere founder, Sir William Logan.

Logan, the first Canadian scientist to be knighted, had died in 1875, the year before Joe entered the University of Toronto, and admiration for Logan's famous achievements had influenced many young men to pursue geology. Logan had made his reputation in Wales, investigating the then mysterious relationship between coal beds and fossilized trees, and as head of the Geological Survey of Canada from 1842 to 1869, he had defined and mapped the rock formations of much of eastern Canada. In 1851, his display of Canadian minerals at the Crystal Palace Exhibition in London was praised as the best of all, and in 1855, a similar display won the Grand Medal at the Paris Exposition. Logan was the first Canadian to be elected a fellow of the Royal Society of

London, and the first Canadian to receive the Geological Society of London's prestigious Wollaston Medal.

Logan had been a paragon. His hand-coloured geological maps were works of art, his sketches of geographical features beautiful enough to hang in a gallery. In appearance he had been elfin, but his endurance and stamina had been inexhaustible; hammer in hand, he'd clamber up and down cliffs from sunrise to sunset, oblivious to hunger, injury, or fatigue. He took a perverse delight in looking filthy and unkempt; strangers often mistook this ragged, busy little fellow with the fly-away hair for an escaped lunatic.

After one field trip, Logan described himself: "hair matted with spruce gum, a beard red, with two patches of white on one side, a pair of cracked spectacles, a red flannel shirt, a waistcoat with patches on the left pocket, where some sulphuric acid, which I carry in a small vial to try for the presence of lime in the rocks, had leaked through – a jacket of moleskin, shining with grease and trousers patched on one leg and with a burnt hole in the other leg; with beef boots – Canada boots as they are called – torn and roughened all over with scraping on the stumps and branches of trees, and patched on the legs with sundry pieces of leather and divers colors, a broad rimmed and round-topped hat, once white but now no color and battered into all shapes."

When Logan travelled by canoe, he lived like a voyageur. His tent might be only a flimsy canvas sheet, his "sleeping sack" two blankets stitched together. He lived on salt pork and hardtack, but he was not entirely indifferent to food: "It requires considerable time to arrange a porcupine for cooking when the skin is to be left on it," he notes in his journal. "It is necessary to pluck off all the quills, as the feathers are plucked off a bird, and then to singe the small and long fine hairs, and scrape them off with a knife. The skin is thick, and there is a great deal of nourishment in it."

Logan's backwoods persona enhanced his reputation for brilliance, and the extent of his eccentricity was hushed up outside scientific circles. Dr. Robert Bell, a senior geologist with the

Survey who had worked for Logan, described Sir William's lodgings as a single, sparsely furnished room that served as office, mapping room, parlour, bedroom, and wardrobe; the walls were decorated with work clothes and instruments hanging from nails, the floor cluttered with old boots. No stranger meeting Logan in his shabby workman's clothes would have guessed that this little tramp was one of the richest men in Montreal; when the Survey budget ran a little short, or a storage warehouse was needed, Logan simply reached into his own pocket to cover the cost.

Joe's office at the survey bore a striking relationship to Logan's dirty cubby, as did his tiny room at Mrs. Adams's boarding house. Logan had casually stored hundreds of boxes of rock samples and fossils in his warehouse without labels or inventory. It was no wonder that the Geological Survey was a model of improvised chaos.

Well, Joe had proven his Spartan mettle out west, and he'd eaten roast porcupine too, one he'd shot himself. He couldn't draw worth a damn, but he could learn to take photographs, and he'd teach himself to make maps. But Logan had never been west of Ontario, and his obsession with collecting wasn't any help when it came to deciphering the *meaning* of the rocks and the fossils in them. Why had multitudes of certain plants and creatures thrived during one era, not earlier or later? Why had they disappeared? And were the survivors superior, or merely different? Logan, Canada's pre-eminent scientist, had ignored or evaded the furious international controversy over evolution.

It was a destructive legacy. In the rest of the western world, evolution had come to be considered a reasonable, even authoritative, explanation for Nature's patterns and complexities, although it meant accepting apes as human ancestors, but in Canada scientists dared not openly question the Book of Genesis: "In the beginning, God created . . ." To believe in "natural selection" was to admit to Godless "materialism" or "socialism," heresies so shocking to Christian society and the Church-run colleges that suspects were vilified and ostracized. The words *agnostic* and *atheist* were obscenities spoken in whispers, if at all.

The scientist responsible for this Christian orthodoxy, William "Elder" Dawson, Little Doc's father, was the world's leading proponent of Creationism. In a torrent of books, tracts, and lectures, he attempted to force scientific observation to conform to the "evidence" of the Bible, which he believed to be God's revealed truth.

"The Bible can have no conflict with science," Dawson stated in *The Origin of the World According to Revelation and Science*, published in 1877. "The study of nature is an inquiry into the ways of God." This view, promulgated by Protestant theologians for generations before *Origin of Species* was published, comforted Victorian Christians frightened by the concept of a violent, amoral, and irrational universe.

"The winds and the clouds are so arranged as to afford the required supplies of moisture to the wilderness where no man is, to 'cause the bud of the tender herb to spring forth,'" Dawson wrote. "For similar objects the tempest is ordered, and the clouds arranged 'by wisdom.' The adaptation of the wild ass, the wild goat, the ostrich, the migratory birds, the horse, the hippopotamus, the crocodile, to their several habitats, modes of life, and uses in nature, are most vividly sketched and applied as the consummate wisdom of the Creator, which descends to the minutest details of organization and habit."

Elder Dawson's interpretation of scripture as science would have had less impact had he not been a respected friend and associate of Logan, and Sir Charles Lyell, who praised Dawson's research in his popular classic *Principles of Geology*. By 1884, Elder Dawson's scientific prestige was so great that he was elected president of the British Association for the Advancement of Science; later that year he was knighted.

Canada had no Thomas Huxley, Darwin's fearless, eloquent advocate in Great Britain, and science itself was considered useless or, worse, subversive. University positions were scarce and

"Elizabeth Burr Tyrrell, circa 1885." (TFRBL, J.B.T. papers, F3593)

research opportunities in private industry virtually nil. Canadian scientists avoided self-incrimination by shrugging off evolution as one of many dubious theories, or by not discussing it at all.

Joe Tyrrell had been dodging God all his life. His earliest memories would have included the Methodist summer camp meetings in some nearby meadow, with the preacher's soaring incantations invoking God's presence, and the congregation shouting *Amen!* and *Praise the Lord!* God was at church too every

Sunday, and He presided over the dinner table, but mostly He lived in Joe's mother's sitting room.

Elizabeth Burr Tyrrell belonged to a prominent Quaker family that had moved to Ontario from New Jersey after the American War of Independence, but her father, Rowland Burr, a contractor and land speculator, had left the Society of Friends to marry a French Huguenot Anglican, Hester L'Amoreaux. They compromised on Methodism, with its Quakerish code of hard work, plain living, and good conduct, but evangelical Elizabeth had accepted God as her Saviour; His presence in her heart governed her every waking hour.

Joe's father, Methodist by marriage, Anglican by tradition, regarded religion as the business of women. William Tyrrell was quite willing to abide by his wife's strictures against having liquor in the house, but meetings of the York County council were held in taverns, and Conservative party gatherings, especially with Sir John in attendance, were notoriously well lubricated with whisky. Joe and his brothers were not encouraged to hunt and fish on Sundays, but since the Methodists valued healthy exercise and the exploration of "God's works," they could freely roam the woods and meadows in the Humber River valley. The Tyrrell children read Romantic poetry, popular novels, and the Toronto newspapers, and, unlike stricter Methodist families, they had a piano. When Joe rebelliously took up smoking in college, his father seems to have approved of this effort to fit in with the other fellows.

A stubborn, unrepentant "unbeliever" by the time he reached the Geological Survey in Ottawa, Joe nevertheless went to church on Sundays, varying the denominational menu by attending all the Protestant churches in turn. It was an opportunity to meet people, and, if lucky, be invited to someone's home for tea. Although shy and tongue-tied with strangers and stand-offish in his manner, Joe enjoyed congenial company, especially if the girls were as pretty and lively as his sisters Minnie, Annie, and Lizzie. Most doors in Ottawa, however, were closed to him. The greatest proportion of the city's thirty thousand residents were

Roman Catholic, either Irish or French Canadian; tradesmen, servants, and working people, they lived east of the Rideau Canal in Corktown and Lower Town. To the west of Parliament Hill, on The Flats, lived a rowdy population of shantymen employed by the shrieking sawmills that straddled the Ottawa River. Joe would no more think of visiting The Flats than the lumber kings who owned the mills, Booth, Eddy, Gilmour, Bronson, would dream of inviting an obscure government clerk into their dark brick mansions.

Joe was glad for the cheerful company of his devil-may-care younger brother James, a surveyor with Ottawa's Dominion Land Survey, who shared Joe's pleasure in long rambles through the woods. Sir John and Lady Macdonald did not ask the Tyrrell brothers to tea, and few other politicians lived in Canada's capital; they camped there briefly while the House of Commons was in session from February to May. The tiny civil service was rigidly stratified; only the senior echelons were invited to join the Rideau Club, or to attend banquets and receptions at the governor general's residence, Rideau Hall. Yet during the winter, Their Excellencies, Lord and Lady Lansdowne, hosted tobogganing and skating parties on the grounds for everyone who had signed the guest book in the entrance foyer.

Joe couldn't skate. Skating was dancing on ice, and he had never learned to dance. He excelled, however, at the latest craze: snowshoeing. The handsome young British officers, Lansdowne's aides-de-camp, had taken it up in Quebec, and completed their *coureur de bois* costume with moccasins, a toque, and a striped, white Hudson's Bay Company blanket coat bound with a bright, plaited sash. Joe, proud, shabby veteran of the North-West, scoffed at the officers' music hall getup, but envied their popularity; all the fashionable young women, decked out in identical blanket coats, toques, and sashes, stumbled about on their snowshoes and fell helplessly into the snowbanks in fits of giggles. Their laughter and rosy cheeks aroused Joe as much as their infatuation with the officers annoyed him. Robert Bell, who had been everywhere in the North, gave Joe a pair of his snowshoes and showed him how to walk on them. They hurt like hell until his muscles got the hang of it, then he outdistanced everyone.

It was only a game. The Lansdowne crowd liked to call Ottawa their "Arctic" posting, as if they were among Esquimaux, or trapped in the ice like Sir John Franklin, frozen to death with all his pitiful crew. Frolic and flirtation served to while away the long, dull hours; there were no republican rebellions to put down, no invasions of, or from, the United States, and, although there were warnings of discontent, no uprisings among the Red Indians in the North-West. For an active soldier, Ottawa was an exile; all the action was in Egypt.

In the spring of 1884, Canada, with the rest of the British Empire, was aflame with excitement and alarm over the plight of General C.G. "Chinese" Gordon, besieged in Khartoum. Exactly why the eccentric British general had gone to Khartoum, a desert outpost on the Upper Nile in the vast wasteland of Sudan, was not clear: never mind, the telegraph wires had been cut and the city was surrounded by a fanatical army of Sudanese tribesmen led by the Mahdi, a charismatic, self-proclaimed Mohammedan messiah who had declared *jihad*, or holy war, on the infidels, whether Egyptian, Turk, or British. If Khartoum fell, the Mahdi would rule Sudan.

Rumours circulated that General Garnet Wolseley, hero of the campaign to quell Louis Riel's Metis rebellion at Red River in 1870, intended to lead a British expedition up the Nile to relieve Khartoum, and that Wolseley wanted his boats to be manned by the fearless Canadian voyageurs who had transported him to and from Red River.

Joe had been only eleven when the special train carrying Wolseley's troops north from Toronto had passed right through Weston, and all the village had turned out to wave and cheer. The rebellion had been a bit of a bust: Riel fled before the British troops arrived, but *The Great Lone Land*, written by Wolseley's scout, William Francis Butler, had made the North-West seem wonderfully melancholy and romantic. Butler, a burly, bewhiskered Irish soldier, had travelled by canoe, horse, and dogsled as far as the Hudson's Bay Company's post at Rocky Mountain House, then, two years later, to the Peace River country west of Lake Athabasca, an adventure he told in a sequel, *The Wild North Land*. Now, Butler was in Egypt to build the Canadian voyageurs' boats for the Nile expedition.

Joe had never lifted a paddle or an oar in his life, but brave Nor'westers were suddenly all the rage, and a Canadian naval officer, Lieutenant Rawson, had led Wolseley's army to a surprise victory against Egyptian rebel forces by guiding them across the desert at night, navigating by the stars.

Joe practised making astronomical measurements and redoubled his efforts at map-making. He took boxing and fencing lessons, although he was no good at physical combat, and got a licence to shoot birds, for scientific purposes, in the Gatineau Hills. He gave a lecture on fleas to the Ottawa Field Naturalists Club. His two beautiful *suctoria* were not new species, but he'd obtained them from a Rocky Mountain chipmunk and a field mouse he'd shot in the Kicking Horse Pass, so they had an exotic interest for his appreciative audience.

Fleas, mites, snails, eggs, skins of birds, snakes, mountain sheep, and grizzly bears; antlers, arrowheads, hundreds of pressed plants, tons of rock samples – Survey geologists were encouraged to ship back to their museum anything that struck them as curious or unusual. Mounds of stuff piled up, yet during the winter months they had time to go through only a fraction of it. The Survey couldn't afford to employ expert specialists to evaluate the quality of their collections, even though their cramped and shabby building, an old hotel, was Canada's official museum, and, much to the politicians' astonishment, thousands of people came to peer at the displays.

Joe learned to catalogue his own plant specimens, and helped Richard McConnell puzzle over some strange bones he'd found northwest of Fort Macleod and in the Cypress Hills, north of the U.S. border. McConnell was Joe's age, and as new to the Survey as he was, but McConnell was already a seasoned frontiersman, having spent the winter of 1882–83 in Fort Calgary, as pretty much the only white man in the area except for the police and the smugglers. Joe and McConnell both knew buffalo bones, the prairie was strewn with them, but they had never seen bones like these before, even in illustrations. The brittle bones had broken into pieces when McConnell excavated them, and he was having a devil of a time trying to put them together again.

No one at the Survey was a vertebrate biologist, or a surgeon expert in anatomy, and it was hard to know if these skeletal remnants belonged to birds, fish, reptiles, or mammals, or to some mythological creature, a gryphon perhaps, or a unicorn. The common term, *dinosaur*, was unhelpful: it meant simply "terrible lizard." Skeletons of these grotesque, gargantuan creatures, some of them larger than whales, were being dug up in England, Europe, and the United States, but apart from indicating that areas now desert were apparently once seas or swamps, their significance was a mystery.

The bones McConnell had found would have to be sent to paleontologist Edward Drinker Cope in Philadelphia for identification. Cope was one of the two most famous, or infamous, fossil hunters in North America. The other was Othniel Charles Marsh, paleontologist with the Peabody Museum at Yale University, New Haven, Connecticut. The two had been locked in venomous rivalry since 1871, when Cope, uninvited, had followed Marsh into a newly uncovered fossil quarry at Fort Bridger, Wyoming. Monstrous bones had been turning up in the American Midwest since railway construction had disturbed the ground, but this graveyard was a treasure trove of extinct mammals, reptiles, and fish, never before known or imagined. Marsh refused to share the Bridger Basin with anyone, but Cope quickly found promising sites in Kansas, Montana, and Colorado, and the two scientists fought it out at Como Bluff, Wyoming. Each hired local men to scour the land and dig out the fossilized bones, and they bought every bone they could from amateur collectors. Money was no object: Cope was wealthy, and Marsh was an heir to the Peabody fortune.

Each man shrouded his activities in secrecy, hired spies to discover what the other was up to, and bribed employees to switch sides. Marsh travelled with a U.S. Army escort, and at one point hired Buffalo Bill Cody as a scout and guard. Stories circulated of threats, sabotage, and fist fights. Cope and Marsh publicly accused each other of lying, theft, plagiarism, and incompetence, and their jealous battle revealed to all their own ugly, obsessive acquisitiveness.

Other scientists were excluded from their collections. Apart from the few specimens Cope and Marsh chose to exhibit, there was no way of independently checking the accuracy of their identifications; skeletons were incomplete, and the location of a fossil's excavation was often unknown. Marsh, who had a large staff and mountains of bones at Yale, published cautiously, while Cope, with no assistants, trumpeted his findings in a blizzard of telegrams, bulletins, and self-published journals. Cope claimed to have discovered hundreds of species, but in his rush to be first, he was notoriously incomprehensible and inaccurate.

Marsh was silent and lugubrious, Cope verbose, excitable, and frank to the point of insult. Marsh, an expert on the evolution of the horse from an extinct three-toed mammal, was championed by Darwin and Huxley; Cope, a Quaker, appealed to Christians, among them Elder Dawson. When Cope was bankrupted by investing unwisely in Colorado silver mines, he found part-time work identifying fossil fragments for the Geological Survey of Canada.

Not that Cope invited the Canadians to inspect his collection, explore his excavations, or discuss his research methodology; their fossils were shipped to him in Philadelphia, where they were examined, identified, if possible, and returned. Perhaps it was just as well. The public generally believed that these beasts had perished in Noah's Flood; if a scientist contradicted popular opinion, what better explanation for their existence and extinction could he offer?

Were other marvels waiting to be found? Canadian scientists had only started to tickle Earth's scarred and wrinkled skin, and Joe was anxious to continue his exploration of the Rocky Mountains. A little placer gold had been found decades earlier in a region of British Columbia called the Cariboo; a vein might be nearby, or diamonds, as in South Africa, or a lost civilization. Cariboo, come to think of it, had as wild a ring to it as Khartoum.

Joe was delighted when Selwyn told him he'd be going back to the North-West for the summer of 1884, and crestfallen that his area of exploration was to be the open prairie between the Red Deer and North Saskatchewan rivers.

I'll be accompanying Dr. Dawson again, I assume, Joe said, trying not to sound dismayed.

No, said Selwyn. This is your expedition, Mr. Tyrrell. You're on your own.

‿

August 1, 1884, somewhere between the Battle and Red Deer rivers
"We have certainly commenced the month very badly today as it rained almost all day and we were scarcely able to move out of our tents. It is now about nine o'clock and it is still raining."

Joe was feeling as low as he ever had in his life. It had rained most of the time since he headed north from Calgary on May 30. The rain was as unexpected as it was miserable. His Palliser expedition map clearly designated this area as "Arid Plains." Joe had passed through areas marked "Great Herds of Buffalo" with no buffalo, and he was amazed to come across one small herd of about twenty at an alkali slough. His Native wagon men, Matthew and Joseph Cook, said that the buffalo went away long ago, when they were children. Nor was there a "Blackfoot Camp" where it was marked on the map; the Blackfoot were now on their reserves far to the south. Captain Palliser, although an army officer, and armed with an arsenal of weapons, had been too timid to venture on to this unknown prairie between the Red Deer and Battle rivers. In those years, 1857 to 1860, the "Great Plains," as he had labelled them, were the scene of frequent bloody skirmishes between Blackfoot warriors and Cree raiders from the north. Strange interlopers fled, or were murdered.

Joe was proud to have been given the sole assignment of exploring and mapping this dangerous land, but aside from a brief visit to Fort Edmonton in early July, he'd hardly seen a soul. The monotony was wearing him down. The rain and mist made it hard to see any distance, or to take his bearings, and the low hills, like the rolling prairie, were covered in dense grass. The only rocks to be seen were on the eroded sides of the creeks and riverbeds, but the rain had made the cutbanks too steep and slippery to climb. Joe was stuck for a week in Calgary buying a few provisions because the Bow River had flooded and swept away the bridge. The ferry had stopped running, so they finally loaded everything into their wagon and forded the torrent at a shallow crossing. A miners' wagon next in line was swept downstream, and the horses drowned.

So far, Joe's first expedition as leader had been a complete washout, so to speak. He had had to let the Cook brothers go when one of them was accused of stealing a horse; then his cook, Fitzpatrick, injured his eye. Joe had wasted five days on a side trip to the Methodist mission at Morley following up a false rumour that silver had been found there. He worried about trying to cover the rest of the 45,000 square miles he had been assigned before the snow covered the ground.

At least he had proven Palliser's map right, or almost right, in one location: on the Red Deer River, near some nameless creeks, it notes: "Coal and Ironstone, Sicilified wood and Lignite, Gypsum. Freshwater shells." In Palliser's 1860 report, his geologist, Dr. James Hector, gives a graphic description of the junction of a creek he called Deadman's and the Red Deer River: "A little above this place the lignite forms beds of great thickness, one group of seams measuring 20 feet in thickness, of which 12 feet consists of pure compact lignite, and the remainder of carbonaceous clays. At one point the seam was on fire, the bed exposed in a cliff of about 300 yards in length being at many places in a dull glow, the constant sliding of the bank continuing to supply a fresh surface to the atmosphere. For miles around the air is loaded by a heavy sulphureous and limey smell, and the Indians say that for as long as they can remember the fire at this place has never been extinguished summer or winter."

Hector gives the location as "latitude 52°5' N; longitude 115°30' W," but floating down the Red Deer River in a canvas canoe, Joe found no sulphurous fumes or perpetual fire. Then, on June 12, three miles above the junction of the Red Deer River and Rosebud Creek, he spotted a coal seam nearly three feet thick. He found fossil plants – a clue to coal – red iron oxide stains on the riverbanks where coal seams had burned away, and a few dinosaurian bones.

The tortuous Red Deer River valley was a perfect exhibit of seventy million years of geological history: the steep, water-worn banks rose in undulating, alternating layers of mudstones, sandstones, shales, clays, and coal. The layers, shaded from pale grey to ochre, brown, and black, looked like stripes in a clumsily knitted sock, and in places the rock had been weathered into weird, almost human shapes. Joe had noticed many unmapped gullies running into the Red Deer River north of Rosebud Creek. He decided to take a look.

On August 3, they broke camp in a cloud of flying ants and headed southeast across the open prairie towards the river. The sod was rough and full of badger holes; on August 5, the wagon's rear axle broke. They circled far to the west to avoid the deep coulees that barred their path; it took much longer, but saved wear and tear on the wagon. Nonetheless, the wagon's front axle broke. Joe was furious with Fitzpatrick and his partners, Gough and Mulligan. Lazy good-for-nothings. It's their wagon, and they're too clumsy to keep it in repair. It took them a day of searching in the coulees to find a green tree branch to make a new axle. Sunday was so sultry Joe declared a day of rest.

The next day, August 10, they followed an old Indian trail into a deep valley. The decline was so steep and slippery they had to lock the wagon wheels, but the stream at the bottom was fresh and cool, and they camped on a meadow shaded by bushes laden with ripe serviceberries. Joe would tell various versions of the events of the next few days, but he writes his first account to his father on August 13:

"My dear Father,

"The next day I had plenty to do examining the rocks along the creek, but found out too that it would be quite impossible to get up the other bank – the trail was too steep and rough. It is a very old indistinct Indian trail that we were following. It was almost as impossible to get back, for the hill was steep and about 300 feet high.

"This morning I intended to try but it commenced to rain and we waited until this afternoon. First we took up the buckboard with about 30 pounds on it and with one man pushing behind, one at the horse's head and the other alongside of him pounding him, we managed to get that up in about half an hour.

"Then came the wagon. We threw off about half the load, and our load is in all about half a ton, and hitched another horse on to the front of the tongue by the tail, but the three of them could not pull it up, so we threw out all but about 100 pounds of the clumsiest things and at last we managed to get to the top. One man had to ride the front horse and keep him well pounded on.

"Then the stuff had to be got up, so we took down the horses to be saddled, packed the outfit on their backs and thus in two or three trips we managed to get everything to the top. This was about four o'clock so we thought we would pull on a few miles, but in hitching in the horse into the buckboard, he became fractious and broke the whiffletree and part of the harness so we camped to get things mended.

"I am having a fine time just at present, gaining plenty of experience for the men don't know how to do anything and are thin-skinned and afraid of getting themselves a little damp. They have to be shown how to do everything, and though they are good enough natured we cannot make the same progress that we could if they knew what to do in any emergency. . . .

"While down in the bottom of the last coulee, I found a head of one of the large extinct reptiles that used to roam over the country, the first as far as I know that has been found in any part of Canada, but unfortunately it was too heavy to move and too brittle, and though I have got a large portion of it, it is now in so many pieces that it is doubtful whether it can be put together again. It would have been worth a good deal to have it just as it was in the Museum room in Ottawa. I also found a number of other very fine bones but am not able to carry them away, as we have a wagonload already. I may come back for them in the Fall, when the rest of the work is done.

"Love to all at home,

"Your affectionate son, J.B. Tyrrell

"PS: You must not consider that I am enduring hardships. I am not in my blankets five minutes before I am asleep and there is a charm about this life that for a young man is not in any other and there is no chance of any accident to any person."

In his field notebook, Joe gives a few more details about the "Dinosaurian bones." He had found them "in an excellent state of preservation, though very brittle, among them a large head almost perfect and we spent the afternoon in excavating them out of the bank." The next day, Joe "packed such of the bones as we could carry up to the top of the hill, leaving the rest at the bottom of the bank." The weather, he writes, was cold and dreary, "like a damp day in November."

Short of food, they rattled full tilt across the open prairie towards Calgary, a "very rough and disagreeable journey" in the rain. A wagon axle broke again. They were living on pancakes and pork when they reached Calgary on August 22 and Joe shipped the dinosaur bones to Ottawa. The next eight weeks he spent exploring the Red Deer River area in rain and snow. On October 22, he writes in his notebook: "I went with Gough and two horses to get the fossil bones which we had left here in August. This occupied us till dark and we took our supper by fire light on the hillside in a clump of spruce. . . . I wrapped up some of the fossils." On October 23: "We were obliged to repair the wagon and then I wrapped up the rest of the fossils . . . we then climbed up the bank of the creek about 200 feet." On October 30, Joe left for Ottawa. Nowhere in his field notebook does he record the exact location of the dinosaur excavation. The creek is nameless.

The dinosaur skull, or rather a fragment of it, was the only fossil bone, of two apparent wagonloads, to be sent to Edward Cope for analysis. Cope identified it, and a second skull fragment later found nearby by the Survey's field paleontologist T.C. Weston, as *Laelaps incrassatus Cope*. In 1905, it was renamed *Albertosaurus sarcophagus*, carrion-eating reptile, in honour of the new province where it was found.

CHAPTER THREE

What was Joe thinking? Years later, in an article in *Science* magazine, he described finding the dinosaur skeleton virtually complete: "I walked up the bank close to camp, and at an elevation of between forty to eighty feet found a number of Dinosaurian bones in an excellent state of preservation, though very brittle. Most of them were heavy and massive, such as those of the limbs, etc., but among these was a large and fairly perfect head of *Laelaps incrassatus*, a gigantic carnivore. We spent the afternoon excavating these bones from the rock, but unfortunately we had no appliances but axes and small geological hammers. We worked with all the care that the tools and time at our disposal would allow, but in spite of all we could do some of the bones, teeth etc. were broken. Then, after we managed to get them out of the rock, we had no proper means of packing them, and no boxes but the wagon box to put them in. However, we got together the skull and some of the best of the leg and other bones and then found that we had a heavier load than we were able to carry with us. We were therefore obliged to leave a small pile of bones at the bottom on the bank just north of the creek, on the chance that we might be able to pick them up at a later date, which fortunately we were able to do two months afterwards."

Joe knew that he had made a rare and significant discovery: he called it "one of the most enjoyable thrills of my life." Why then did he and his teamsters hack the skeleton to pieces, toss bones helter-skelter in their wagon box, and leave the rest in situ or piled by a creek in the vague hope they might be retrieved? Did Joe not know that an excavation on this scale ought to take weeks or months of painstaking labour, and that ideally the bones should be left in their stone casing, then wrapped for shipment in layers of burlap soaked in flour paste? Why did he not carefully record the site, then return with expert help? T.C. Weston had made numerous fossil discoveries in the region the year before, and both G.M. Dawson and Richard McConnell were working in the foothills of the Rockies not far to the west; Dawson had excavated fragments of dinosaurian fossils in 1874 and 1881, and Edward Cope had determined that McConnell's strange bones had belonged to an extinct horse, rhinoceros, and wild boar.

Did Joe panic? Was he afraid that Fitzpatrick, an American, would steal the fossil and sell it? Cope and Marsh paid high prices, and they weren't choosy about where their bones came from. Or was he simply following the amateurish, slapdash practice of the Survey? Weston, a jeweller's lapidary by training, had no more expertise than Joe at excavation, and Dawson's dinosaurian fossils had been too fragmentary to identify a species. In Ottawa, Joe's discovery seems to have caused no excitement; the Survey's annual report for 1884 simply lists "the skull of a dinosaur" among "about 400 specimens of plants, invertebrates and vertebrates" that Joe had collected that summer.

What became of the rest of the skeleton? If the wagonloads of bones Joe claimed to have shipped to Ottawa from Calgary ever arrived, they were lost, discarded, or sent on to Cope in Philadelphia, where, as Joe phrased it, they "were probably not sufficiently perfect for identification." As it was, even the remnant of the skull was so incomplete that Cope waited four years, until Weston found a complementary specimen, before making his identification. Another two decades passed before the Survey, prodded and assisted by the Americans, began to probe the vast, astonishing dinosaur graveyard a few miles down the Red Deer River.

Joe's career as a paleontologist came to an abrupt halt, however, and for the rest of his life he remained silent or disingenuous about his dinosaur discovery. At the time, his successful survey of rich coal beds on the Red Deer River was infinitely more significant, and he was assigned to spend the summers of 1885 and 1886 on an almost recklessly dangerous mission: investigating rumours of coal, gold, and silver in the eastern Rockies and along the North Saskatchewan River.

When Joe had written his father from the prairie in the summer of 1884, "there is no chance of any accident to any person," he was being less than truthful. The miners swept away crossing the turbulent Bow River by wagon had barely escaped drowning, and Joe's whole trip had been marred by accidents, including a runaway campfire that scorched his tent. Joe no doubt wanted to allay his father's fears, but he had also learned to adopt a demeanour of calm bravado to convince calloused frontiersmen that he was not a coward. As commander of an expedition, no matter how small, he had to earn the respect of the older men he expected to accompany him to unknown places on, to them, incomprehensible errands. As a field geologist he had no uniform to give him authority, and his brass instruments sometimes aroused a good deal of laughter and incredulity; if he appeared irresolute or frightened, his men might strand him in the middle of the prairie, or take him wherever they pleased. As it was, Joe's scientific route was largely determined by pasture for the horses and wood for the campfire.

Joe slept in his own tent, and ate ahead of his men. He helped with the horses and wagon repairs if necessary, but he didn't cook, wash dishes, carry water, or gather wood. They all shared the same campfire, unlike James Carnegie, the Earl of Southesk, who, on a grizzly bear hunting expedition in 1860, had insisted on his own noble fire, and Joe did without Southesk's rubber bathtub. Joe's inventory of his camping gear for five months shows it comprised only the bare necessities: "tent, floor cloth, rubber sheet, 2 pr blankets, buffalo robe, rubber pillow, pack saddle and saddle blankets, plant bags, gold [panning] basin, camp chair and table, candles, tin plate and cups, 2 frying pans."

For clothing, he packed: "2 hats, 2 coats, 1 riding vest, 3 pr pants, 4 flannel shirts, 2 pr drawers, 2 pr hobnail boots, 1 pr waterproof slippers, 6 pr socks, 6 handkerchiefs, 1 overcoat, 1 macintosh, 1 pr leggings and 2 pr spectacles." In addition to his field glass, watch, wallet, and scientific instruments, he carried towels, soap, toiletries, matches, cutlery, penknives, writing supplies, fish hooks and line, a rifle, and a revolver. He shared the men's daily diet of bannock, porridge, beans, and bacon, varied with rice, dried peas, corn, apples, and all the ducks and rabbits they could shoot.

As commander, Joe was no long the Kid; at twenty-five, he was the same age as fur trader Sir Alexander Mackenzie had been when he reached the Arctic Ocean in 1789. Four years later Mackenzie had become the first European to cross the Rocky Mountains to the Pacific Ocean: "I could perceive the termination of the river, and its discharge into a narrow arm of the sea," Mackenzie casually recorded in his journal. In the preface to his narrative of his journeys, *Voyages from Montreal* . . . , published in 1801, Mackenzie presented himself as the ideal explorer: "Being endowed by Nature with an inquisitive mind and enterprising spirit; possessing also a constitution and frame of body equal to the most arduous undertakings, and being familiar with toilsome exertions in the prosecution of mercantile pursuits, I not only contemplated the practicability of penetrating across the continent of America, but was confident in the qualifications, as I was animated by the desire, to undertake this perilous enterprize."

Mackenzie's self-assured tone, coupled with his tales of his own Herculean strength, daring, and quick wits, created a daunting model for succeeding explorers to emulate. Forging ahead despite impassable terrain, mutinous guides, and threatening tribes, Mackenzie travelled at breakneck speed. On the great river that bears his name, he made a round trip of 3,000 miles from Lake Athabasca to the Arctic Ocean in 102 days. The 2,300-mile round trip to the Pacific, through deep gorges and across mountain passes, took a few days longer, but Mackenzie's expedition, through unknown territory, still averaged 20 to 36 miles a day.

Mackenzie, his lieutenant, Alexander McKay, and his Canadian canoemen all returned safely, and while they kidnapped local Natives to guide them, they murdered no one.

Speed, boldness, and risk-taking, joined with Sir William Logan's self-imposed privation, were expected of all exploration geologists. In the spring of 1884, bureaucrats in Ottawa's Department of the Interior, which administered both the Geological Survey and the Indian reserves, had been panicking at rumours of an "Indian uprising" in the North-West, but no one had thought twice about sending Joe into the isolated, unpopulated area between the Red Deer and Battle rivers where the only trails had been made by Indians. The presence of a lone "government man" may have been calculated to reassure the Indians that the omniscient, benevolent Queen was everywhere, but Big Bear's restless, angry Cree had not yet settled on a reserve, and Joe had returned to Ottawa only months before Big Bear's warriors murdered an Indian agent and eight other white men at Frog Lake, north of Edmonton, in April 1885.

When Joe arrived back in Calgary in the summer of 1885, Big Bear's fugitive band was still at large on the North Saskatchewan River. General T.B. Strange, a Calgary businessman and militia officer, was in hot pursuit, with a force of a thousand Canadian soldiers, scouts, mounted police, and almost all Calgary's able-bodied men. Had the surrounding Blackfoot, Blood, Piegan, and Sarcee chosen to massacre the little frontier town's remaining population, they could have done so easily, but they remained aloof from the bloody, short-lived rebellion.

The North-West Rebellion had broken out, almost by accident, on March 26, 1885, near the hamlet of Prince Albert on the North Saskatchewan River. A year or so earlier, Metis leader Louis Riel had returned from exile in the United States to lead political agitation for self-government in the North-West. Ignored and rebuffed by the Canadian government, the Metis had formed a provisional government with its headquarters at the village of Batoche. Anticipating an attack from the North West

Mounted Police, Metis scouts confiscated a trader's store at Duck Lake, then fought off a rescue party of ninety-five mounted police and local settlers. Nine police, three volunteers, and five Metis were killed in the skirmish. Prime Minister Sir John A. Macdonald immediately dispatched an armed force of Canadian militia to crush Riel and end the Metis's demands for an independent nation.

In this second Riel Rebellion, General Wolseley, still far away in Egypt fighting the Mahdi, was replaced by another British general, Frederick Middleton, and Riel, during fourteen years of exile in the United States, had been transformed into a messianic leader with his own devoted, skilful, guerrilla warriors. After two months of fierce fighting through the coulees of the Saskatchewan River watershed, the Metis were defeated in a pitched battle at Batoche on May 12, 1885; Riel surrendered three days later. Big Bear turned himself in on July 15.

Ottawa's constant ally in this racial and religious civil war was the old Blackfoot chief Crowfoot. Crowfoot, now a peacemaker, had suffered too many battle wounds at the hands of the Cree and their kinsmen, the Metis, to join their cause. In 1874, he had welcomed the mounted police when the whisky traffic at Fort Whoop-Up was destroying his people, and in 1877 when he had signed Treaty 7, he'd pledged loyalty to Canada and the Queen. In return, Crowfoot had been favoured over other chiefs, feted, interviewed, and photographed until, like the refugee Sioux chief Sitting Bull, he had achieved celebrity status. Crowfoot had chosen passive accommodation to the invader, yet, as Joe discovered, the Blackfoot diplomat had his subtle ways of exacting a price.

↵

September 5, 1885, on Crowfoot Creek, west of the Red Deer River
"We were up this morning before it was fully light and while Blake and Jack, two of the horses, were standing near nothing could be

seen of the others. . . . When the horses were not back by noon, I rode over to McDonnell's store to ask him if he had seen anything or heard anything from the Indians of them. He said he would send an Indian over to look for them in the morning.

"Sept. 6: A little after ten an Indian boy came into camp with a letter from McDonnell saying that he had seen my horses while looking for his, and would bring them in for $2.00. I gave him the $2 and sent him off, but did not see anything of him for the rest of the day. In the meantime, we kept riding around the country as much as we could with the tired horses that we had."

The next day, Joe went back to McDonnell's store. McDonnell said the Indian was still out hunting for the horses. Joe checked in at the Indian agency: no one had seen the horses and the boy had not returned.

"Sept. 8: This morning I rode over to the Indian Agency and while going up to Mr. Beggs an Indian called to me, and asked me to go and see Crowfoot. He came out of his teepee and brought me over to the halfbreed who acted as interpreter and then he told me that the day before his boy had seen my horses and would bring them in if he was paid enough.

"I told him that I would give him ten dollars which satisfied him and he at once sent his boy for a horse. I then rode over to McDonnell's store for some bacon, and while there the Indian boy rode up and wanted some tobacco and matches. I gave them, and he started off while I went back to camp.

"About 7 o'clock in the evening, while we were eating supper, he came riding into camp with the four horses."

Having lost four days, Joe was in no mood to haggle, and he had no illusions about how his horses had "strayed." Already the summer was almost over. The Rebellion had cost him eight weeks; he'd been stuck in Ottawa cooling his heels while a lot of Sunday soldiers from Toronto traipsed around the prairie. Good thing, though, that Britain hadn't sent Wolseley back to the North West. To liberate Khartoum and defeat the Mahdi, Wolseley had recruited nearly four hundred Canadian voyageurs, among them some first-rate Iroquois, shantymen, and fur trade veterans, but eleven had drowned in the Nile, and most had been sent home when their boat brigade was only halfway up the river. Those remaining never made it. When British scouts discovered that Gordon and the Khartoum garrison had been butchered by the Mahdi's hordes, the British retreated and left the Mahdi lord of Sudan.

Now imperial attention was on Canada's wild North-West. The strategy for pacifying the Red Man was to populate the prairie with hard-working, Protestant farmers from Ontario and Great Britain. The promise of free land drew homesteaders by the trainloads, and now Joe had less to fear from the Indians than he did from the speculators, bootleggers, loan sharks, con artists, thieves, and tramps who were pouring in with hopes of making a fast buck. There was always a stampede of some sort going on, and Sheriff J.J. Healy, the infamous founder of Fort Whoop-Up, was usually in the middle of it.

Having built his thriving saloons in all the mushrooming little prairie settlements, Healy had developed a sideline as a mining promoter. In 1882, J.J. and his gang claimed to have discovered a fabulously rich silver vein on Castle Mountain, west of the Stoney Indian reserve at Morley. They staked claims and enthusiastically sold shares; within the year a sprawling shantytown, Silver City, had sprung up on the mountainside. When Joe Tyrrell and Dr. Dawson investigated in 1883, they had found traces of copper and lead, but no silver. The boom soon collapsed amid rumours that the rocks had been salted with nuggets stolen from silver mines in Colorado.

At the end of September 1885, Joe Tyrrell returned to the Morley area, this time to examine mysterious springs of "coal oil." Once more, the land around had been staked by hopeful prospectors, but Joe dismissed the "oil" as a scum of black dust washed down from nearby coal seams. His next task was to explore the upper reaches of the Red Deer and Little Red Deer rivers,

"Unidentified group of Stoney Indians at Morley, soon after the North West Rebellion, 1885." From Tatanga Mani: Walking Buffalo of the Stonies, *by Grant MacEwan.* (Hurtig, 1969)

and he needed to hire a Stoney to guide him along the tortuous trails the hunters followed.

The Stonies were a small band, and poor, but they knew the mountains, and they were sober, dependable Christians. The first Wesleyan Methodist missionary in the area, Robert Rundle, had begun visiting the Stonies, or the Assiniboine, as they were formally called, about 1844, and for decades after Rundle returned to England, some families retained vestiges of Christian observance. In 1873, John and Dave McDougall had built their church, school, and trading post on a site near the Bow River they named Morleyville. Now, John, the missionary, acted on the side as an agent for the Canadian government. Visitors scratched their heads: was Morley a family homestead, a mission, a company, or a feudal estate?

At least Methodist Joe Tyrrell could be assured of a friendly welcome. He was from Ontario, like the McDougalls, and God

knows how many Stoney schoolboys had been clothed in his out-
grown flannel shirts and mended breeches. Even the brightest
Stoney boys did not take well to school, to the church's great frustration, but some learned enough English for Joe's purposes. The
Stoney children were all given English and Scottish names, often
those of missionaries, and on Dave McDougall's advice Joe hired
a young man named William Campbell for $1.50 a day.

William proved to be a sure-footed guide through the maze
of foothill creeks and gullies. Troubled by a nagging cough that
nothing in Joe's medicine kit could alleviate, he was still a good
shot – they feasted on rabbits, ducks, and grouse, except on
Sundays, when William refused to hunt or make a fire – and an
encyclopedia of information about the country.

Apart from scattered glacial boulders of Laurentian granite,
similar to those he had argued with Dawson about in 1883, Joe
found little of geological interest, so he recorded many of
William's observations in his notebook: "On Sheep Creek, eight
days journey from where it flows into the Saskatchewan, there is
a large seam of coal; also there is coal on a creek above this called
in Stony 'where the man was shot in the head.'" William was an
historian as well. Joe notes: "Riding back over the flat between
the Saskatchewan and the Clearwater, the Indian said that this
was a favourite battleground for the Blackfeet and Stonies, point-
ing out the place where a number of Blackfeet had been killed."

Joe was giving credibility and respect to an Indian inform-
ant; William even drew him a map. This was unusual. Indians
were seldom listened to, and almost never believed. Joe listened,
and believed. Of course, Joe could read latitude and longitude,
and scribble lines on a sheet of paper, but he was following a more
reliable atlas in William's memory, a map he would never be able
to reproduce. It was beginning to dawn on Joe that he was no
Adam in a Garden of Eden: *Someone has been here before me.*
Nowhere was this feeling stronger than at his destination, the old
Hudson's Bay Company trading post, Rocky Mountain House.

Rocky Mountain House. Photo by J.B. Tyrrell. (TFRBL, J.B.T. papers, F5398)

"It is now a deserted ruin," Joe writes, "nothing but the forge house and three of the corner towers being left standing, these latter being used only by partridges and ravens. A considerable quantity of timber is lying close to the back of the river, having evidently been part of the houses at one time."

The fort's huge timber bastions gave it a medieval look, as if it had recently been sacked by Richard Lion Heart. It had been there as long as William Campbell could remember, and it had been a busy post in 1870 when Captain Butler observed the arrival of a band of Blackfoot eager to trade:

"When the Blackfeet arrive on a trading visit to the Mountain House they usually come in large numbers, prepared for a brush with either Crees or Stonies. The camp is formed at some distance from the fort, and the braves, having piled their robes, leather, and provisions on the backs of their wives or their horses, approach in long cavalcade. The officer goes out to meet them, and the gates are closed. Many speeches are made, and the chief, to show his 'big heart,' usually piles on top of a horse a heterogeneous mass of buffalo robes, pemmican, and dried meat, and hands horse and all he carries over to the trader. . . .

"Sapoomaxica, or the Big Crow's Foot, having demonstrated the bigness of his heart, and received in turn a tangible proof of the corresponding size of the trader's, addresses his braves, cautioning them against violence or rough behaviour – the braves, standing ready with their peltries [furs and hides] are in a high state of excitement to begin the trade. Within the fort all the preparations have been completed, communication cut off between the Indian room and the rest of the buildings, guns placed up in the loft overhead, and men all get ready for anything that might turn up; then the outer gate is thrown open, and a large throng enters the Indian room. Three or four of the first-comers are now admitted through a narrow passage into the trading shop. . . . The first Indians admitted hand in their peltries through a wooden grating, and receive in exchange so many blankets, beads, or strouds [woollen cloth]. Out they go to the large hall where their comrades are anxiously awaiting their turn, and in rush another batch, and the doors are locked again."

Butler noted approvingly that the Hudson's Bay Company had stopped using rum in the trade: "The trade usually began with a present of fire-water all round – then the business went on apace. Horses, robes, tents, provisions, all would be proffered for one more drink at the beloved poison. The fire-water, although freely diluted with water, soon reduced the assemblage to a state of wild hilarity, quickly followed by stupidity and sleep."

The most westerly and heavily fortified of the company's prairie posts, Rocky Mountain House invited violent confrontations between rival trading parties of Blackfoot, Cree, and Stonies, but Reverend Rundle had held prayer meetings on the meadow, and when Toronto artist Paul Kane visited in the spring of 1848, he found a tranquil camp of Stonies. Kane writes in his memoir, *Wanderings of an Artist*:

"The Assiniboines, who reside in the vicinity of this fort, I found the most kind and honourable of any tribe that I met with.

They constitute a very small part (say forty or fifty families) of a very large tribe who live in a more easterly direction. Mah-Min, 'The Feather,' their head chief, permitted me to take his likeness, and after I had finished it, and it was shown to the others, who all recognized and admired it, he said to me, 'You are a greater chief than I am, and I present you with this collar of grizzly bear's claws, which I have worn for twenty-three summers, and which I hope you will wear as a token of my friendship.'

"The second chief, Wah-he-joe-tass-e-neen, 'The half-white Man,' seeing that I was so successful with his head chief's likeness, and probably feeling a little jealous, came and requested me to take his also, which I willingly did, as he had one of the most extraordinary countenances I had met with for some time."

Kane himself made an indelible impression on the Stonies; in 1882, artist Lucius O'Brien, travelling in the foothills, encountered an old chief who clearly remembered the white medicine man with the bushy red hair and beard.

Ten years after Kane, another powerful, bearded stranger arrived among the Stonies. Called The Sun, for his habit of habitually squinting towards it through his brass sextant, Dr. James Hector was searching for the Great Divide, the height of land in the Rockies that separated the eastern-flowing North Saskatchewan River and its tributaries from the Columbia, Thompson, and Fraser rivers to the west. Hector depended on his Stoney guides' knowledge of the mountain passes, translated for him by the best interpreter in the North-West, Peter Erasmus. Son of a Scandinavian father and Cree mother, Erasmus had been educated by Anglican clergy at Red River; he was fluent in all the plains languages, and could read and write English, Cree syllabics, and a little Greek. Erasmus had rejected the church for the free life of a plainsman, and he was contemptuous of anyone, especially snobbish Englishmen, who demanded all the comforts of home on the trail.

"Dr. Hector alone of all the men of my experience asked no quarter from any man among us, drivers or guides," Erasmus recalls in his memoir, *Buffalo Days and Nights*. "He could walk, ride, or tramp snowshoes with the best of our men, and never fell back on his position to soften his share of the hardships, but in fact gloried in his physical ability after a hard day's run to share in the work of preparing camp for the night, building shelters from the wind, cutting spruce boughs, or even helping to get up wood for an all-night fire. He was admired and talked about by every man that travelled with him, and his fame as a traveller was a wonder and a byword among many a teepee that never saw the man."

Hector climbed mountains effortlessly too, but he would be remembered most by an accident in the Rockies that nearly killed him. Writes Erasmus: "We were following along a river bank as the easiest way in the direction we wanted to go when one of the horse's packs came loose. The horse lost his balance and tumbled backward into the river. The river was quite deep and the banks steep. We all left our saddle horses and rushed down to save the brute. Losing the pack would have been quite serious in our present situation as it contained most of our food supplies. Sutherland, an old cow puncher, roped the horse and we were able to finally get him on safe ground.

"The doctor went to pick up his own horse which was feeding among some spruce with his lines trailing. The instant the doctor reached for the lines, the horse whirled and kicked him with both feet in the chest. The doctor was knocked unconscious.

"We all leapt from our horses and rushed up to him, but all our attempts to help him recover his senses were of no avail. We then carried him to the shade of some big evergreens while we pitched camp. Dr. Hector must have been unconscious for at least two hours when Sutherland yelled for us to come up; he was now conscious but in great pain. He asked for his kit and directed me to prepare some medicine that would ease the pain. I had him sign a document stating the facts of the accident in case his illness might prove serious. He readily agreed that it would be the proper thing to do." Hector recovered, and the Stonies christened the river the "Kicking Horse."

But Hector had used a more northerly pass the next year to cross the Rockies to the Columbia River. On Joe's map it was marked "Howse Pass." Who was Howse? There was no Howse listed among Hector's or Palliser's colleagues, family, or friends, although Hector, according to custom, had named mountains for the expedition's financial backers in England. Joe knew of no more recent surveyor or geologist who had crossed the Rockies by this path. Before deciding on the Kicking Horse Pass as the route, the CPR had chosen the Yellow Head Pass, even farther to the north than the Howse.

Howse was only one of many mysterious names and routes marked on his map. If, as it seemed, Palliser's expedition hadn't named most of these mountains and rivers, or, as their own marked route showed, even visited them, who had? The question had begun to nag at Joe in the summer of 1883 as he and Dawson had followed the Columbia River north through British Columbia to the Kicking Horse Pass. The well-marked trail they had followed along the river was assumed to be an old Indian path – but had there been an unknown Indian or trapper or fur trader with the skill, or inspiration, to make such a detailed and accurate map? And who had named Mount Nelson? It made sense that it would have been named for Admiral Nelson in honour of his victory and death at Trafalgar in 1805, but if the British Admiralty had later sent an exploring expedition into the Rockies, surely it would have been trumpeted around the world. It couldn't be Captain James Cook; he had rarely sailed close to the Pacific coast south of Alaska, and Captain George Vancouver didn't venture up the coastal rivers and inlets, although if he had, he might have bumped into Alexander Mackenzie arriving across the mountains. Mackenzie's route was too far north, and the route of the Lewis and Clark expedition in 1806 was too far south. According to Palliser's report, his expedition had relied on "the maps of Mr. Arrowsmith which gave very correctly on the whole the great general features of the region explored." But Arrowsmith was a British publisher of maps, not an explorer or map-maker, and Arrowsmith had since gone out of business.

Someone has been here before me. Ever since Joe had arrived in the North-West he had been following in invisible footsteps. Rocky Mountain House was part of the enigma. When had it been built, Joe wondered, and why had it been destroyed? The Hudson's Bay Company's Fort Edmonton, which Joe had visited briefly the previous summer, was rotting, but it was still an active trade centre in a new little townsite. And what did Joe know about the Hudson's Bay Company? Nothing but its nickname, "Here Before Christ." In school, he'd learned about the French-Canadian explorers Radisson and Groseilliers, old "Radishes and Gooseberries," and how the Iroquois and missionaries and fur traders had paddled up the Humber River, right past his house, but somewhere around Georgian Bay, Etienne Brule got eaten, the missionaries were martyred, and the voyageurs vanished into the Lake Huron mist. Fort Edmonton was the first Hudson's Bay Company post Joe had seen outside of a picture in a book or a newspaper. At Rocky Mountain House, he felt he'd stumbled upon the ruin of a lost empire.

> My name is Ozymandias, king of Kings,
> Look on my Works, ye Mighty, and despair!
> Nothing beside remains. Round the decay
>   Of that colossal Wreck, boundless and bare
>   The lone and level sands stretch far away.

Joe knew *Ozymandias* by heart, and making friends with his Stoney guide William had set him brooding over the unsettling news that his Calgary lawyer friend, Jimmy Lougheed, had married an Indian, a niece of the Hudson's Bay Company's big man in the North-West, Chief Factor Dick Hardisty. *Squaw* was the word flying around Weston, but according to Dave McDougall, Belle Hardisty was only part Cree, and Jimmy was busting his buttons at snagging a real princess of the country's aristocracy.

Although Chief Factor Hardisty's own mother was Cree, his sister had married Donald A. Smith, one of the biggest financiers behind the CPR, and Hardisty's wife Elizabeth was the Methodist McDougalls' sister. Jimmy Lougheed said they were all great pals of Sir John's, and Hardisty would make it to the Senate before long.

. Back east in Ontario, it would be outrageous to imagine a half-breed being appointed to the Senate, a position that after all these years still eluded Joe's own father. In Ontario, "going native" did not usually mean going up in the world, but in the summer of 1886, Joe made a point of calling on Chief Factor Hardisty in Fort Edmonton. Hardisty, Joe had learned, was born and raised in the North-West, and knew it as well as any man living. He, if anyone, would know the identity of the mystery map-maker. Critics of the Hudson's Bay Company's arrogant, monopolistic practices complained, however, that the company did not acknowledge maps, except those in its own employees' heads, because maps attracted interlopers, like surveyors and geologists, who made more maps, as well as peddlers, lunatics, and kiss-my-ass big-game hunters who quarrelled with their guides, got the Indians drunk, poisoned traps, and expected the company to act as nursemaid. Hardisty may have been forthcoming enough to tell Joe that Howse Pass had been named for Joseph Howse, an enterprising company trader who had left Fort Edmonton to investigate the mountain pass on July 18, 1809; Howse crossed it the next year and wintered on the Columbia River. Howse, however, left no journal and had not mapped his route. Did Hardisty tell Joe that ten years earlier, as an economy measure, he had destroyed Rocky Mountain House?

Joe's immediate reason for visiting Fort Edmonton was to rent a scow to look for gold on the banks of the North Saskatchewan River. Joe and his Survey assistant, Donaldson Bogart Dowling, drifted lazily downriver like Huck Finn and Tom Sawyer, but without reward or adventure. The countryside was becoming civilized; telegraph lines were being strung – earlier, near Sounding Lake, they had encountered a line repairman – and the old Indian campsites, their weathered lodge poles still standing, were deserted. At one campsite, they had been accosted by a posse of mounted police under the impression they were Indians who had left their reserve without permits. Everywhere, settlers were fencing and ploughing; soon, the prairie's dappled carpet of grasses, roses, and lilies would be an ocean of grain. Joe was fed up with investigating rumours, or evaluating other men's mines, and bored by classifying almost imperceptible differences in rock formations.

The Survey geologists were assured it was perfectly fine to discover nothing significant at all; at least the ground had been covered, and expectations satisfied with factual, if negative, information. But that was no way to make a man's reputation! Perhaps, Joe thought, he was being punished for messing up his dinosaur, or being encouraged to quit, but he had been assigned to examine an area of rolling hills that amounted to nothing more than an immense, lumpy pile of dirt.

A surprise, however, was waiting for him in Ottawa. An old surveyor, Andrew Russell, retired assistant commissioner of Crown lands for Ontario, told Joe that stored away in the bowels of the Ontario lands department in Toronto was a large map drawn in 1813 by David Thompson, a long-dead Crown surveyor, along with many of Thompson's journals. Prior to surveying the boundary line between Canada and the United States from the St. Lawrence River to Lake of the Woods, between 1816 and 1826, Thompson had been a fur trader and explorer with the North West Company of Montreal. Russell had met Thompson briefly in 1848, and remembered him as a little old white-haired man, sober, religious, and active for his advanced age. Russell understood that two of Thompson's daughters were still living, one, Mrs. G.E. Shaw, nearby in Peterborough, but Joe's most important contact would be Charles Lindsey, an elderly political journalist best known for his biography of his father-in-law, the leader of the 1837 Rebellion in Upper Canada, William Lyon Mackenzie. Lindsey, on good terms with Ontario politicians of all stripes, had apparently acted as agent for Thompson's son Joshua in 1859 when he'd sold his late father's journals to the government for six hundred British pounds.

Joe unearthed Thompson's map and journals and pored over them during his long Christmas vacation in 1887. The faded, brittle map, when unfolded, measured more than six feet by ten feet! Signed by Thompson, and drawn from surveys conducted between 1792 and 1812, it traced the rivers, hills, and mountains of the North-West from the eastern end of Lake Superior to the Pacific Ocean, south to the Missouri and Mississippi rivers, and north to Lake Athabasca and Hudson Bay. Joe was incredulous that one man could have covered such an immense area in only twenty years.

Sure enough, there were Nelson's Mountains, and the Columbia River, but the range Joe knew as the Selkirks was called McGillivray's Mountains. Joe had never heard of a McGillivray. The Red Deer and Saskatchewan rivers around Rocky Mountain House were meticulously drawn, but the fort itself wasn't marked; in fact, no posts, camps, or settlements were identified. Fortunately, Thompson's journals, with their astronomical and meteorological readings and descriptive notations, gave a meticulous account of his travels, including descriptions of the trading posts where he spent the long winters. Many places bore standard English names – Cumberland, Buckingham, Manchester, George – but others – Missinippi River, Seepaywisk House, Methy Portage, Ithenoostosequan Lake – were in a Native tongue. Thompson was a methodical, indefatigable traveller, undeterred by ice, storms, or swamps; on April 27, 1798, after struggling for weeks through a maze of small streams and wild rice meadows, he arrived at Turtle Brook, the outlet of Turtle Lake. "This is the source of the famous Mississippe," Thompson writes with characteristic assurance, "since it is from here that the river takes its most direct course to the sea."

Joe was amazed. Thompson's unknown, unheralded achievement, more significant to North Americans than the much-ballyhooed discovery of the source of the Nile, was a mere junket for him compared to the years, 1807 to 1812, that he devoted to exploring the headwaters and upper reaches of the Columbia River and the Kootanie plains, trading for furs in a series of posts he built among the Kootanie Indians. Thompson's jumping-off place had been the North West Company's fort, Rocky Mountain House. Arriving at the newly built Mountain House for the first time in 1800, Thompson had recorded the presence of coal on the riverbanks, and he and his voyageurs had travelled south to the Bow River through the same foothills Joe had just crossed with his Stoney guide, William. In 1807, and again in 1810, Thompson had set out from the Mountain House to cross the pass later named for Howse; in 1811, Thompson had descended the Columbia River to the Pacific Ocean.

To Joe, David Thompson was North America's Marco Polo. He was astonished that apparently nobody else in the Geological Survey had read Thompson's journals, or looked at his marvellous map. Nor did anyone but Joe seem to care. Joe was coolly received by Thompson's daughter Mary, Mrs. Shaw. All he could ascertain from her was that Thompson was born in 1770 in Westminster parish, London, England, had married fourteen-year-old Charlotte Small at Île-à-la-Crosse in 1799, and that both died, in extreme poverty, in 1857 at Longueuil, Quebec, near Montreal. Undaunted by the scanty, unreliable biographical details he could obtain, Joe delivered a lecture, "A Brief Narrative of the Journeys of David Thompson in North-Western America," to the Canadian Institute on March 3, 1888.

It was fortunate for Joe that he published his lecture; his verbal recital of dates, times, solar observations, and incomprehensible names of places his Toronto audience had never heard of roused no interest. Charles Lindsey, however, was sufficiently impressed by Joe's diligence to share a secret: Lindsey owned David Thompson's unpublished, handwritten manuscript describing his travels throughout the North-West. Lindsey had been struggling for years to rewrite Thompson's quaint, idiosyncratic prose into a popular story, but he was handicapped by his lack of personal knowledge of the remote geography Thompson described. Would Joe, with his expertise, consider a collaboration, the book's profits to be shared equally?

Joe agreed with alacrity, but there was a complication. A second daughter, Charlotte, Mrs. W.R. Scott, was incensed that her brother, Joshua, had sold their father's papers without his sisters' knowledge and permission and had pocketed all the money. As far as Charlotte was concerned, all David Thompson's maps and papers, including those in the possession of the Ontario government, rightfully belonged to his living heirs, who were entitled to any proceeds from publication. If Joshua had acted illegally, as she claimed, there would be no profit in publishing Thompson's *Travels*. The royalties had to go to his aggrieved children. And to tell the truth, aside from his familiarity with the Milk, Red Deer, and upper Columbia rivers, Fort Edmonton, and Rocky Mountain House, Joe didn't know any more than Lindsey about the landscape of Thompson's travels. He'd never been there.

He would go, then. Here was an opportunity for him to retrace Thompson's routes, and possibly find new ones as yet unmapped. David Thompson's commanding voice, almost audible in the delicate, hasty scratches of his pen, filled Joe with anticipation. It was a calm voice, sometimes brusque, but not cruel, and Thompson's personality – observant, passionate, boyishly curious – was fascinating. A physical description of Thompson as a young man, although based on hearsay, seemed to fit: "Tall and fine-looking, of sandy complexion, with large features, deep-set, studious eyes, high forehead and broad shoulders, the intellectual was well set upon the physical." Joe could imagine Thompson standing on a rocky outcrop at night, head back, smiling at the constellations, starlight gleaming on the broad river at his feet.

David Thompson's ghost became Joe Tyrrell's guiding star, a companion in Joe's own obscurity; Thompson's *Travels* was an inspiration, his map a hairy, inky claw grasping the heart of a continent.

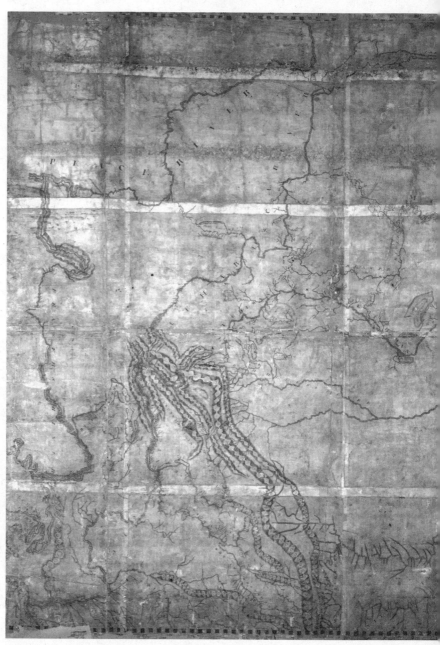

David Thompson's map. The six- by ten-foot copy Joe discovered in the Ontario Lands Office in 1887 is displayed in the Archives of Ontario reception room, Toronto. (AO, 15031)

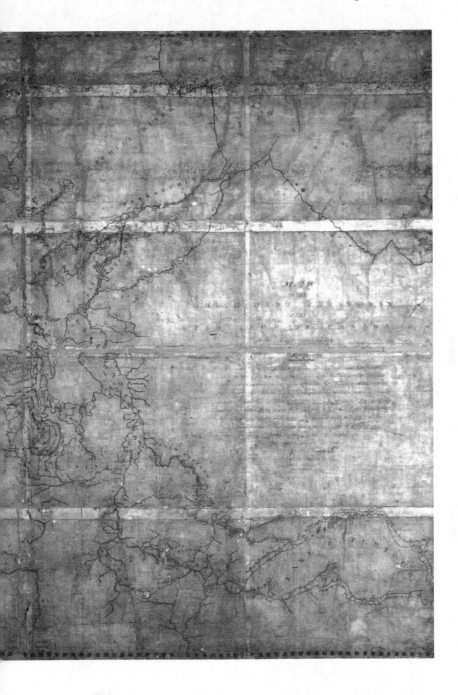

CHAPTER FOUR

At the end of the geological epoch which preceded the uplifting of the Alps, the earth was covered by a huge sheet of ice which buried the Siberian mammoths and reached just as far south as did the phenomena of erratic boulders. It extended beyond the shores of the Mediterranean and Atlantic Oceans and even covered completely North America and Asiatic Russia.

– Louis Agassiz, 1837

With this dramatic statement, spoken before an assembly of distinguished scientists at Neuchatel, Switzerland, the brilliant young Swiss paleontologist, Louis Agassiz, sent a seismic shock through the world of natural science. Extreme and erroneous in many aspects, Agassiz's theory of an *Eiszeit*, or Ice Age, based on his thorough study of glaciers in the Alps, was the first attempt to explain the peculiar scoured topography so characteristic of Scandinavia and Scotland. Naturalists, only then becoming accustomed to looking downwards through the dizzying depths of the volcanic and sedimentary layers of Earth's crust, now had to look up, way up, and imagine a sheet of Arctic ice, high as a mountain, creeping over half of the globe. At first, the majority scorned and ridiculed the Ice Age theory. "There has not been at any time a polar ice cap," William "Elder" Dawson loudly and persistently proclaimed, "and the theory of great continental ice sheets covering the northern parts of the two great continents is also baseless." Canada, with its Rocky Mountains and immense expanses of bare, eroded rock, would have been a prime location for Ice Age investigation, but Elder Dawson's intransigent, life-long opposition stifled such heretical exploration.

To the south, however, American scientists were more open-minded and adventurous. In 1846, Louis Agassiz had been invited to join the faculty of Harvard University. Here, surrounded by Boston's intellectual and financial elite, including Ralph Waldo Emerson and the Transcendentalists, Agassiz became a charis-matic lecturer and celebrated scientific guru. Perhaps because Agassiz's specialty, fossil fishes, was reputable, and he remained a Creationist, his Ice Age theory was accepted by American geo-logists examining glacial moraines and other curious landforms in the more northerly states. During the 1870s, Warren Upham, a young researcher with the Geological Survey of Minnesota, investigated near the Canadian boundary a wavy line of gravel ridges he believed formed the ancient shores of a freshwater glacial lake. He named it Agassiz.

As Upham travelled from east to west along the height of land that divided the Arctic watershed from the Mississippi, he looked north over an undulating, swampy terrain of lakes and streams he concluded could only have been formed by a long-vanished *mer de glace*, a sea of ice:

> The portions of the earth upon which natural lakes abound are further characterized by surface deposits of clay, sand, gravel, and boulders, mixed together in the same mass, which is called till, boulder-clay, hardpan, or unmodified drift. The rock-fragments are of very diverse material and origin, having been gathered from ledges in widely separated districts. The direction in which these boulders and pebbles have been carried is from north to south, or to the south-east or south-west, throughout the United States and adjoining British territory. In these and all other drift-covered regions the bed-rocks are

marked by parallel scratches and furrows, called striae, that run in the direction in which the boulders have been transported. The glaciers of the Alps and of Greenland show us such markings and similar deposits of drift now in process of formation, and there are no other known agencies capable of producing these effects.

It is therefore a necessary conclusion that the last period in the geological history of this region brought a very cold climate in which a vast ice-sheet was accumulated, each year adding something to its depth by the excess of snowfall over melting and evaporation. Its greatest thickness was far to the north, where the solid ice probably became several miles deep; and the pressure of this vast weight caused it to flow slowly outward in all directions from its deepest part. The superficial materials formed by decomposition of the rocks before this glacial period were then ploughed up, mingled with large additions by erosion of the underlying ledges, and carried forward in the direction of the ice-current. It appears also, by shells and trees found deeply buried between glacial deposits, that this very cold period was not one unbroken reign of ice, but that this retreated and readvanced, or was possibly at some times nearly all melted and then accumulated anew.

During the glacier's final melt, Upham argued, the runoff drained south until the ice-sheet had shrunk within the bowl of the Arctic watershed. Then, blocked by the ice itself from flowing north, the water pooled into a broad depression, enclosed by granite hills and glacial moraines, to form Lake Agassiz. Upham estimated that the lake, from 200 to 300 feet deep, was 600 miles long and up to 200 miles broad: some nine thousand years later, the

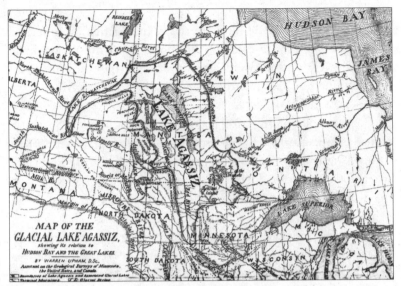

Warren Upham's map of glacial Lake Agassiz, Geological Survey of Minnesota. From The Ice Age in North America, *by G. Frederick Wright, 1920.*

lake's dried bottom became the broad, shallow Red River valley, deep in peat and soil deposited by glacial rivers and meltwater.

Upham's study, first published in 1879 by the Geological Survey of Minnesota, mapped part of the southern edge of the vanished North American ice-sheet, but, to Upham's frustration, most of it, and of Lake Agassiz, had been in Canada. The Canadian government allowed Upham to venture into Manitoba to explore Turtle Mountain, which was on the boundary line, but in light of the American doctrine of Manifest Destiny – the inevitable conquest by the United States of the entire North American continent – the motives of any U.S. exploring expedition were suspect. Canadians generally believed, rightly or not, that the 1869 Riel Rebellion in Red River had been a pretext for an American invasion of the North-West. David Thompson had surveyed the headwaters of the Mississippi River in 1798 because his North West Company, based in Montreal, was anxious to ascertain if its fur trade posts were on the British or American side of the proposed international boundary, and most Canadians, including Thompson, were furious when Britain did not insist on claiming for Canada the upper valleys of the Mississippi, Missouri, and Ohio rivers.

Yet in spite of lingering jealousies, the Geological Survey of Canada could hardly let politics or hard feelings stand in the way of an American colleague's scientific research. Finally, in 1887, when Joe Tyrrell was feeling most discouraged by his unrewarding work on the Canadian prairie, it was agreed that he would chart, for Upham, Lake Agassiz's Canadian shores.

Joe was in luck. He found Upham to be a friendly, meticulous scholar with whom he could frankly discuss glacial theories and observations. The contours of Lake Agassiz, far from being a mystery, were so striking that they had been remarked upon by earlier explorers.

"The vast ocean of level prairie which lies to the west of Red River must be seen in its extraordinary aspects before it can be rightly valued," Canadian naturalist Henry Youle Hind had reported in 1857.

> It must be seen at sunrise, when the boundless plain suddenly flashes with rose-coloured light, as the first rays of the sun sparkle in the dew on the long rich grass, gently stirred by the unfailing morning breeze. It must be seen at noon-day, when refraction swells into the forms of distant hill ranges the ancient beaches and ridges of Lake Winnipeg, which mark its former extension; when each willow bush is magnified into a grove, each distant clump of aspens, not seen before, into wide forests, and the outline of wooded riverbanks, far beyond unassisted vision, rise into view. It must be seen at sunset, when, just as the huge ball of fire is dipping below the horizon, he throws a flood of red light,

indescribably magnificent, upon the illimitable waving green, the colours blending and separating with the gentle roll of the long grass in the evening breeze, and seemingly magnified towards the horizon into the distant heaving swell of a parti-coloured sea. It must be seen, too, by moonlight, when the summits of the low green grass waves are tipped with silver, and the stars in the west disap-pear suddenly as they touch the earth. Finally, it must be seen at night, when the distant prairies are in a blaze, thirty, fifty, or seventy miles away; when the fire reaches clumps of aspen, and the forked tips of the flames, magnified by refraction, flash and quiver in the horizon, and the reflected lights from rolling clouds of smoke above tell of the havoc which is raging below.

Joe's destination in the summer of 1887 was the escarpment of densely wooded hills, the Porcupine, Duck, and Riding moun-tains, that had formed Lake Agassiz's western shoreline. After four summers on the bare, windy prairie, it was a joy for him to be in a leafy forest, with clear, cold lakes and fresh streams to bathe in. Lake Agassiz's old beaches were the trails he travelled on; local people, native and newcomer, used them by habit because they were high and dry. All Joe had to do was measure the ridges' contours and calculate their height above sea level. He surveyed hundreds of square miles, on foot, by horseback, and by wagon, and climbed both the Duck and Riding mountains, but his four-month expedition was as pleasant as a picnic. Home-steads, and a string of tiny settlements – Minnedosa, Strathclair, Russell, Rossburn – provided fresh vegetables, home baking, and news; settlers were eager to help, and the drill core from a home-steader's new borehole well told Joe at a glance everything he needed to know about the earth beneath his feet.

The hills were bedrock shale and limestone buried in an

"Tyrrell's survey party, 1886." Left to right: Joe Tyrrell, D.B. Dowling, G. Dickson, J. Robison, F. Hastings. (TFRBL, J.B.T papers, F3597)

"Our party after lunch, 1887." (TFRBL, J.B.T papers, F3594)

"Valley River, looking east." The photo shows part of an old Lake Agassiz shoreline. (TFRBL, J.B.T papers, F3595)

immense moraine of gravel, sand, and clay pushed up by the advancing ice-sheet. Evidence of glaciation stared Joe in the face everywhere he looked. On the Valley River, he notes: "Overlying the shale, the boulder clay was filled with glaciated pebbles and boulders. One that was lying in the river was very large and showed some beautifully striated surfaces. It was of white limestone containing fossils and corals."

Gazing northeast from the top of Duck and Riding mountains, it was easy to visualize Lake Winnipeg and her numerous sparkling sisters, Lake Agassiz's remnants, as a single sheet of clear, turquoise water lapping at his feet, but Joe was more intrigued by the lake's mother ice cap, which he imagined looming on the northern horizon.

Who knew anything about this Arctic glacier? No one. It was one thing to poke about in the muck the ice-sheet left behind, but it was like examining a pile of bear dung. Where was the bear? David Thompson had gone no farther north than Lake Athabasca, and the Geological Survey's investigations of Hudson Bay had been largely confined to weather and navigation; Joe's brother James had spent the winter of 1885–86 making meteorological observations on an island in Hudson Strait. Reluctant to challenge his father's open Arctic Sea theory, Little Doc Dawson now hypothesized a "Laurentian" or "Laurentide" glacier that had curled southwest around Hudson Bay from Labrador; yet Warren Upham visualized a polar ice-sheet originating north of Hudson Bay. Both men were guessing, and Upham didn't even bother to give Lake Agassiz's glacier a name. A great deal was now known about how it had melted, but Joe wondered how and where it had come into being, and how long it had lived.

As Joe squinted out over the Lake Winnipeg basin, speckled with the shapeless, puddle-like lakes characteristic of a post-glacial landscape, it seemed plain that the long, narrow lakes were water-filled troughs. Had they been gouged by the glacier itself, or eroded by runoff as it melted? But if the glacier had ground its way down from the north or northeast, why did the lakes' axis lie to the northwest? It appeared as if at least some of the ice may have flowed southeast, filling a basin of limestone and sandstone already hollowed out by millennia of exposure to wind, waves, and rain.

Lake Winnipeg's Dr. Jekyll and Mr. Hyde personality had puzzled observers since Alexander Mackenzie had noted in his journals: "Along the west banks is to be seen, at intervals, and traced in the line of the direction of the plains, a soft rock of limestone, in thin and nearly horizontal strata. It is also remarkable that, at the narrowest part of Lake Winipic, where it is not more than two miles in breadth, the West side is faced with rocks of this stone thirty feet perpendicular; while, on the East side, the rocks are more elevated, and of a dark-grey granite."

Limestone, with its multitudinous marine fossils, meant that from 500 to 200 million years earlier, Lake Winnipeg had been the bed of a tropical sea. It was possible that there been swamps

here too, with giant lizards and dense jungles that died and com-
pacted into coal, and Joe might be lucky enough, perhaps, to find
a mammoth, or an extinct rhinoceros.

Joe's highly praised work on Lake Agassiz in 1887 earned
him the opportunity to survey the entire Lake Winnipeg basin,
with its innumerable lakes and their progeny of bays, inlets,
streams, and swamps. He was thrilled to be entering country
described by David Thompson in his journals, the watery northern landscape of the fur trade, and he would have the pleasure of
camping on the exact spots where Thompson had beached his
canoe a hundred years earlier. In the summer of 1888, Joe and his
assistant, D.B. Dowling, were provided with a small sailboat, the
Pterodactyl, but Joe preferred to leave the sailing to Dowling and
trust his safety to the local Indian canoemen.

After years of hard saddles, bouncing buckboards, and
wooden wagon seats, Joe found it a treat to sit among the tents
and dunnage bags in a canoe, dragging his Massey log like a
gigantic fish lure as he leisurely recorded the distance travelled
while the Indians rhythmically paddled. He could dip his cup in
the lake for a drink whenever he wished, and splash along a white
sandy beach while the men pitched the tents. Still, the blackflies
and mosquitoes ate him alive when he was out of the wind in a
marshy bay, and Joe spent much of his time in such marshy bays
probing the underbrush for remnants of Thompson's old fur
trade posts.

In addition to collecting fossils and mapping enough limestone to build a thousand shining cities, Joe located a deposit of
gypsum northeast of Fairford, a Hudson's Bay Company post,
Indian agency, and mission on the northern shore of Lake
Manitoba. The local chief guided him to this strange "medicine"
rock. "The two days spent on this trip with Chief Wekemowskunk
were among the hardest that I ever travelled," Joe recalled. "The
days were hot and moist, the mosquitoes and black flies were in
incredible numbers, and the Chief was a fast walker, enjoying the
heat, although the flies bothered him a little. . . . On reaching the

lake I was almost exhausted."

Joe's gypsum find, in July 1888, was nearly his last; on August 6, as he stepped out of his canoe at Fairford, he fell unconscious on the shore. The Anglican missionary dosed him with brandy, and the Hudson's Bay Company ferried him by boat down the lake. A doctor in Portage la Prairie diagnosed typhoid fever. Delirious, Joe was taken by train to the Winnipeg General Hospital. He recovered very slowly. It was late October before he was strong enough to return home to Weston, and January 1889 when he went back to work in Ottawa. Yet as soon as spring came, he declared, "The lakes are waiting!"

The lakes revealed what Joe had hoped for: tadpole-shaped drumlins, glacial islands of clay and boulders, tailing to the northwest, and polished stone outcrops scarred by deep, parallel grooves that ran in the same northwest–southeast direction. It was proof enough for Joe that somewhere west of Hudson Bay, an Arctic glacier had pushed south, then hooked a giant finger to the east.

Lake Winnipeg's prevailing northwest winds were a constant reminder of the old glacier's path. To the Cree, the lake was Mistehay Sakahegan, the Great Lake; David Thompson called it Sea Lake, or Big Lake, and both Native people and fur traders paddled close to its shores. Blowing unimpeded across a vast expanse of open, shallow water, the winds churned up towering, white-capped waves and steep, rolling swells that capsized small boats or smashed them against the rocks.

"We have been windbound all day, and the boat [*Pterodactyl*] has been lying at the island a little to the south of here," Joe writes in his notes on October 4, 1889. "In moving her last night after the wind rose, Mr. Dowling was knocked overboard by the boom, and had a narrow escape from drowning."

Old-timers on Lake Winnipeg were full of chilling stories of *La Vieille*, the Old Woman, as the voyageurs called the wind, and tedious as it was to wait, sometimes for days, for the wind to drop – "Nothing to do. No birds to shoot," he writes in another entry – Joe had learned caution. On September 4, 1890, he was surveying the shoreline around the Hudson's Bay Company post, Norway House, in a small dinghy, when a violent storm forced his crew to take refuge on a rocky sandbar, Spider Island. They were glad to find company: the mounted police patrol's new sail-boat, *Keewatin*, was sharing their crude harbour. As soon as the wind dropped the next day, Joe's boat made a quick run for the mainland, but their progress southward on the lake's eastern shore was delayed for days by high winds and cold, incessant rain. Joe was cranky and impatient by the time they reached safe har-bour on September 12 at the Berens River Indian agency and trading post.

Joe liked to spend as much time as possible talking with the old Bay men and Indian agents who knew stories about the early days of the fur trade and the locations of many posts that had fallen into decay. Surprisingly, the big northern posts were still going strong, including the oldest, Cumberland House, estab-lished by Samuel Hearne in 1774 on the Saskatchewan River, not far, it was said, from the remains of Fort Bourbon, built by the French La Vérendrye some forty years earlier. One old trader Joe met, Robert Campbell, claimed to have discovered the source of the Yukon River, and had established the first trading post at Dease Lake.

Joe may have shrugged off some old-timers' memories as tall tales, but earlier at Grand Rapids, where the Saskatchewan River tumbled into Lake Winnipeg, trader Henry McKay had allowed him to read company post journals that gave the details of daily life dating back for decades: weather, population, visitors, sickness, skins traded, shortages of goods or food, and any strange event worth remarking on. Joe had had no idea such journals existed. And there they were, mouldering away in old trunks in the attic of a log storeroom!

At Berens River, Indian agent Angus McKay had been with

the Indian department for a relatively short time, but the innumerable McKays in the North-West knew everything about everybody for countless generations. Joe had given up trying to figure out McKay family relationships; somewhere back there was a Scotchman, or a clan of them, but these days McKays were as likely to be French and Cree, like Angus, and their name was spelled and pronounced a dozen different ways, in various languages, not unlike Tirel, Tirrelle, Terrell, Terry. Joe's own name was pronounced in the Irish way, *Ti-rill*, but it came from France and may have originated in Tyrol, in the Alps.

Angus McKay and Joe Tyrrell had another thing in common; they were both friends of Sir John, and Angus could thank Prime Minister Sir John A. Macdonald for his Indian department appointment as much as Joe could thank him for his job at the Geological Survey. Growing up, Joe had believed that his father belonged to the prime minister's inner circle; he had learned since, of course, that Sir John's dearest friends, scattered from sea to sea, numbered in the thousands. Crowfoot himself had been to Ottawa and had shaken Sir John's hand.

Now, however, Angus McKay was on the "outs" with Ottawa: he argued on behalf of the Berens River Indians in his charge, and their grievances were many. McKay allowed Joe to pitch his tent on high ground behind his house, but left him to fend for himself. Joe was anxious to push off again the next morning, but the wind made it impossible to leave the bay. Finding nothing else to do, Joe passed the time visiting with the Methodist missionaries Mr. and Mrs. Butler. "In the course of conversation," Joe notes on September 16, "he [Mr. Butler] said that an Indian had found a skiff on the shore with a wooden leg in it."

The peg leg was on everyone's mind the following evening when Angus McKay hosted a dinner party for a visiting friend, LaTouche Tupper. McKay, Joe writes, "had gone over to see the skiff found by the Indian, and the wooden leg, and found that the latter was a riding boot in which was a last, and on the last was written the name Morphy. The skiff had spoon oars and the Indian said that many other pieces of wreckage were lying along the shore; this looked very much as if the Police Yacht had been wrecked, and Mr. McKay at once sent an Indian for the boat and stuff.

"He returned after a long time without them, saying that the man's wife would not let him have them. Mr. McKay then went himself with three men and brought the skiff oars, boot and a piece of board, all of which were recognized as belonging to the Police Yacht. One of the men with McKay was Sinclair, my cook, who also thought that he recognized a valise and pair of trousers as having belonged to de Beaujeau, one of the policemen, but they were not brought along."

The wind dropped, and Joe packed up ready to leave the next morning, September 18: "We started out at daylight, and sailed out Berens River Bay where we found some of the islands to the south composed in part of black schist. . . . I struck straight across to Pigeon Point where there are several little coves making a safe harbour for a small boat. . . . The rock is dark grey, light weathering, rather greenish coarse granite gneiss, often very massive, but in places showing a well marked foliation striking N35E. It is cut by a few veins of fine red granite, but is without inclusion. The surface is striated in direction S.41 W. Quite a number of boulders of gneiss and granite are scattered along the front of the rock but none are of limestone.

"The Point is wooded with poplar, birch & B. pine.

"Lying turned upside down on the south side of the point is the Grub-box of the Police Yacht, marked on the lid N.W.M.P. Norway House. The lid has been fastened on with leather hinges and these have been violently torn off. The lid was lying close to the box.

"The shore of Pigeon Point has been very generally a little bank or cliff of light grey clay strewn over with a thin coating of sand. Little or no peat covering. . . . Four more pieces of the yacht, one the lid of a box, and 3 pieces of the boat itself are lying half-buried in the sand."

Instead of returning to Berens River to report the wreckage,

"James Inesace and squaw, October 16, 1887." (TFRBL, J.B.T. papers, F3596)

Joe methodically continued his geological examination along the lakeshore. The next morning, September 19, they were having breakfast on Flathead Point when McKay stopped by briefly to report yacht debris he had found. Joe writes:

"Shortly after McKay had left for Berens River, an Indian boat was sighted coming down the lake, and he gave us the intelligence that they had found the boat between Flower Point and Rabbit Point and lashed on her was an old man, but that two young men who had been with him were drowned. That the old man was now with a half-breed at Rabbit and was being well taken care of but that he had been 7 days on the boat. For three of those days the boat was on shore but he was not able to get off her.

"The rock here is a grey gneiss very much weathered and cut and broken by many wide veins of red granite. In it are regular inclusions of darker gneiss. Striae S 38° W."

The Indians returned the next day: "Two of them were

going to Norway House, and two to Berens River. Their names are Thomas Colin, and Charlie Keeper of Norway House, James Meskinsot and Timothy Macdonald of Berens River. Tchipatoos is the Indian who found the skiff and who brought the first information to Berens River." Joe gave Colin and Keeper a letter confirming their information for them to take to the police sergeant in charge at Norway House. On September 22, Joe was at the Dog's Head Point post office when the steamer *Aurora* docked on its way south to Red River; on board he briefly spoke to the *Keewatin*'s rescued captain, Matthew Watt.

Joe continued on his way, making detailed geological notations about the islands and shoreline; he found no bodies and saw no more wreckage, but when he docked at his base port, Selkirk, on October 12, he found himself hailed as a hero in a sensational tragedy.

The story had begun to unfold on September 26 on the front page of the Selkirk *Record*:

> WRECKED!
> The Sailing Vessel Keewatin Foundered on Lake Winnipeg.
> Two Mounted Police Drowned.
> Matthew Watts [*sic*], Of Selkirk, Was In The Gale.
> He Drifts About For Ten Days Without Food.
> He Is At Last Picked Up By Indians Almost Dead.

The *Record* quoted from Watt's daily log:

"Sept. 7 – Left Spider Island twenty minutes to six o'clock a.m, wind north, single reef. Got in sight of Swampy Island about 7:50 p.m. Put three reefs in foresail. Blowing very heavy. Could not get into Swampy Island. Let anchor go in bay outside. Anchor chain parted when out about one hour. Could carry no sail at this time. . . . Two men bailing with pails all night.

"Sept. 8 – At about four o'clock in the morning went over a

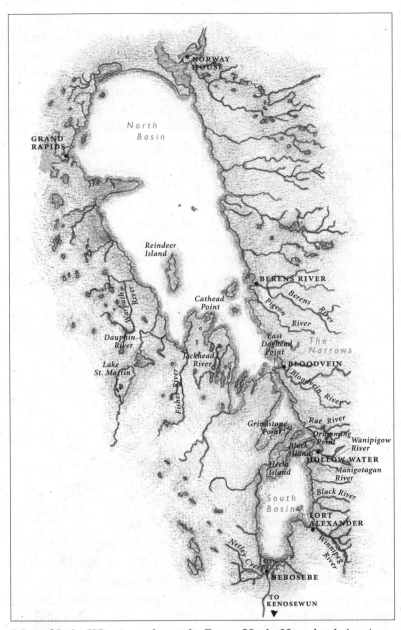

Map of Lake Winnipeg, drawn by Dawn Huck, Heartland Associates, Winnipeg. From Mistehay Sakahegan/The Great Lake, *by Frances Russell.* (Heartland, 2000)

reef. Could not see it. Took in a large quantity of water which caused her to founder and go on her beam ends. Corporal Morphy and the boy, Rene, got up on her side. Morphy had hard work to get the boy up on side. The poor boy seemed to go crazy and sunk very fast for about four hours, when Morphy had to let him go. I saw him no more. I did not succeed in getting on the side of the boat until about four o'clock p.m. Had to hang to cleat on deck, the sea washing continually over us. Morphy got blind. Through the night he fell or slipped off, when I succeeded in getting him on again. Through the night he tried several times to sleep with his head on my lap. Towards morning I noticed he began raving and I got him up beside me.

"Sept. 9 – He raved continually and slipped off the boat about sunrise, when I succeeded in getting him on again, and kept him beside me until about 8 o'clock. Both of us were stretched out on her side, with our heads towards each other and had hold of a piece of cotton which I fastened to side of boat. We both had our heads down and immediately I heard a splash in the water."

After Morphy slipped off, Watt lashed himself to the boat and drifted at the mercy of the waves until the boat came to rest on a sandbar close to shore near a point named Split Rock. On September 17, the Indians found the wreck and took Watt, more dead than alive, to shore. Reviving him by rubbing his body with kerosene, they carried him to the nearby home of a Metis, James Creight. Creight cared for Watt until September 22, when the *Aurora* transported him to Selkirk.

The *Record*'s reporter did not interview or even name the Indians; he spoke instead to Indian Agent Angus McKay: "Mr. McKay, who had been out with Mr. Tyrell [*sic*] of the geological survey in search of the boat, gave the incidents of their trip. Mr. McKay says that as soon as he heard of it he and Mr. Tupper and Mr. Tyrell organized a party and started to make a search. They travelled along the shore until they came to the wrecked boat, when they were informed that Mr. Watts [*sic*] had been the only person found with the boat, and had been taken to Creight's house."

Joe's role had grown even more dramatically by October 2, when the *Manitoba Weekly Free Press* took up the story:

"A gentleman who arrived Thursday from Lake Winnipeg says that enough credit could scarcely be given Mr. Tyrrell, of the geological survey, who upon hearing of the disaster, at once put out in the darkness of the night in a tempestuous sea to render aid to the lost ones. No effort was lost, no opportunity unseized, to aid the shipwrecked ones, and if the two are lost today, as they are, it is not for lack of effort in rescuing them by Mr. Tyrrell and his subordinates."

Joe's arrival in Winnipeg on October 12 was featured in a *Free Press* story headlined MATTHEW WATTS DEAD. "For the past two weeks he was completely out of his mind," the newspaper reported, "and while in this distressful mental condition he lived over again the scenes and sufferings he experienced while drifting about in the cold, merciless waves during those long ten days. He encouraged his companions to hold fast and cried out in despair as he saw them slip off the boat and disappear beneath the icy waters. He went again through the agonies of starvation, rendered more intense by the cruelty of the elements, and called on both God and man to save him. Towards the end he calmed down and slowly sank, passing away peacefully."

After noting Watt's funeral arrangements, the *Free Press* added, "Mr. J.B. Tyrrell of the geological survey arrived yesterday from Lake Winnipeg. Mr. Tyrrell was the first white man who saw Watts after his rescue from the wreck by Indians. . . . Mr. Tyrrell says that the charges made against the boat that it was unseaworthy, are not true. The boat was the best sailing vessel of its size on the lake."

That was a fib – Joe was no judge of boats – but it was no worse than the newspapers' garbled falsehoods about his role in the search. He did not venture out at night, or in a storm. Seen poking among boulders along the shoreline, Joe might have given the impression that he was searching for bodies or debris, but the wreckage he found was incidental to his interest in the rocks.

Why did Joe not give the reporter the names of the Indians he knew deserved the credit for the search and rescue, or acknowledge the role played by his own cook, Donald Sinclair, in identifying Rene de Beaujeau? Or did the reporter suppress all this information? Would attempting to set the record straight now only cause more confusion and embarrass everyone involved, including Joe himself? It would definitely be risky to contradict Manitoba's lieutenant-governor, Dr. John Christian Schultz, obviously the *Free Press*'s anonymous, effusive "gentleman" who had heaped praise on Joe's head. Schultz had taken command of Captain Watt's rescue and the search for the missing policemen. Schultz owned the *Keewatin*; he had hired Watt, an Ontario man, to build her and sail her, and, according to rumour, Schultz had designed the broad-beamed, duck-beaked boat himself.

In Manitoba, everything from Ontario was suspect, especially Dr. Schultz. Schultz had arrived in the Red River colony in 1860, a big, brawling, red-haired Orangeman posing as the champion of Protestant Ontario's right to the North-West, beginning with the dispossession of the Indians and Metis in favour of rapacious Ontario opportunists like himself. Once his goal had been accomplished with the suppression of the Riel Rebellion, provoked to a large degree by Schultz himself, Schultz was rewarded with lucrative and prestigious political appointments. Crude, unscrupulous, mistrusted by all, Schultz was the best political ally the Geological Survey had. Fancying himself a botanist and historian, Schultz was angling shamelessly for election to Canada's Royal Society while sniffing around the Survey for the inside dope on property, minerals, or anything valuable he could grab. When Joe had been recovering from typhoid, Schultz had put him up at Government House, and when Joe had paid Schultz a courtesy call this spring, he'd been received like the prodigal son. On October 16, 1890, Joe writes in his field notes: "I drove up to the Government House and spent the afternoon and evening with Dr. and Mrs. Schultz, most of the conversation being on the wreck of the *Keewatin*."

Two Joe Tyrrells left Winnipeg on the train for Ottawa that night. The first, Geologist Joe, was the pragmatic, unemotional researcher who had quietly gone about his work in a crisis, leaving more experienced men to take charge; the second, Celebrity Joe, was the chimera in the newspaper clippings he carried in his suitcase, a figment of political expediency and journalistic imagination, *the first white man* to distinguish himself in this dramatic rescue.

Which personality would Joe now present to the world?

CHAPTER FIVE

He *is* handsome, Ellie!

Not!

Is so!

He has a fat face.

It's . . . it's his beard. He looks like a Viking!

In spectacles?

He reads a lot, that's why! Just ask Father.

Dumb as a post, Dollie. Mr. Tyrrell is the hardest man to talk to I ever met.

I didn't talk to him! Dollie wanted to shriek at her so-superior sister. Instead, she tossed her head, gave a little shrug, and smiled to herself: *I listened, like Desdemona, to every word he said, admiring his splendid physique, and thinking of the courage and strength of purpose he had needed to accomplish the things he had done!*

Dollie Carey fell in love with Joe Tyrrell at first sight. Neither Dollie nor Joe recorded the date of their meeting, but Joe later recalled it as the spring of 1891. Reverend George Carey, his wife Mary, and three of their four daughters, Alice, Eleanor, and Mary Edith, nicknamed Dollie, had moved to Ottawa from St. John, New Brunswick, in November 1889. George Carey was the new Baptist minister, and the manse, at the corner of Gloucester and Metcalfe streets, was only two blocks south of 92 Metcalfe, Mrs. Buchanan's boarding house, where Joe, Richard McConnell, and several of their unmarried Survey colleagues had rooms for the winter months. Mrs. Buchanan's was a more genteel establishment than Joe's old digs with Mrs. Adams, and when parliament was in session, Mrs. Buchanan's best suite was occupied by a Conservative senator, John Boyd, and his wife, from New Brunswick. The Boyds and Careys had been good friends during the many years the Careys had lived in St. John, and the Boyds were always among the convivial crowd invited to the Carey home for supper after the Sunday evening service. Senator Boyd, famed as a storyteller and mimic, could usually be counted on to bring interesting guests, and Joe Tyrrell's dramatic role in the wreck of the *Keewatin*, so soon after his near death in the wilderness from typhoid, had made him an object of curiosity and admiration.

"One Sunday evening," Dollie writes in her memoir, *I Was There*, "we found several people sitting in our pew. There was no room for me. I sat behind and entertained myself by looking at a tall man with fair hair and beard, who listened to the sermon much more attentively than I did."

Dollie was twenty, Joe thirty-two. During ten winters in Ottawa, Joe had called on almost every eligible young woman, and he had reached an age when his family was wondering when he was going to settle down; James, nearly five years younger, had married in 1890. Eleanor and Alice Carey seemed ideally suited for a scientific man: both had attended Wellesley College in Connecticut and, like their father, were fluent in Latin and Greek; Lissie, the oldest, had studied medicine before marrying a doctor in Michigan. Dollie, the sickly baby of the family, had been educated largely at home, and, frankly, she preferred to read romantic novels and poetry.

So did Joe. He had grown up with the works of Sir Walter Scott, especially *Ivanhoe*, with its reference to Wat Tyrrel, the Norman knight who had killed King William Rufus, and Shakespeare's plays, of course, Tennyson, Byron, the Bröntes, Jules Verne's thrilling *Journey to the Centre of the Earth* and *Twenty Thousand Leagues Under the Sea*, with their mad scientist heroes and Ned, the Canadian voyageur, Mark Twain, and, secretly, the Wild West dime novels and illustrated magazines of which his

Mary Edith Tyrrell as a young woman. (TFRBL, J.B.T. papers, F3591)

mother so disapproved. Joe's father had given him his grandfather's ancestral shotgun when he was barely old enough to walk, and Joe prided himself on being as good a shot as any man in the North-West, Indians included.

But conservative Joe Tyrrell was too much a Quaker at heart to be an outlaw or a military man, and he had only contempt for all the Yankee Indian fighters, army deserters, and jailbirds he met out west. For all Joe's Viking vagabond pose, he missed the loving companionship of his three sisters and the comforts of a cozy home. He hated having his room at Mrs. Buchanan's rented out to a stranger while he was away, and he'd been devastated on his most recent return from the West to find his office at the Survey occupied by a new man. He'd had to raise an unpleasant row to get it back.

People often asked Joe how he could bear the loneliness of travelling in wild, unpopulated country for six months of the year, and he always replied, with a shy smile, that he had loved solitude since, as a boy, he had wandered the Humber Valley as far south as the villages of Thistletown and Etobicoke. In truth, Joe was helpless in the North-West without his cook, and he lived in such cramped, intimate contact with his assistant, Dowling, his teamsters and canoemen, that they grated sorely on one another's nerves; Joe unjustly complained that patient, indefatigable Dowling was dirty and lazy. Joe's expeditions crossed paths with others, and he stopped regularly at settlements for provisions and mail, rushing with a pounding heart into some back-of-beyond outpost hoping against hope for a packet of little white envelopes with familiar handwriting from home. The letters, often damp and dog-eared, were weeks old, and the homely news predictable, but Joe preserved them all in the blotting papers he used for pressing plants.

One letter had caught him off guard, and it remained a painful, guilty memory. Joe had picked it up in Calgary in mid-November 1886, and torn it open impatiently while waiting to pay off his summer's accounts before catching the train home. The date, October 9, was five weeks old, but the postmark, Detroit, Michigan, told him it was from his dearest sister, Minnie, Mrs. Lennox. This would be a treat: he hadn't heard from Minnie since, when? Last spring, not long after the birth of her second baby. Minnie had seemed wonderfully happy, the little girl healthy and strong. Ordinarily, Joe would put the letters in his pocket to read at leisure on the train, but he noticed that the paper was strange, like scraps of a child's scribbler, and the crabbed handwriting was his sister Annie's.

"My own dear brother – Our darling Minnie left us yesterday morning. . . . She had been ill for three weeks. . . ." Sorrowful, yet calm, Annie spared no details of Minnie's deathbed: three doctors in attendance, their brother Rob among them, Minnie lucid, "*so happy and bright,*" disposing of her trinkets and treasures, saying goodbye, "tell Joe to meet me in Heaven and I will watch for him," then delirious, and finally, "she just quietly ceased to breathe." Her husband, Lambert, prostrated with grief, Minnie laid out in her wedding clothes, looking almost as she did on her wedding day, three years ago, except that "glory was written all over her face now."

Minnie, six years older, had been Joe's loving teacher and protector, and he had been her young confidant when their father broke her heart. In July 1874, Minnie had written to Joe: "About Mr. Duncan, Joe dear, I don't know what to do. You can't know how hard it would be to break it off now, when we have been engaged for more than a year. He seems almost part of myself now. Then he is thirty years old and I am the first person he ever loved, and how will he feel. I would not like anybody to treat you that way. I would rather die than be false. Then again, how can I do what Papa does not wish me to do. You are all so good and kind at home. I cannot bear to hurt any of you. I think you could not find a more difficult position for anybody than I am in. I earnestly beseech God our Father that He will not let me do anything wicked but will guide me right. Pray for me, dear Joe, as I do for you."

Minnie ended her engagement to John Duncan. Her letters don't reveal her father's objection, but it was late, arbitrary, and cruel. Her subsequent, sad letters to Joe at university refer repeatedly to "the trouble" and "the dark cloud." Although Joe was only fifteen when the family crisis occurred, he took Minnie's side: "I shall never forget, Joe," she writes to him in 1878, "how good you were to me when I was in such dreadful trouble, for I utterly despised myself when I broke my engagement with Mr. Duncan. I did not think I could be as mean as to treat a man like that. . . . I need not say anything more about that, only to thank you over and over again for being so kind to me."

William Tyrrell had already blighted Minnie's life. Minnie, like her mother, had attended a Methodist ladies' college to become a teacher, but William had insisted that Minnie open her own little school in Weston, under his thumb. When Lambert Lennox, a Methodist circuit preacher, proposed, Minnie had seemed happy, at least happy to be getting married.

By the time Joe learned of Minnie's death, she had been a month in her grave, and when he got home to Weston, her little daughters were living with his parents. Joe felt almost a stranger in his own family. He had missed Minnie's wedding – he'd been wading through mountain streams in the foothills of the Rockies – and while Minnie was dying, he'd been heedlessly drifting down the North Saskatchewan River in a scow. Joe could not believe that Minnie was rejoicing in Heaven with her Saviour, and his sore heart knew that during her short, passionate life, she had celebrated and suffered and died without his presence, even, in her dying, without his knowledge. He had been, as the Irish say, *away*.

Lambert Lennox grieved little more than a year before he married Annie. Annie had been acting as nursemaid to the children, and the children needed a mother, but the wedding was such a hasty, surreptitious affair, on a Monday night, with no advance notice, that it appeared certain Lennox had seduced her. Joe didn't have to be a prude or a cynic to blame Minnie's death on a loveless marriage, loveless at least on her husband's part. He never forgave Annie.

Minnie's hurt, and death, made Joe leery of marriage in general, fathers in particular. And what did he have to offer a wife? What sort of father would allow his daughter to marry a man who was absent, virtually incommunicado, six months of the year, and spent the rest of his time buried in rocks in a museum?

Then there was the religion question. It was one thing to attend a church service as a guest, quite another to join a church, especially the Bible-thumping Baptists, and sell his scientist's soul. As much as Joe enjoyed the Careys' hospitality, he was, after all, an eligible suitor.

"During the winter," Dollie observes, "my father was preaching a series of sermons on the Book of Ezekiel. One of his most interested hearers was young Mr. Tyrrell, and early in the week following each of the sermons he called in to discuss the problems of the Book more fully with my father. He purchased a Commentary on Ezekiel and brought his profound geological knowledge to bear on the Valley of the Dry Bones. He was well informed on the vision of the Red Horses, and the White Horses, and never even gave one look at me where I sat listening.

"My father was delighted to find a scientific man so deeply interested in the splendours of the Old Testament, but he got a rude jolt when Mother said decisively, 'George, leave the young people alone. The young men would rather talk to the girls.'

"Father replied warmly, 'There you go, putting nonsense into the children's heads. These young men come to see me; especially Tyrrell, who is an intelligent and clever scientist. I'm learning a great many things from him.'"

Dollie was accustomed to sitting quietly in her father's study, reading, listening, and watching, and she too had learned a great many things. Too gawky and homely to play the coquette, Dollie charmed visitors with her dramatic flair, teasing, and playfulness. She pretended, with her family's connivance, to be still a child, and whenever she was angry, or frustrated, she threw a temper tantrum and sulked off to her sickbed until she was mollified or grew bored.

Talkative, impulsive, imaginative, Dollie loved dressing up, and, depending on the circumstances, the drama might be *Pride and Prejudice*, the Book of Esther, or "The Lady of Shalott." Dollie was always the prima donna, and now Joe, her "bearded young giant," was cast as her leading man.

Joe indeed may have come to visit her father. Reverend Carey, in popular demand as a preacher, was also a distinguished biblical scholar who skirted dangerously close to the heresy that the Old Testament, like the *Iliad* or *Odyssey*, might be a secular work of history or mythology. Carey's interest in the history of the Mediterranean and the Holy Land included archaeology and paleontology, and an invitation to visit his library, one of the best in Ottawa, was an honour. Joe loved reading as much, or more, than tramping around outdoors.

Joe's sparse diary is mute about Miss Edith Carey until the spring of 1892, but two entries show her influence: Joe joined the Ottawa Rifle Club, and he bought a commission as a lieutenant in the Governor General's Foot Guards. Improving his shooting skills made practical sense – Dollie called Joe her "mighty hunter before the Lord" – but why was this clever scientist playing Sunday soldier? For one thing, the scarlet uniform showed off his splendid physique; for another, the Careys were the only Baptist family in Ottawa, possibly in all Canada, who belonged to "society."

Dollie's mother, Mary, was a Killmaster, a clan of prosperous merchants and landowners near Port Rowan on Lake Erie, and Mary's share of the Killmaster fortune allowed the Careys to enjoy luxuries and privileges some in their puritan congregation might call unchristian. Dollie and her sisters wore expensive, fashionable clothes; they attended the governor general's balls, and a regular, two-mile walk to sign the guest book at Rideau Hall became part of Joe and Dollie's courtship ritual. Joe no longer envied or despised the British toffs who swanned around Government House; he learned to dance, and on May 29, 1892, Miss Edith Carey agreed to become his wife.

Dollie'd had to do some nudging. "Dear Mr. Tyrrell," she writes on March 31, "We have found the two books we mentioned to you. Perhaps you might care to look over them while you are in Toronto – Surely you are going to come and say good-bye to us when you will be away for so long, and if you care for the books you may have them then. Yours Sincerely, Edith Carey."

Joe's departure for a summer's survey in the area east of Lake Athabasca was still two months away, and as the date approached Dollie's tone became more peremptory: "Dear Mr. Tyrrell, Please come down for a few minutes this evening to tell us all about your picnic. I cannot let a day go by without seeing you when you are going away so soon." The hand-delivered note, dated simply "Saturday evening," was likely written on May 28, following the Foot Guards' annual Victoria Day celebration on May 24. "Father must have been a little dazed when Joe asked him for me," Dollie recalled, "for he turned to me saying, 'You poor, deluded child; the last thing in the world you need is a husband.'"

Joe seems to have agreed – they expected that their engagement would last five to ten years. Dollie was unfazed. "My own dear Jo," she writes on June 7, "You looked, my own dear Jo, so strong, brave and true when you went off last night and I am the very happiest girl in all the world to think that you love me, and I am proud, very proud, to think of the clever grand things you can do. . . . You don't know, dear, that I have been a very dirty girl since you left, for I would not wash my face excepting just around my eyes where it was red. I wonder, would it get very dirty if I did not wash it until you come back? Your own true loving Edith." Then, the next day, in case Joe felt badly about going away: "You know, my own dearest Jo, that I do not wish in any way to stop you in your work and to feel that because you love me you cannot fill your place in the world or live your part of Canadian history."

Joe addressed her as "My dearest Edith," and he signed his first letter "Fondest love, from your true lover, J.B. Tyrrell." He broke the exciting news to his parents in Weston en route to Lake Athabasca. They were pleased but flummoxed; they had never heard of Miss Edith Carey, much less met her. Joe's mother took the trouble to send Edith a note warning her that

Joe was not a Christian. Dollie replied that she didn't care: Joe was "good and noble."

Dollie could lay on the flattery, but there was a knife beneath the honey: "You will be sure to telegraph to me as soon as you get out of that horrible wild place, won't you?" she writes to Joe as he embarked on his "old horrid geological expedition," then she adds: "You must go and gain the highest scientific honours that any man can have." One minute Dollie would be speculating about coming to live with "Mr. Pterodactyl" at Lake Athabasca for two years, the next, she'd remind Joe of a rival suitor, Donald McLean. A reference to a past quarrel seems to have provoked Joe to write Edith a revealing, if defensive, letter on June 10: "Your home on Gloucester St. will be remembered and known as the home where I spent so many happy hours, and where I won my love, even if she was almost lost to me at one time. The idea of such loss makes me shudder every time it rises before me. But that merely arises from my own egotism which is unnecessarily strong. A solitary life tends to make one egotistical, but in future your interests will lend a higher motive to existence, and a constant thought for another will develop a higher and fuller manhood in me."

Dollie's ambitions for Joe were not her fantasies: she was holding up a mirror to his own avid, restless need for recognition. There must have been times during their courtship when Joe felt that Dollie was the only person in the world who believed in him. Professionally, it was a time of frustration and disappointment. Joe was not satisfied that Victoria College in Cobourg had awarded him a Bachelor of Science, and the University of Toronto a Master of Arts, based on his research for the Survey. Thanks to his outstanding Lake Agassiz work with Warren Upham, he had been elected a fellow of the Geological Society of America, and at the society's meeting in December 1889, Joe had presented the first analysis of the great continental *mer de glace* that had once spread from the Arctic over the Canadian plains and across the forty-ninth parallel. Pulverized rock, muck, and boulders dragged by the ice had created the lumpy topography of hills, knolls, and ridges in the North-West that Joe had examined for six years, and he pointed out that, contrary to the accepted theory of south-westward movement, the glacier had swung to the southeast down the Lake Winnipeg and Assiniboine River valleys.

This paper, published by the society the following year with the brain-numbing title "Post-Tertiary Deposits of Manitoba and the Adjoining Territories of Northwestern Canada," made Joe Tyrrell a leading expert on North American glaciers, but it did not bring him a prestigious job offer or the slightest encouragement to continue his research. The Survey rejected his requests to study abroad, and his applications for university teaching positions in Canada were unsuccessful in spite of excellent letters of recommendation. Edward Chapman, Joe's professor at the University of Toronto, praised him as "a careful and patient investigator," who stood "high in the esteem of his professors." George Wallace, headmaster of the Weston High School, testified that his former pupil's character was irreproachable, "his manner courteous and highly obliging."

No longer. Joe had developed an exaggerated and obstreperous opinion of his own worth. He applied for a university teaching position before it had been advertised, bragging, "I expect to have secured it by then." He wasn't offered it at all. He published his geological studies in journals before they had appeared in the Geological Survey's own reports, and mailed copies of everything he wrote to the newspapers. Joe's dislike of the Survey's director, A.R.C. Selwyn, amounted almost to paranoia: "It is the policy of the director to keep the men down as much as possible," he complained to his father. "The less they are known, the less he has to pay them." Far from being grateful that the Survey had kept him on, at full pay, during the many months of his illness and recovery from typhoid, Joe badgered his father to write to Sir John, and other influential government figures, to further his career:

"A letter from you to Sir John asking him to speak to Mr. Dewdney, Minister of Interior, on my behalf, would be of considerable service to me. A letter from you to Mr. Burgess, Deputy Minister of Interior, asking him to do what he could for me would also help me. You might also write to Dr. Selwyn saying that I had told you that he would recommend me for promotion and thanking him for it. He has promised to recommend me, but of course he may forget it, and if he got a letter thanking him it would serve to remind him. I can get promotion if I push hard for it, but I will have to push very hard."

A formal citation from Manitoba's Lieutenant-Governor Schultz commending Joe's role in the *Keewatin* rescue helped to boost his salary to $1,500 a year, yet he was one of the leaders in a vicious agitation to push Selwyn out. "He is endeavouring to crush me," Joe writes to his father in March 1891. "I am doing all I can to get at his throat." Selwyn did recommend Joe's dismissal, but then Selwyn had been threatening to fire his entire rebellious staff. Unanimously fed up with being underpaid and classified as "clerks," they insisted that the government recognize the sciences as professions, not the hobbies of aristocrats or last resorts for academic misfits.

A compromise was reached: the senior men's demand for recognition as "technical officers" was granted, but while Selwyn was nearly seventy, he remained as director. The root problem was that in a depressed economy, with a moribund, parsimonious Conservative government, the Survey could not afford raises, promotions, or even extensive field trips, and its old museum building was, literally, falling down. The death of the Old Chieftain, Prime Minister Sir John A. Macdonald, in June 1891, left the country rudderless. The public was disillusioned. The completion of the Canadian Pacific Railway to the Pacific Ocean in 1885 had brought prosperity only to the railway's financiers and the Hudson's Bay Company, which, between them, had been awarded nearly seven million acres of prime land. Scattered gold finds and oil booms had come to naught, and coal did not excite enthusiasm. Yet voters and politicians still dreamed of undiscovered mountains of silver and sapphires, and rivers glittering with gold. Why hadn't the Geological Survey found King Solomon's Mines?

"The very existence of large regions of which little or nothing is known is, of course, stimulating to a fertile imagination, ready to picture to itself undiscovered 'golden cities a thousand leagues deep in Cathay,'" Dr. G.M. Dawson admonished the Ottawa Field Naturalists' Club on March 7, 1890, "but such unscientific use of the imagination is far removed from the position of sober seriousness in which I ask your attention to the facts which I have to present." However, instead of sober facts, Dawson, backed by a map of Canada showing sixteen vast "unexplored regions," presented an enticing vision of the North as a yet-undiscovered Garden of Eden:

"Beyond Winnipeg is the great area of prairie, plain and plateau, which runs on in one form or other, though with diminishing width, to the Arctic Ocean. This is, generally speaking, an alluvial region, and one of fertile soils. Very fortunately, and as though by a beneficent provision of nature, the climatic features favour the utilization of this belt." Warm summer isothermals, Dawson argued, would permit crops to ripen as far north as York Factory on Hudson Bay and at Great Bear Lake in the Arctic. If agriculture failed, there was plentiful timber, and with respect to mineral resources, "it is probable that the value of those which exist in the unexplored regions will be found, area for area, to be equal to those of the known regions."

Dawson's pitch, blithely ignoring the contrary evidence of all earlier explorers, was crudely aimed at industrialists and financiers: "Though the explorer himself may be impelled by a certain romanticism in overcoming difficulties or even dangers met with in the execution of his task, his steps are surely and closely followed by the trader, the lumberer, or the agriculturalist, and not long after these comes the builder of railways and his iron road. It is, therefore, rather from the point of view of practical utility that an appeal must be made to the public or to the Government for the further extension of explorations."

The oil sands of the Athabaska region and the Mackenzie River valley were well known, and in 1887 Dawson himself had seen gold dust in the headwaters of the Liard and Pelly rivers east of Alaska. By rekindling the mysterious vision of northern treasure that had prompted Queen Elizabeth I to dispatch Martin Frobisher to the fabulous North-West in 1578, Little Doc cast himself, and his colleagues at the Geological Survey, in the popular role of Arthurian knights in quest of the Grail. The fact that they had to undertake these long, dangerous journeys with nothing more than the shirts on their backs was perfectly appropriate.

Of Dawson's sixteen unexplored regions, stretching from Labrador to the Alaska boundary, Joe chose number 9: "Area south-east of Athabasca Lake, 35,000 square miles. This may be compared in extent to Portugal." The traditional route of northern trade and exploration led through the west end of Lake Athabasca to the Mackenzie River, but David Thompson had spent a great deal of time on the Churchill, or Missinippi, River system to the south and east. His map and journals, which Dawson seems to have ignored or rejected, told Joe exactly where to begin.

Unhappily, Joe had to return Thompson's unpublished *Travels* to Charles Lindsey. Lindsey's attempt to rewrite the manuscript as a biography was an admitted failure, and the seven-hundred-page manuscript itself, clearly and closely written in ink on sheets of lined foolscap, was so amorphous, fragmented, and disorganized that it stymied attempts to put it in readable order. Parts were missing; there were no chapters or paragraphs, punctuation was absent or erratic, and, as was customary in his time, Thompson spelled words in a variety of ways.

His voice, however, spoke clearly and forcefully, and the stories he told were mesmerizing: hunger and hardships during his travels through the mountains and to the Pacific Ocean, bloody battles between the Piegans and Snakes, the curious customs of the Nahathaway, the name the Cree called themselves, observations on the habits of owls, grouse, ermine, and beaver, quarrels with rival traders, and, at Cumberland House in 1789: "By too much attention to calculations in the night with no other light than a small candle my right eye became so much inflamed that I lost its sight."

Thompson was then only nineteen, and he had yet to learn surveying. The astronomer Joe now praised as North America's greatest geographer had been blind in one eye! More remarkable . was Thompson's insouciant attitude. Bravery, "manliness" as he called it, he admired above all. Proud, intelligent, and opinionated, censorious towards those who drank (everyone in the fur trade but himself), quick to take offence and nurse a grudge, Thompson regarded the Nahathaway, his wife's people, with admiration and affection. He admitted, half jokingly, to only one weak spot: "Hudson's Bay is a country that Sinbad the Sailor never saw, and he makes no mention of Musketoes."

The Nahathaway called Thompson "You who look at the stars," and believed that the Great Spirit spoke to him as he studied the night sky. Joe Tyrrell, while not averse to taking a drink, could see himself mirrored in the narrator of the *Travels*. Lindsey allowed Joe to keep a typewritten copy, but Joe feared that Lindsey intended to sell the original.

On June 6, 1892, a week after his engagement to Dollie, Joe left Ottawa to spend the summer exploring the region southeast of Lake Athabasca. It was a big expedition, with a budget of four thousand dollars. Joe was again accompanied by D.B. Dowling, who would independently survey the lake's south shore, and his own assistant, McGill University student John Gwillam. Joe and Gwillam travelled by train to Prince Albert on the North Saskatchewan River, then by Hudson's Bay Company wagon and barge to their jumping-off point, Île-à-la-Crosse. Joe brought his own wood canoe, and apart from a camp stove, his outfit was the bare minimum for four months in the northern bush: "2 coats – 1 leather, 1 serge; 3 pr. trousers – 2 wool, 1 moleskin; 1 vest, 6 pr. socks; 3 shirts – 2 flannel; 3 undershirts – 1 wool; 2 pr. drawers;

1 long boots, 1 short boots; 2 rubbers; 1 straw hat, 1 cloth, 1 nightcap; 1½ pr. blankets; 2 towels, 2 silk handkerchiefs; 2 cakes soap; mosquito nets and tent, mosquito oil; 1 45/90 rifle, 100 cartridges; 1 44/40 revolver, 50 cartridges; 1 small camera; instruments; medical case; pocket Shakespeare; awls and needles; sponge and rubber mat for canoe; alarm clock, very small."

Joe's baggage included a photo of Dollie, which he propped up beside his writing case every evening. "You know, darling, that you are a very, very large part of my life," he writes from Prince Albert on June 14, "and you must not think that because fate is carrying my body farther away from you it is separating our souls. We are bound together by the powerful bonds of love, the strongest bonds that can be formed in this world or next, and nothing can separate us now.

"Last year, I did not believe in heroism that had not self interest or amusement as the main motive. Now everything appears in a new light. That there is such a thing as pure, sweet unselfish love I now know, and I would not give it up for everything else that this world could bestow.

"You must not think, darling, that you can wash all traces of me from your face, for every night, before I roll up in my blanket, I shall breathe you a fond kiss, which the little spirits of the forest will carry down to Ontario and leave with my own true love."

At Île-à-la-Crosse, Joe stocked up on provisions at the Bay post. The hospitable manager, H.J. Moberly, found him four canoemen, Joe Parker, Pierre Girard, a Metis, and two young Chipewyan, Ithingo and Wolverine. Shortly after they set out, they met three American hunters arriving from the north. This was disconcerting. Perhaps this area was better known than they had believed. With the spring hunting season well over, and the autumn season months away, there were historical grounds to suspect that the "hunters" might be U.S. Army scouts.

Canada's claim to the North-West Territories derived from the Royal charter given to the Hudson's Bay Company in 1670, the company's venerable chain of fur trade posts, trader Samuel

Hearne's overland journey from Hudson Bay to the mouth of the Coppermine River between 1769 and 1772, Alexander Mackenzie's voyage to the mouth of the Mackenzie River, and numerous expeditions, by sea and land, led by an assortment of fur traders, Royal Navy officers, including Sir John Franklin, and British explorers searching for Franklin's lost ships.

The two most recent expeditions, however, had been American. Between 1860 and 1869, Charles Francis Hall, an eccentric publisher from Cincinnati, Ohio, had lived for several years on the Arctic islands north of Hudson Bay with two English-speaking Inuit, Ebierbing and Tookolito, known to the whalers as "Joe" and "Hannah"; ten years later, between 1878 and 1880, "Joe" guided a successful overland expedition, led by Lieutenant Frederick Schwatka of the U.S. Army, from Chesterfield Inlet on Hudson Bay to the site of the Franklin expedition's wreckage on King William Island. Both Hall and Schwatka had professed to be searching for relics and survivors – Schwatka discovered skeletons, graves, and a few remnants of clothing – but the fate of British sailors, long since documented, seemed an odd interest for the wealthy, prestigious American Geographical Society, which had financed the explorers, and Schwatka, accompanied by reporter William Gilder of the *New York Herald*, had the nerve to name an Arctic river "Hayes" after the U.S. president.

The presence of Americans gave Joe's expedition an urgent political as well as an economic purpose: Canada must stake a clear claim to any "unexplored region." Striking north up the Caribou River at the end of June – Joe called it Mudjatick, or Bad Caribou, River – the expedition entered a flat, monotonous wasteland of sand and sandstone that revealed a secret. Joe notes: "The sand was almost certainly deposited at the mouth of an ancient river. The whole valley that we have followed appears to have been a great drainage channel from the face of the ice field to the north. The current has been so swift that sand and pebbles alone were left in this valley while all the fine clay rock flour was carried farther south."

On July 1, Joe writes to Dollie: "I am sitting like Abraham on the ground at the door of my tent looking out to the setting sun which is just sinking behind the trees on the opposite side of the river. The day was rather a hard one, as this morning we paddled against a dead head wind and made two long portages, and this afternoon we have been struggling upstream against a current of four miles an hour so that the men have had little rest." Although Joe was in a rush, he tried not to work his crew too hard until they got used to their daily routine.

And on July 3:

"My tent has been pitched on the west side of the Caribou or Deer River at the foot of a rapid, the ground is covered with little trailing berry vines with hard waxy leaves and tall pines with few branches throw a little shade. My Indians are in good humour as they set the net last night at the foot of the rapid and this morning found in it some fine whitefish and a beautiful large trout. Their food is almost all they think of as in this rather inhospitable land they have always been kept busy providing a mere subsistence for themselves and their families. The exultation of war has always been unknown to them. Those with me are very cleanly in their person and appearance and are withall very pleasant fellows. Their language is very gutteral and aspirate, but one of the three [Girard] speaks English and it is not unlikely that he will be to a certain extent the boss of the expedition.

"Prices are high at the Trading Post of the Hudson's Bay Company where they are obliged to trade and they do not get very much for all the fur that they manage to procure. For instance, common grey cotton is fifty cents a yard and one of our men paid a dollar for a common cotton flour bag. Wages are correspondingly high and I am obliged to pay all my men forty dollars a month, and of course their board.

"I think of you every leisure hour, and in the evening, lying in my tent, you are very near and dear to me, Your true lover, J.B. Tyrrell."

Ten days later, Joe writes from Cree Lake: "I have enjoyed the continuous pleasure of travelling over its perfectly transparent water and camping on its pine-clad shores which only four white men have ever seen before, and they were all hunters or traders for the Hudson's Bay Co. The lake is only about forty miles in length and is so broken up by wooded islands that nowhere can a stretch of more than ten or fifteen miles be seen at one time. It is very deep, and the water is clear so that as we travel along the shore in the canoe we can readily see the bottom fifteen or twenty feet below. It also contains plenty of beautiful trout which we can catch in abundance with a trawl.

"Last night I was sleeping under a mosquitoe [*sic*] net with the door of my tent open as usual, and my valise outside the net close to my head. Just at dawn my compass fell from where it was lying on the valise and waked me, and looking through the net I saw a porcupine perched on the valise not two feet from my face. I did not want to raise the net as the mosquitoes were thick so I lay and watched him for about half an hour. He would go to sleep for a while, then wake up, brush some mosquitoes off his nose, try to climb up the side of the tent, and failing in that would go to sleep again. I could talk as much as I liked but he did not notice it at all, except occasionally to turn some of his sharpest quills in my direction. At last I put out my hand and pulled over the valise and threw him between it and the side of the tent. He left a lot of his quills sticking in the side of the tent and the heavy leather of the valise and walked slowly out into the open air."

The Indians killed the porcupine that afternoon. With two Joe had shot the day before, it made a succulent feast before the start of their descent of the Cree River. Joe wrote in his notes: "The river is one of the most difficult and dangerous to follow in all the northern country. From its source to its mouth it is a roaring, boiling torrent either rushing along at a furious rate in a narrow defile or spread wide over a bed of boulders." Sharp exposed rocks punctured the canoes and cut the men's feet as

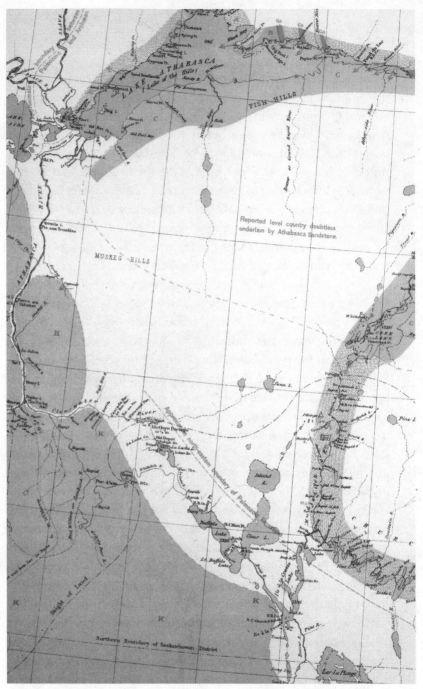

Map of the country between Lake Athabasca and the Churchill River, drawn J.B. Tyrrell, 1897. (TFRBL, J.B.T. papers, M10049)

by D.B. Dowling to accompany a Geological Survey of Canada report by

"Hudson Bay Company post, Fond du Lac, 1892." Photo by D.B. Dowling. (LAC, PA-038197)

they dragged the craft over the shoals; their hands and faces were swollen and bloody from blackfly bites. It was a miserable trip, and it was with relief as much as pride that Joe writes in his notebook on July 24: "We have ascended the Deer [Caribou] River to its source, crossed the height of land, surveyed and explored Cree Lake, that hitherto unknown body of water, and descended Cree River, being the first white men to come down its surging rapids."

Joe didn't really know whether he and Gwillam were the first white men on this river, nor how anyone in the North would define a "white man." The rivers already had names, and the area was known to Pierre Girard, Ithingo, and Joe Parker. Joe Tyrrell was completely dependent on his Native guides and manpower, and his situation caused him anxiety: "My Indians seem inclined to stay with me as they promised to do," Joe writes to Dollie. "This is the great difficulty in this country, that the Indians are not willing to leave home for three or four months at a time to go off with a stranger, they prefer to stay at home and perhaps have poorer fare but have the company of their wives and families. They readily promise to go with you, but after a short time they become homesick and no inducement can be offered sufficiently strong to detain them."

At the end of July, the expedition gladly reached the harbour of Fond du Lac, an old Hudson's Bay Company outpost at the eastern end of Lake Athabasca. Apart from a Roman Catholic mission, where a priest spent the winters, the permanent settlement consisted of a few log houses surrounded by a rough palisade. Joe was charmed to meet the trader, seventy-five-year-old Joe Mercredi, who had been at his post without interruption for forty-seven years: "He is a very nice gentlemanly old fellow. He knows nothing of the world, and the doings of the great mass of mankind are of no interest to him. One journey a year, or perhaps two, to the next Trading Post two hundred miles away, gives him the news of the Company for the year and a priest occasionally comes and stays here for a little while. Beyond that he has nothing to think of but the obtaining of caribou meat for the Trading Posts on the Athabasca and Mackenzie rivers."

Mercredi, who spoke only French, was an invaluable source of information, and Joe was intrigued to be given directions he had not anticipated. On July 29, he writes in his notes: "Information was gathered about a route up Yellow Knife River, and also a route north from Grease Mountain River. Both these routes lead up to the Barren Grounds and to a great river that flows down into the sea on which the musk oxen are plentiful, and which is only travelled on by Esquimos. It must flow into Chesterfield Inlet. No one knows all the country north to Great Slave Lake."

David Thompson, to his regret, had never visited the Barren Grounds, but he gives a vivid description in his *Travels*: "There are no Woods, all is Rock and Moss; on these barren lands, in the open season the Rein deer are numerous; they have food in abundance, and the constant cold nights puts down the flies. The Natives cannot stay long; the Moss, when dry, makes a tolerable fire, but in wet weather, which often happens, it holds the rain like a sponge, and cannot be made to burn; this want of fire often obliges them to eat the meat raw, and also the fish; the latter I have seen them [eat] by choice, especially the pike, and a Trout is no sooner caught than the eyes are scooped out and swallowed whole, as most delicious morsels."

Paddling east up the Stone [Black] River from Fond du Lac to Black Lake, Joe's expedition, now joined by Dowling, was overtaken by a small flotilla of Chipewyan canoes. "They are going to the Barren Ground to hunt, up the river that empties into the north side of Black Lake," Joe notes. Joe had taken to heart Thompson's wise example: "I had always conversed with the Natives as one Indian with another, and been attentive to learn their traditions." With Pierre Girard's help as translator, and small gifts of tobacco, Joe was able to glean more information on July 30 when they stopped for lunch at a Chipewyan camp:

"Here we met a Chipewyan named Andrew and had the good fortune to obtain from him a map of a good canoe route northward from here, on which the Indians travel to the Barren Grounds in their large canoes. The trip to Rabbit Mountain Lake generally takes 20 days to go and return. From Rabbit Mt. Lake a large stream flows down into a great river that flows into the sea. He has been to this river, but he never descended it."

Joe's diplomacy had won him the trust of the suspicious Chipewyan. The first canoemen he'd tried to hire had refused to go: "They were afraid of having their hunting grounds explored and before long spoiled by the general advent of the white man." Ithingo, however, now drew a more detailed map for Joe. "In talking with Ithingo about the route from here northward," Joe notes on August 4, "he says that he remembers long ago going much farther than is marked on his map of yesterday. He went down the river to a great lake called To-bon-tna lying far out in the Barren Grounds with no wood at all on its shores. It has no islands, and is of great extent. The lake is reported to be close to the sea. It would take about six weeks to make the trip from here to there and return."

At the next Chipewyan camp, Joe acquired a third map: "One of the two old men made me a map of the route from

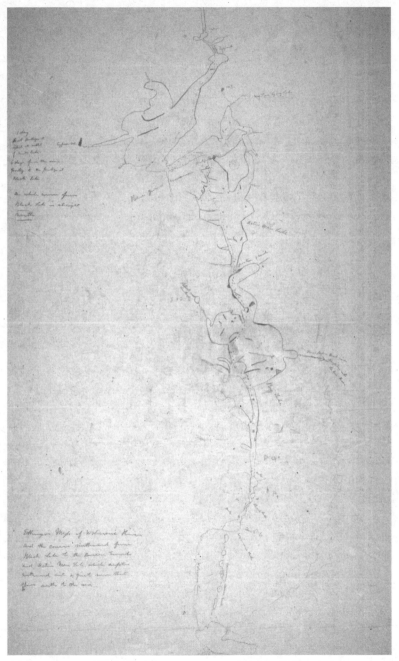

Ithingo's map. (TFRBL, J.B.T. papers, M10019)

Reindeer Lake to White Partridge Lake and thence to the sea, at the same time saying that the route was an easy one. He also said that he knew To-bon-tna and that there was a still longer lake farther north of the same great river, which was never entirely free of ice, though a person could go for a short time between the ice and the shore. Name of this lake is Ta-hiate-tna or Snow Lake."

Joe put this information and the maps carefully aside for future reference. He had no time for a Barren Grounds expedition this year: his path continued up the tumultuous Black River, full of rapids and waterfalls, to Wollaston Lake. At the first waterfall, Joe stopped to pay tribute to David Thompson: here, ninety-six years before, Thompson had nearly drowned. The falls were exactly as Thompson described in his *Travels*:

"A bold perpendicular sided point of limestone rock projects at right angles to the course of the river, against which the rapid current rushes and appears driven back with such force that the whole river seems as if turned up from its bottom. It boils, foams and every drop is white; part of the water is driven down a precipice of twenty feet descent; the greater part rushes through the point of rock and disappears for two hundred yards; then issues out in boiling whirlpools. The dashing of the water against the rocks, the deep roar of the torrent, the hollow sound of the fall, with the surrounding high, dark frowning hills form a scenery grand and awful, and it is well named the Manitou Fall . . . my companions were so awe struck, that the one gave a ring, and the other a bit of tobacco."

After portaging around the Manitou Fall, Thompson's canoemen, Kozdaw and Paddy, had walked along the riverbank, dragging the loaded canoe against the current with a towline while Thompson remained in it to steer: "They came to a Birch Tree, growing at the edge of the water, and there stood and disputed between themselves on which side of the tree the tracking line should pass. I called to them to go on, they could not hear me for the noise of the fall, I then waved my hand for them to proceed, meanwhile the current was drifting me out, and having only one hand to guide the canoe, the canoe took a sheer across the current, to prevent the canoe upsetting, I waved my hand to them to let go the line and leave me to my fate, which they obeyed.

"I sprang to the bow of the canoe took out my clasp knife, cut the line from the canoe and put the knife back in my pocket, by this time I was on the head of the fall, all I could do was to place the canoe to go down bow foremost, in an instant the canoe was precipitated down the fall (twelve feet), and buried under the waves, I was struck out of the canoe, and when I arose among the waves, the canoe came on me and buried [me] beneath it, to raise myself I struck my feet against the rough bottom and came up close to the canoe which I grasped, and being now on shoal water, I was able to conduct the canoe to shore."

Cut, bruised, and exhausted, Thompson lay down on the shore while Kozdaw and Paddy ran downstream to retrieve the paddles and Thompson's cork-lined tin box containing his sextant, maps, and survey notes. Nothing remained in the canoe but an axe, a small tent of grey cotton, a pewter basin, and Thompson's gun:

"We had no time to lose, my all was my shirt and a thin linen vest, my companions were in the same condition, we divided the small tent into three pieces to wrap around ourselves, as a defence against the flies in the day, and something to keep us from the cold at night, for the nights were always cold. On rising from my rocky bed, I perceived much blood at my left foot, on looking at it, I found the flesh of my foot, from the heel to near the toes torn away, this was done when I struck my feet against the rough bottom to rise above the waves of the fall of water. A bit of my share of the tent bound the wound, and thus barefooted I had to walk over the carrying places with their rude stones and banks.

"The Indians went to the woods and procured Gum of the Pines to repair the canoe, and when they returned, the question was how to make a fire, we had neither steel, nor flint, I pointed to the gun from which we took the flint. I then produced my pocket knife with its steel blade, if I had drawn a ghost out of my pocket it would not more have surprised them, they whispered to each other, how avaricious a white man must be, who rushing on death takes care of his little knife. . . . I said to them if I had not saved my little knife how could we make a fire, you fools go to the Birch Tree and get some touchwood, which they soon brought, a fire was made, we repaired our canoe. . . .

"It was now our destitute condition stared us in the face, a long journey through a barren country, without provisions, or the means of obtaining any, almost naked, and suffering from the weather, all before us was very dark, but I had hopes that the Supreme being through our great Redeemer to whom I made my short prayers morning and evening would find some way to preserve us; on the second day, in the afternoon, we came on a small lake of the river, and in a grassy bay we saw two large Gulls hovering, this lead us to think they were taking care of their young, we went, and found three young gulls, which we put in the canoe . . . these gulls gave us but a little meat. They had not four ounces of meat on them. It appeared to sharpen hunger.

"The next day as we proceeded, I remembered an Eagles Nest on the banks of a small Lake before us. I enquired of my companions if the young eagles could fly, they said, they are now large but cannot yet fly . . . accordingly we came on the Lake and went to the Eagles Nest, it was about sixteen feet from the ground, in the spreading branches of a Birch tree, the old ones were absent, but Kozdaw was barely at the nest before they arrived, and Paddy and myself, with shouts and pelting them with stones, with difficulty prevented the Eagles from attacking Kozdaw, he soon threw the two young eagles down to us, they placed themselves on their backs, and with beak and claws fought for their lives, when apparently dead, Kozdaw incautiously laid hold of one of them, who immediately struck the claws of one foot deep into his arm above the wrist. So firm were the claws in his arm, I had to cut off the leg at the first joint above the claws, even then when we took out a claw, it closed in again, and we had to put bits of wood under each claw until we got the whole out.

"We continued our journey to the evening, when as usual we put ashore, and made a fire, on opening the young eagles their insides appeared a mass of yellow fat, which we collected, and with the meat, divided into three equal portions: Paddy and myself eat only the inside fat, reserving the meat for next day, but we noticed Kozdaw, roasting the meat; and oiling himself with the fat: in the night we were both awakened by a violent dysentry from the effect of the eagles fat, Kozdaw now told us that such was always the effects of the inside fat of the fishing Eagle (the bald headed) and also of most birds of prey that live on fish, Paddy bitterly reproached him for allowing us to eat it, we had to march all day in this state, in the evening I filled the pewter basin with Labrador Tea, and by means of hot stones made a strong infusion, drank it as hot as I could, which very much relieved me. Paddy did the same with like effect. We continued our voyage day after day, subsisting on berries, mostly the crowberry, which grows on the ground, and is not nutritious.

"To the sixteenth of July; both Paddy and myself were now like skeletons, the effects of hunger, and dysentry from cold nights, and so weak, that we thought it useless to go any further but die where we were. Kozdaw now burst out into tears, upon which we told him that he was yet strong, as he had not suffered from disease. He replied, if both of you die, I am sure to be killed, for everyone will believe that I have killed you both, the white men will revenge your death on me, and the Indians will do the same for him; I told him to get some thin white birch rind, and I would give him a writing, which he did, with charcoal I wrote a short account of our situation, which I gave him, upon which he said now I am safe. However we got into the canoe, and proceeded slowly, we were very weak, when thank God, in the afternoon we came to two tents of Chepawyans [*sic*], who pitied our wretched condition; they gave us broth, but would allow us no meat until the next day: I procured some provisions, a flint and nine rounds of ammunition, and a pair of shoes for each of us on credit, to be paid for when they came to trade, also an old kettle;

we now proceeded on our journey with thanks to God, and cheerful hearts."

Joe's party ascended the river, Thompson's hair-raising misadventures burned into Joe's imagination, without mishap, and when they reached the height of land separating the rivers flowing west to Lake Athabasca from those flowing towards Hudson Bay, the men celebrated by sheering the lower branches from a tall spruce to create a traditional lobstick – and passing around a keg of whisky. "You would hardly know the reddened creature that the sun and the black flies have made of your Ottawa lover," Joe jokes to Dollie, "but my health is excellent."

Dowling and Gwillam's task would be to continue southeast to survey Reindeer Lake, described by Thompson as a "wretched country of solitude, which is broken only by the large Gull and the Loons," while Joe returned from Reindeer Lake to Île-à-la-Crosse through an unexplored jungle of muskeg, forest, and lakes.

"None of the Indians now with us know anything more about this route than that it is said to exist," Joe notes on August 15. "Without some fairly definite information this year is almost too far advanced, and the supplies are too low to try any chance exploration." For ten days Joe hunted caribou, with scant success, waiting for the arrival of a family of Chipewyans who were reputed to know the way. The Chipewyans provided him with moccasins and tea, but no reliable directions. Undaunted, Joe set out on August 25 with only Girard, Ithingo, and Joe Parker, all of them unfamiliar with the country.

"When I shall reach Île-à-la-Crosse is impossible for me to conjecture," Joe notes, "but my provisions will not last more than ten days and after that we shall have to hunt." Girard, cook and interpreter – Joe spoke no Chipewyan, "a frightfully guttural language" – took charge of the expedition. "He is lazy," Joe writes to Dollie, "but quick-witted and has the knack of making the Indians do nearly all the work and still keep in good humour. It is due entirely to the fact that they are all homesick that I was able to undertake this part of the journey at all . . . the route was the shortest way home. They are much pleasanter than white men to travel with for they never grumble or make all sorts of stupid suggestions, but of course if they don't like you they will simply leave you."

Ten days later, living on moose and bear, they were utterly lost in a labyrinth of swamps and streams that meandered off in all directions; Joe's compass was screwy, and on September 5, the main spring of his watch broke. Without a watch, he couldn't measure longitude, but knowing his exact location was less urgent than getting the hell out of there: "As no one has any idea of the course we have to follow, we have to search the shores of all the lakes for signs of the portages, and these are all very old, no Indian having been here in the summer for a great many years. The portages when found are all blocked up and have to be chopped out." On September 6, they were camped near a stream flowing northeast: "We are going to follow this stream, but where it will lead us no one here knows."

Luckily, the stream led them into a country that began to look familiar to Girard, and by September 14 they were paddling for their lives towards Île-à-la-Crosse. Joe gave up any pretense of conducting a scientific survey of the country: "Unfortunately I am unable to examine it at all thoroughly as we are entirely out of provisions. We are living on ducks but they are not very plentiful, and we are either hunting ducks or hurrying on." During the remaining six days before reaching the Hudson's Bay Company post, they survived on potatoes, bacon, and dried moose meat supplied by the Indians they met, and Joe acquired from a Chipewyan a map of the country he had just traversed.

Next trip, he resolved, he would get directions in advance, and his imagination was already afire with the Chipewyan stories of a route to the sea across the Barren Grounds.

CHAPTER SIX

The Chipewyans' accounts of a Great Northern River seemed to confirm a story Joe had heard earlier on Lake Winnipeg from an old Hudson's Bay Company trader named King:

> Speaking of the country in the north, he says that there is a canoe track all the way from Fort Rea [Rae] to the head of the Chesterfield Inlet, and that the Indians travel the distance in a month. That the journey could readily be made from Ft. Rea and back in a summer and that the Indians there would be willing to go with a party, though they were rather afraid of the Esquimaux in the lower part of the distance.
>
> The route is first through a chain of lakes connected by portages and then down a large river that flows into the Inlet. He has himself been more than half way, and he found the country for a way wooded, and then he struck on the barren grounds. These were generally pretty smooth and easily travelled over but there is one tract 30 miles wide of rough coarse grained gneiss of a pepper and salt colour which is on edge striking N.W. & S.E. which is very rough. There is always a little short grass, but no wood, but little blueberry bushes and willows as big as a slate pencil.

The reindeer leave Ft. Rea about June and travel to the sea coast to have their young and return in the autumn and anyone travelling would need to follow the deer both going and returning, and in that way an abundant supply of provisions could be obtained. Barren ground bears, wolverines, musk ox etc. are also very plentiful, besides wild fowl, and the lakes are teeming with fish. A party going would need largely to live on the country.

This river also appeared to be the one mentioned by Sir George Back in his *Narrative of the Arctic Land Expedition to the Mouth of the Great Fish River*, published in 1836. While Back was wintering at the eastern end of Great Slave Lake, the Indians tried to persuade him to take a much simpler route to the sea along a river that ran through a wooded valley where caribou and musk oxen were plentiful: "The traders travel to it from the establishment at the Fond du Lac in four days. It is known to them by the names Riviere Noire and Thlewndiaza." Wishing to go to the Arctic Ocean, not Chesterfield Inlet on Hudson Bay, Back ignored it, but, from all accounts, the Thelon, as it was commonly called, had more navigational potential than the rocky, treacherous Great Fish River (renamed the Back River in the explorer's honour). Back had also collected "singular" and "remarkable" granite and volcanic rocks in the eastern Barren Grounds, and reported clear evidence of glaciation: sand hills, with gigantic granite boulders strewn about on their tops.

Back's route across the Barren Grounds had veered north, but a more southerly passage through a labyrinth of lakes and rivers had been rudely mapped and described by Hudson's Bay Company trader Samuel Hearne in *A Journey from Prince of Wales's Fort in Hudson's Bay to the Northern Ocean, 1769, 1770, 1771, & 1772*. Hearne, travelling to and from the Coppermine River with a band of Chipewyan, used their names for the major waterways – Whooldyah, Doobaunt, Yath-kyed-whoie – but these did not match the names Joe's Chipewyan informants had given: Active Man Lake, Rabbit Mountain Lake, Snow Lake. It seemed certain that the Thelon, the Great Northern River, was as yet uncharted. George M. Dawson had designated this entire area, some 178,000 square miles, as No. 12 on his list of "unexplored regions," saying contemptuously of Hearne, "Not even roughly approximate accuracy can be assigned to his geographical work."

Could the Barren Grounds be Joe's "Open, Sesame!" to fame and riches? Within a few weeks of returning to Ottawa, and after consulting with his surveyor brother James, Joe had woven his rough drawings and anecdotes into an audacious proposal, which he put before Dr. Selwyn early in 1893:

"In reference to an exploration through the Barren Grounds from Lake Athabasca to the west coast of Hudson's Bay, I beg to state that during the past summer while travelling on Athabasca Lake, Black river and other lakes and streams south of those mentioned I had as one of my canoe men a Chipewyan Indian who had spent his early years on Wollaston Lake and had travelled with canoes northward from Black river to some large lakes which discharge northward by a magnificent stream with a moderate current, but no serious rapids or portages. He had followed this stream down as far as Doobaunt Lake, which he stated to be an extensive sheet of clear open water. He also gave me an excellent map and description of the route.

"Another Indian, whom we met on Black river, stated that he had crossed Doobaunt Lake, and had descended the Great River flowing from it to Tath Kyed Lake which is not far from the sea. The Eskimos come up to this lake, and no Indians will travel beyond it for fear of them, but he had heard that the river was good all the way to the sea.

"On reaching the sea, either Chesterfield Inlet or the west coast of Hudson's Bay, the expedition would turn southward down the unexplored shore of the bay to Fort Churchill. Thence the men might be sent home in canoes by York Factory, and Lake Winnipeg, while I and my assistant would take passage in the 'Erith,' the Hudson's Bay Co.'s steamer, and return through Hudson's Straits, where still further observations could be made on the important question of their navigability.

"The region which would thus be passed through has never been entered by a white man since Samuel Hearne crossed it with a wandering band of Indians in 1770. It is described by him as rocky and barren.

"An area of Huronian rocks, which may be found to be rich in such minerals as gold, silver, nickel etc., striking northeastward from Athabasca and Black Lakes, and the boulders which were found in abundance on Black river, and which have been transported by glaciers from the north, show a considerable proportion of similar rocks, indicating the existence of an area, probably of large extent, of Huronian or copper bearing rocks which both in Canada and the United States are constantly rich in valuable minerals.

"If valuable minerals were discovered in that country, where on account of the uncovered condition of the rocks, they might be expected to be readily found if they do exist, they would be within a few hundred miles of the sea coast on the west side of Hudson's Bay, whence the ore could be shipped to all parts of the world.

"Furthermore, the east end of Lake Athabasca is only four hundred and twenty miles from Fort Churchill, the best harbour on Hudson's Bay and a railroad between these two points would open up direct communication between the sea and the magnificent inland water stretches of the Mackenzie river and its tributaries, on which there is almost continuous steamboat navigation for 750 miles. If the Vermilion Falls on Peace River and the rapids at Fort Smith were overcome, the steamboat navigation would be continuous throughout the whole distance.

"When the various precious metals have been discovered in the country north and east of Lake Athabasca, abundant supplies can be cheaply transported to the mines from the fertile country along Peace River.

"As shown by the appended estimate the proposed expedition would not be an expensive one, for the party would be small and well chosen, and the herds of reindeer that roam over the country would furnish us with provisions for part of our journey. Indians would be taken as far as Doobaunt or Tath Kyed Lakes, but it would be impossible to induce them to go farther. For the rest of the distance it would therefore be necessary to have an Interpreter. The only man known to me who could communicate with any Eskimos whom we might meet who could fill that office is Mr. J.W. Tyrrell C.E., P.L.S. of Hamilton, Ontario, who spent a winter on the north side of Hudson's Straits, and two summers on Hudson's Bay with Com. Gordon, and who talks the Eskimo language fluently. He is an accomplished traveller, and a good surveyor, having spent several years on the Geological Survey as Assistant to Drs. Bell and Lawson in the exploration of Lake of the Woods, while the surveys and maps of Hudson's Bay and Straits, carried out under the charge of Com. Gordon, were also made by him. He has taken a live interest in the question of the navigation of Hudson's Bay, as will be seen from the papers attached, as well as from several other papers which he published in the *Mail* and *Empire*.

"I accordingly wrote to him asking him if he would be willing to accompany me as Topographer and Eskimo interpreter in case I should be sent out on the exploration, and the appended letter was received in reply. His employment for five months would not cost as much as is now paid to my assistant, Mr. Dowling, and the expedition would therefore not be as expensive as that undertaken during the past summer, or much more expensive than the expedition to the east side of Lake Winnipeg, and would be infinitely more fruitful of important results. Mr. J.W. Tyrrell's services as Eskimo interpreter would however be absolutely essential to its success, as without them the short summer of that region might be wasted in unavailing attempts to reach the seaboard by impracticable channels, and irreparable disaster might overtake the party."

Joe's pitch was worthy of the circus impresario P.T. Barnum, and Selwyn, knowing the Tyrrells, would have taken the hint that Joe had already circulated copies of his proposal to the Conservative Toronto newspapers, the *Mail* and the *Empire*. The pipe dream of a railway across the north, linked to a transcontinental steamship network, was intended to appeal to politicians and investors promoting a national frenzy of railway and canal building; Joe had found no precious metals, and his optimistic picture of the Barren Grounds was based on hearsay and wishful thinking.

How could the Tyrrells do a thorough topographical and geological survey of this vast area in the short period of time, June to September, when the waterways were free of ice? How accurate were the Indians' maps and estimated distances? And how could Joe claim that the west coast of Hudson Bay was "unexplored," when his brother James, and Dr. Robert Bell of the Survey, had served aboard the *Alert* on the expedition that had recently explored it? As early as 1612, Captain Thomas Button had sailed down the west coast of the bay to the Nelson River, and British and American whaling ships had been plying the coast for more than one hundred years. As for unexplored Chesterfield Inlet, the British Admiralty had already sent Joe navigational charts, and the mysterious lake Tath Kyed was almost certainly Baker Lake, named in 1761 for Sir William Baker, governor of the Hudson's Bay Company, and his brother Richard. Both Chesterfield Inlet and Baker Lake had been mapped by Captain William Christopher of the Hudson's Bay Company during the eighteenth century, and one expedition had ascended a river at the lake's western end for thirty miles. Most recently, renowned Arctic overland explorer Dr. John Rae, who was still living, had twice sailed up the bay's western coast, investigated the inlet, and wintered farther north at Repulse Bay. Had Joe done so little advance research he did not know that the steamer on which he expected to sail home was named the *Eric*?

Selwyn's response to the Tyrrell brothers' impetuous adventure was to stall. True, Dr. Bell had recommended further study

of the rocks on the western shore of Hudson Bay, and a good
Canadian map of the Doobaunt area, if the Tyrrells could make
one, would justify the relatively small cost, less than four thousand dollars, Tyrrell was proposing. The Americans were being
worrisomely aggressive in the North. A U.S. Navy officer, Robert
Peary, had recently spent a year exploring Greenland, with his
wife and a Negro servant, of all things! The Danes could take care
of him, but at this very moment, a sneaky young scientist from the
University of Iowa, Frank Russell, was on his way to Great Slave
Lake supposedly to study musk oxen, but really, as he'd let slip,
"to pick up everything else I could lay my hands on." Two years
ago, Russell had been at Grand Rapids on Lake Winnipeg posing
as an ornithologist collecting bird skins, but he'd been observed
surreptitiously digging up Cree graves and examining the con-
tents. How many skeletons had he stolen? The Schwatka expedition had earlier carried off the remains of one of Franklin's
officers. Did the American Museum of Natural History intend
to put human cadavers on display?

The British had transferred jurisdiction over the Arctic
archipelago to the Canadian government in 1880, but the question
of actual title remained in limbo. Who would defend Canada's
North, if necessary? The Canadian government saw no need to
have any official presence in the Far North, not even a police officer, until, in the words of the official document, "some influx of
the population or other circumstances shall occur to make such
provision more imperative." What was that, an American invasion? The only government presence in the North was irregular
mail delivery to the scattered Hudson's Bay Company posts, and
none of the British Navy's overland expeditions could have been
undertaken without the company's generous cooperation.

Joe Tyrrell's friendly relations with the Hudson's Bay Company were an asset to be cultivated for the Ottawa museum;
company officers across Canada had for decades been collecting
specimens and sending them off to museums in England and the
United States. It was hard to justify another wildlife survey of the

Barren Grounds in light of Sir John Richardson's monumental *Fauna Borealis Americana*, but Richardson had never explored east of the Coppermine region, and his rock collection had been abandoned or lost. The Survey urgently needed specimens of Arctic game animals, especially musk oxen, before hunters like the English madman Warburton Pike, whose recently published adventures, *The Barren Ground of Northern Canada*, was causing a sensation, slaughtered them all. Selwyn had no qualms about grossly exaggerating the commercial virtues of the Canadian wilderness to promote the Survey's work, but if the expedition ended in disaster, his neck would be in the noose.

James Tyrrell also hesitated. Unable, or unwilling, to find permanent employment with the Dominion government – surveyors were hired on a per-project basis – James was struggling to make a living as a civil engineer in the little city of Hamilton at the west end of Lake Ontario. He was concerned about how much Selwyn would pay. At twenty-nine, nearly five years younger than Joe, James had a wife and infant son to support. He wanted at least $75 to $100 a month, and on April 11, 1893, he was happy to sign on for a generous $6 a day. "I suppose you will supply yourself with all available maps of the country, as of course they are indispensable," James blithely writes to Joe, apparently unaware that they would be making their maps as they went, and adds, "I fancy there will be no difficulty in getting down the coast to Churchill if we get through in time."

Joe's schedule called for them to travel to Edmonton by train, then by wagon and canoe to Fort Chipewyan on Lake Athabasca, leaving there for the Barren Grounds on June 15, yet it was May 10 before Joe was able to write to James from Ottawa confirming that their trip was on – they would leave in five days:

"I shall supply you with a light repeating rifle, blanket, tent, mosquito tent and nets, for the mosquitoes are at their worst in that country. You will need to bring your own clothes, but you do not need a large supply, as we must travel as light as possible. I am going to send a box up to Churchill with a few things that we may need in the autumn but it is more and more doubtful whether we shall even go to Churchill at all or not. It may be impossible to come down the shore of the Bay in canoes, and if so we shall find a route inland probably back of Reindeer Lake."

Joe had ordered two eighteen-foot cedar-strip canoes from the Peterborough Canoe Company, and had hired three Iroquois canoemen, brothers Pierre, Louis, and Michel French, from Caughnawaga near Montreal; a westerner, John Flett, would join them in Edmonton as cook. "I have also sent for a canoe and two men from Île-à-la-Crosse," Joe adds, almost as an afterthought, "but whether they will get word in time or not I do not know."

It was a reckless, disorganized beginning to any scientific expedition. How could Selwyn have authorized it? In 1833–34, Captain George Back, commissioned by the Royal Navy and with unlimited financial resources, had taken a full year to build a base of operations, Fort Reliance, at the eastern end of Great Slave Lake, in order to reconnoitre the headwaters of Great Fish River before risking the next year's exploration down the river; in addition to his own men, British and Canadian, Back had been assisted by a veteran Hudson's Bay Company trader, Roderick McLeod, his family, and a band of Chipewyan who supplied the entire party with caribou and fish. Joe and James Tyrrell and their six-man crew would be entrusting their lives to nerve and luck, rough Chipewyan drawings, and Samuel Hearne's journal of the arduous, painful trips he had made on foot 120 years before.

Between 1769 and 1772, Hearne had made three attempts to reach a fabled copper mine near the mouth of a river on the Arctic Ocean, hundreds of miles northwest of the Hudson's Bay Company's Fort Prince of Wales, at the mouth of the Churchill River. "The Indians who were the occasion of my undertaking this journey," Hearne writes, "represented this mine to be so rich and valuable, that if a factory were built at the river, a ship might by ballasted with the oar [sic], instead of stone. By their account, the hills were entirely composed of that metal, all in handy lumps, like a heap of pebbles. But I and almost all my companions expended near four hours in search of some of this metal, with such poor success, that among us all, only one piece of any size could be found." This worthless "jumble of rocks and gravel" was characteristic of the Barren Grounds landscape: "The land throughout that whole track of country is scarcely any thing but one solid mass of rocks and stones, and in most parts very hilly. . . . The surface, it is very true, is in most places covered with a thin sod of moss, intermixed with the roots of the Wee-sa-ca-pucca, cranberries, and a few other insignificant shrubs and herbage; but under it there is in general a total want of soil, capable of producing any thing except what is peculiar to the climate."

Rocks were exactly what Joe was looking for, and Hearne had noted that fish, especially trout, were abundant in the lakes and streams. Migrating geese and swans nested in marshy areas, and caribou were so plentiful in spring and autumn that the Chipewyan families with whom Hearne travelled, numbering at times as many as six hundred people, slaughtered them indiscriminately for meat and skins. If the Tyrrells met up with any of these swarthy, tattooed "gangs," as Hearne had called them, they were in danger of being pillaged of all their goods, reduced to starvation, and abandoned. Or, with providence, they might find a powerful guide and protector, as Hearne had found in Chief Matonabbee.

Joe's planned route, down the Doobaunt River, passed through country Hearne had traversed, and his guide Matonabbee had told Hearne about a mysterious, secluded forest, inhabited by only one primitive family, "situated so far on the barren ground as to be quite out of the track of any other Indians." According to all Chipewyan accounts, this verdant Eden, visited by migrating geese, ducks, and swans "in great plenty," and by caribou "in astonishing numbers," lay along a river and several fine lakes that drained into Baker Lake. "This, however, is mere conjecture," Hearne noted, "nor is it of any consequence, as navigation on any of the rivers in those parts is not only impracticable, but would be also unprofitable, as they do not lead into a country that produces any thing for trade, or that contains any inhabitants worth visiting."

Hearne was a trader and explorer; he had no pretensions to be a scientist or geographer, but he was an acute observer, and his vivid accounts of his personal experiences were harrowing:

> None of our natural wants, if we except thirst, are so distressing, or hard to endure, as hunger; and in wandering situations, like that which I now experienced, the hardship is greatly aggravated by the uncertainty with respect to its duration, and the means most proper to be used to remove it, as well as by the labour and fatigue we must necessarily undergo for that purpose, and the disappointments which too frequently frustrate our best concerted plans and most strenuous exertions. . . . It may justly be said to have been either all feasting, or all famine: sometimes we had too much, seldom just enough, frequently too little, and often none at all. It will be only necessary to say that we have fasted many times two whole days and nights; twice upwards of three days; and once, near seven days, during which we tasted not a mouthful of any thing, except a few cranberries, water, scraps of old leather, and burnt bones. On those pressing occasions, I have frequently seen the Indians examine their wardrobe, which consisted chiefly of skin clothing, and consider what part could best be spared; sometimes a piece of an old, half-rotten deer skin, and at others a pair of old shoes, were sacrificed to alleviate extreme hunger. . . . Those who are conversant with the history of Hudson's Bay, and who are thoroughly acquainted with the distress which the natives of the country about it frequently endure, may consider them as no more than the common occurrences of

an Indian life, in which they are frequently driven to
the necessity of eating one another.

This, then, was the land Joe and James Tyrrell intended to
traverse by an unknown route, to an uncertain destination, in
eight weeks. How much food should they carry? Joe ordered
two tons of staples (flour, oats, rice, tea, bacon, canned beef,
dried fruits, sugar, cocoa) from the Hudson's Bay Company in
Edmonton for delivery, by steamer and barge, to Fort Chipewyan
on Lake Athabasca, and he relied on the company's northern
supervisor, Dr. William McKay, to find him a guide.

Joe was in an anti-social mood when he wrote to Dollie
from Winnipeg on May 19: "A crowd of people, in a city like this,
wearies me beyond endurance, and though the northern life is
very lonely there are none but the powers of nature to struggle
against, and there is no one present to upbraid if you fail, so that
a fresh start is comparatively easy." In his relationship with
Dollie, Joe liked to play the role of Wild Man, a coarse, ugly, solitary creature who inadvertently said disagreeable things that
angered and annoyed her. A few months earlier, he had bluntly
warned her: "I am afraid that life off alone in the wilderness for
half the year makes me entirely incapable of understanding the
feelings of others, even those most dear."

Joe first met his Iroquois canoemen, Pierre, Louis, and
Michel French, at the end of May in Edmonton; contrary to the
popular stereotype of lean, hatchet-faced *sauvages*, they were
stocky and middle-aged, with short hair, moustaches, and ordinary working man's clothes. Joe had hired them sight unseen
because the Iroquois were the reputed aristocrats of the voyageurs,
and because, as strangers in an unfamiliar land, far from their
homes and families, they would not be tempted to desert. They
came highly recommended: Louis had accompanied the Wolseley
expedition up the Nile in 1885, and Pierre, a ferryman on the St.
Lawrence River, had run the ice-choked Lachine Rapids one
Christmas Day, for fun.

The French brothers showed off their whitewater skills on the first leg of the journey, a four-hundred-mile canoe trip down the Athabasca River to Fort Chipewyan. About halfway, the Tyrrells' two canoes met the river steamer *Athabasca* at a portage around the Grand Rapids: here, the steamer, carrying all their food and gear on top of tons of supplies for the missions and fur trade posts downriver, was being unloaded, and its cargo hauled, by a tramway and a flotilla of scows, to a second steamer, the *Grahame*, waiting at the foot of the rapids. The Tyrrells beached their canoes and camped amidst a raucous crowd of half-naked boatmen who drummed and gambled the night away.

Next morning, the French brothers confidently proposed to run the Grand Rapids. Smashing their expensive cedar-strip Peterboroughs into kindling would put a quick, ignominious end to the Tyrrells' expedition, but James observed, "We determined to see what they could do."

Louis took the bow, Michel crouched amidships, and Pierre paddled stern. "As the three daring fellows pushed off from the shore into the surging stream, those of us who gazed upon them did so with grave forebodings," James writes in his memoir *Across the Sub-Arctic of Canada*. "Their speed soon attained that of an express train, while all about them the boiling waters were dashed into foam by the great rocks in the channel. Presently it appeared as if they were doomed to be dashed upon a long ugly breaker nearly in mid-stream; but no! with two or three lightning strokes of their paddles the collision was averted. But in a moment they were in worse danger, for right ahead there were two great rocks, over and around which the tumbling waters rushed wildly. Would they try the right side or the left? Only an instant was afforded for thought, but in that instant Pierre saw his only chance and took it – heading his canoe straight for the chute between the rocks. Should they swerve a foot to one side or the other the result would be fatal, but with unerring judgment and unflinching nerve they shot straight through the notch, and disappeared in the trough below. Rising buoyantly from the billows of foam and flying spray, they swept on with the rushing waters until, in a little eddy halfway down the rapid, they pulled in to the shore in safety."

This display of skill and bravado persuaded the Tyrrells that they too could run the next rapids, baggage and all. Joe rode in the lead canoe with Pierre and Michel, James followed, with Louis in the stern and their frightened, unwilling cook, John Flett, in the bow. At the third rapid, James's canoe swiped a rock, swung broadside, and nearly swamped; nothing was lost, and on shore the gear was spread in the sun to dry. All the rapids were marked on their map, and they usually took the precaution of landing upstream to reconnoitre them from the high, rocky river-bank. At Mountain Rapid, they were too late:

"A bend occurred in the rapid," James records, "and so high and steep were the banks that only with great difficulty could we see the river beyond. . . . So alarmingly swift was the current now becoming that we eagerly looked for some place on the bank where a landing might be made, but none could be seen, as the banks were of perpendicular or even overhanging walls of lime-stone. Retreat was equally impossible against the enormous strength of the river, and all we could do was to keep straight in the current. As we were rounding the bluff, old Pierre suddenly stood up from his seat in the stern . . . right before us there extended a perpendicular fall. We had no time for reflection, but keeping straight with the current, and throwing ourselves back in the canoes in order to lighten the bows, we braced ourselves for the plunge, and in a moment were lost to sight in the foaming waters below. But only for an instant. Our light cedars, though partly filled by foam and spray, rose buoyantly on the waves, and again we breathed freely."

Shaken and chastened, they stopped at the little log outpost of Fort McMurray to pick up the two men who had been sent with a third canoe from Île-à-la-Crosse: Jim Corrigal and François Maurice. Joe had hoped to hire Ithingo and his crew from the previous year, but young Maurice was fluent enough in Chipewyan to act as interpreter, and Corrigal, for all his Irish name, spoke

"Some of our men, 1893." Left to right: Pierre French, John Flett, Jim Corrigal, Michel French, Louis French. Missing: François Maurice. (CHP, James W. Tyrrell collection, no. 215)

Cree more readily than English. The Iroquois spoke French. Joe and James Tyrrell, who spoke English and a smidgeon of Cree and Inuktitut, would have to communicate with their canoemen largely through the lingua franca of the North: sign language.

On June 17, they landed their canoes on the crowded beach in front of the whitewashed log buildings of Fort Chipewyan. From a distance, across the lake, the post's white tower and bastions, with the little steeples of the Roman Catholic and Anglican missions adjoining it, looked like a cathedral. It was, in a way, the Canterbury of the North, a place of pilgrimage with a bloody past: Peter Pond, who built the original post in 1778, was believed to have murdered two of his rivals in cold blood. From here, Alexander Mackenzie had set off down the Slave River to reach the Arctic and Pacific oceans, and David Thompson had discovered a route across the Rockies via the Peace River. Since then, hundreds

"Indian camp at Fort Chipewyan, 1893." Photo by J.B. Tyrrell. (LAC, PA-045362))

of travellers' moccasined feet had trod these pebbly shores: traders, missionaries, hunters, and British naval officers obsessed with the ephemeral Northwest Passage through the Arctic ice.

In 1820, Captain John Franklin, accompanied by midshipmen Robert Hood and George Back (on his first expedition), and naturalist Dr. John Richardson, had stopped in on their way to winter on the Barren Grounds north of Great Slave Lake, then to descend the Coppermine River to explore the Arctic coast. Franklin's expedition, which included some twenty voyageurs, guides, interpreters, and women and children, departed with enough food to last one day. "It was gratifying," remarked Franklin, "to perceive that this scarcity of food did not depress the spirits of our Canadian companions, who cheerfully loaded their canoes, and embarked in high glee after they had received the customary dram."

How many of Franklin's companions died of starvation and exposure on that long, terrible journey? Nine? Fifteen? Who knows? Women and children weren't officially counted, and most bodies were unaccounted for: men simply disappeared into the emptiness, or were left behind where they fell. Did they die, or could they have been taken in by passing Indians? Two men were murdered. Richardson said that he shot an Iroquois voyageur, Michel, because Michel had shot Hood and intended to kill them all, then eat them, as he had already eaten several others. Franklin was knighted for this disaster – testimony, perhaps, to the English fashion for Gothic horror. Franklin later died frozen into the ice of the Northwest Passage, along with the crews of his two ships, *Erebus* and *Terror*, some of whom, the evidence revealed, had eaten each other.

Most recently, however, Fort Chipewyan had become a grand hotel for swaggering big-game hunters like Warburton Pike, and at dinner the Tyrrell brothers met the American ornithologist Frank Russell, on his way north to hunt trophy musk oxen. Shooting musk oxen, ferocious as they looked, was as much sport as shooting sheep in a pen, and Joe and James were glad to turn east off this beaten track towards one of the least civilized parts of North America: no trading posts, no missions, no steamers, no police, no ornithologists, nobody.

They hired a highly recommended Chipewyan guide named Moberly for $40 a month. He had the same name as the Hudson's Bay Company trader at Île-à-la-Crosse, and while his appearance was entirely Chipewyan, he could be as haughty as any fur trade emperor. When, to save time, Joe decided to pack all their outfit into their three canoes rather than ship it two hundred miles to Fond du Lac by company boat, Moberly demanded that he, his family, and his own provisions travel on the boat. Permission was refused, and as Joe's heavily laden Peterboroughs headed east along the north shore of Lake Athabasca, Moberly, his wife, and two children followed, sulkily Joe thought, in their birchbark canoe. The weather was foul: fierce headwinds, rain, and fog frequently forced them to camp on the bare rocks, and poor visibility made it difficult to survey the shoreline. Bedraggled and bad-tempered, they landed at the old settlement of Fond du Lac on June 29 to find almost all the log shanties boarded up. Old Joe Mercredi had died, and the company had closed its post.

Then, Moberly quit. Or was fired. The Tyrrells give several reasons for the row that erupted when they reached a large camp of Chipewyan, "a promiscuous rabble of Indian men and boys," as Joe described it, a few miles up the lake. There was no sign of Ithingo, or any of the other Chipewyan Joe had made friends with here the year before. These people were hostile and suspicious: "They all object to our going into their hunting grounds," Joe noted. Moberly now demanded that his friend Beauvier come along for another $40 a month. Joe angrily protested, but gave in. Then: "Moberly began to make new demands and lying smoking on the beach refused to make a move to get some boxes that he was carrying up to his house, or to proceed. He wants me to give flour to the Indians here; Beauvier wants flour for his family at Fond du Lac. I of course refused these demands."

The Chipewyan were trying to provide for the wives and children they were expected to leave behind, but Joe too was having second thoughts about the deal: "We have now ten men in the party and the provisions will not last long with that number eating them." Joe told Moberly to go to hell ("go back," is the phrase in his notes); Moberly ordered the Tyrrells to get their stuff out of his canoe. "We did this at once," Joe writes, "and started up the river, glad to be rid of the miserable wretch."

On July 1, Dominion Day, they began the exhausting labour of portaging their canoes and supplies uphill past the Stone [Black] River's cataracts towards Black Lake. "Corrigal was unfortunately laid up with an ugly gash in the knee," James records, "so we had only five packers; but being fresh and in good spirits, they went at their work with a rush, notwithstanding a rocky hill of two hundred feet which had to be climbed, and a deep muskeg which obliged them to wade. Before nightfall, however, their spirits were away down as a result of this slavish work. Feet were fearfully blistered, and all complained of pains in one place or another; but each man had carried six loads to the upper end of the portage, which represented a walk of thirty-three miles, eighteen of which were travelled with one hundred pound loads upon their backs, over rocky hills and through swamps knee-deep with mire." To make things worse, Joe adds, the blackflies were "a constant torture."

Anxious as he was to press on, Joe ordered regular rest periods in case the men became discouraged and rebellious, and when he and James weren't collecting plants, examining rocks, or taking measurements, they helped out with the loads. By Saturday, July 8, when they reached the Chipewyan trail leading north into the Barren Grounds, Corrigal's knee had healed and everyone was optimistic: "Beyond this place we knew nothing of the road, or of the country through which it would lead us," James observes. "We were now dependent on our own resources."

Their path led uphill into a maze of swamps, rocks, and scrubby lakes where they had to scour the shoreline to locate their track, but within a week they came out on a large, lovely lake that Joe graciously named Selwyn for the loathed director of the Geological Survey. A breeze swept the flies away, and they enjoyed a bath in the frigid water before heading north. Towards evening the next day, they were astonished to see a canoe in the distance, and, not far away, on a little island, an Indian camp. Firing an excited salute with their shotguns, they paddled over, and were dismayed to find that the Indians were the same people they had encountered at Fond du Lac, wretched Moberly's cronies. They had obviously come by a shorter, faster route.

The Chipewyan appeared to bear them no ill will, and willingly agreed to help portage the Tyrrells' outfit over the height of land the next morning. James tells what happened next:

"During the evening most of the Indians paddled across to where we were, and from some of them sketch-maps and useful information were obtained; but their attention was chiefly devoted to filling our men with alarming stories of the fearful dangers and certain disasters which we would encounter should we attempt to pursue the route we were following. They said we would meet with great impassable canyons, and that the country through which it led was inhabited by savage tribes of Eskimos, who would undoubtedly eat us. These and similar stories produced a deep impression on the minds of some of our men, and might have given rise to serious trouble, and even the disorganizing of the whole party. Jim [Corrigal] went to my brother, and with a sad face unbosomed his trouble. He said that if he were a single man he would not feel so badly, but having a family dependent on him, he could not run into such destruction as he now learned awaited us. The rest of the men – excepting, perhaps, François, who cared for nothing – were equally affected, and it was with some difficulty we managed to reassure them. We told them that these Indians were a set of miserable liars, and were only trying to prevent us from going into their hunting grounds; that I had lived with the Eskimos for nearly two years, and had found them to be far better people than these Indians who were trying to deceive them. We referred them to Moberly, the untrustworthy and false, as a sample of their tribe, and at length persuaded them into disbelieving the stories."

None of them, including the Tyrrells, knew where they were all going, or how far, but at least it would be downhill; the shallow stream they followed, the Doobaunt River that Samuel Hearne had crossed, became broader, faster, a series of rippling rapids that widened into lakes. On either side, the land was a rock-strewn, rolling prairie of pale, variegated lichens and mosses sprinkled with pink rhododendrons and white patches of anemones. On the lakes, they encountered green ice cliffs and floating islands Joe named "moss glaciers": peat moss, frozen to a depth of ten to sixty feet, was topped with a foot or so of living moss, cranberries, and Labrador tea. Apart from sheltered clumps of dwarf birch, spruce, and tamarack, trees had vanished; the men began to gather and dry reindeer moss for their campfires. The moss gave little heat, and didn't burn at all when wet.

"For the last couple of weeks, or since we left the height of land, it has been constantly blowing and raining so that our

"Hoisting the British flag atop a glacial boulder on the Barren Grounds, Tyrrell expedition, 1893." Men unidentified. (CHP, James W. Tyrrell collection, no. 486)

progress is very slow," Joe writes disconsolately on July 27. They were cold and hungry, and loons "made the nights hideous with their screechings." To lighten their load, Joe had left behind much of their canned food at Fort Chipewyan, and, counting on finding plenty of game, they had packed very little meat, yet they had encountered only a black bear, and it had escaped. They pressed on. Two days later, they entered a lake surrounded by dun-coloured hills that seemed to be covered with waving grasses, or the hills themselves were undulating in a mirage: as they drew closer to shore, the landscape sharpened into a restless, milling mass of caribou, their antlers seeming to float above them like a forest of bleached branches.

The grazing deer barely noticed the three canoes that landed on the beach, or the crouching men with rifles, revolvers, and shotguns who fanned out in a semicircle; when the first shot

"Caribou on the shore of Carey Lake." (TFRBL, J.B.T. papers, P10280)

rang out, the herd stampeded, but sixty-eight were killed at almost point-blank range. It was far more meat than the men could eat, or the canoes could carry; they butchered the choicest pieces, starting with the tongues, and spent three days drying the meat over a fire for future rations.

To Joe's amazement, the caribou reappeared the next morning. A herd of inquisitive does, their calves playfully gambolling at their sides, came within a few yards of the camp. Joe exchanged his rifle for his camera: "A large herd was on the side of the hill and I walked quietly up among them, approaching within a few yards of the dense herd, which opened to let me in and then formed a circle around me. Later on, a herd of bucks trotted up and stood about forty yards from us. This was a most beautiful sight for their branching antlers were now full grown though still soft."

To commemorate the gift of the caribou, Joe named the lake Carey (Dollie Lake sounded silly, Lake Mary Edith presumptuous) and James erected a cairn, with a message in a bottle and a Union Jack on a stick, on top of a gigantic boulder. The boulder itself was cause for celebration: a glacier's dropping, it blended perfectly with the flattened, scoured landscape of moraines, drumlins, sand hills, and eskers that ran southward as straight and sculpted as railway embankments. On exposed rocks, Joe was finding glacial grooves striking southwest and southeast, and, best of all, he found a whole countryside of angular, red granite blocks that were lying where they had broken off the bedrock. The absence of abrasion, till, clay, or pebbles suggested that the ice had moved outward from this central, undisturbed spot, the glacier's secret birthplace. It was as if time had stopped thousands of years ago, the day the last ice melted: "This country," Joe writes, "would clearly appear to be just in the condition in which it was left by the glacier."

Or had the glacier really left? On the afternoon of August 6, Joe climbed a hill to scout the route ahead. The horizon to the northeast was shrouded in a dense white mist. Mist, he hoped, meant Doobaunt Lake, but as he peered through his field glasses, the mist thinned enough to reveal a vast expanse of ice. Ice! In August? This was midsummer: was it spring here, or autumn?

Joe despaired that they had reached an impassable barrier, a sea of ice. And it was almost too late to go on. They were barely more than halfway to Baker Lake, and even if a broad, smooth river flowing straight east to Hudson Bay opened at their feet, they would have to paddle thirty miles a day to make the coast by their deadline, August 15. Ice now certainly meant more ice, snow, and storms to come; what would happen if they were frozen in? A return trip to Fond du Lac now would be relatively fast and easy, and there was no shame in turning back; Hearne had failed on his first two attempts to reach the Coppermine River.

Curiosity got the better of the Tyrrells' common sense, and when they reached Doobaunt Lake the next day, they found open water, choked with floating ice, near the shore. They launched their canoes, dodging the floes, but a strong east wind drove the ice pack onshore and forced them to take refuge in a small bay. "We camped on a sloping, stony shore behind a stony beach in a stony plain," Joe writes bitterly. There was no wood, but they had brought a little with them from Carey Lake and fried caribou in a drizzling rain.

Joe writes again on August 8: "Last night the east wind increased in violence accompanied by a very heavy cold rain. The rain was beaten against the side of our tent and came through it in a constant stream, drenching my blankets and everything else on the east side of the tent. Throughout the day the storm continued with unabated fury so that we were unable to move out and the highest temperature seen in the tent was 42°. As there is no wood anywhere in the vicinity we spent a very wet, unpleasant day in camp, one of the most unpleasant days that I remember. Our welcome to Tobaunt [Doobaunt] Lake and the utterly treeless barren grounds or prairies of the far north is about as rough as we could have received."

The wind veered to the north, the rain became snow, and the thermometer dropped to freezing; the ice pack, however, moved offshore, and on August 11, the eight men launched their canoes on the clear, green water and paddled north. For seven days they fought the wind, drift ice, and driving rain; it didn't cheer their spirits to see packs of grey wolves following them on the rocky shore. On August 18, the wind dropped and they heard the low roar of the rapids leading out of Doobaunt Lake into the river that they hoped would take them to the sea.

Beyond the rapids, the swift current carried them relentlessly north, but as they rounded a bend the next evening, a cry went up from the bowmen: "Tipi!" "Tipi!" A single skin lodge stood on the right bank. Through his field glasses, James made out a cluster of people in Inuit dress, a tall man, several women, and children, all staring in their direction. As they drew closer, the women and children darted into the *topik* and closed the skin flap. The man remained, brandishing something in his hand. A gun, a spear? No, a spyglass. He appeared to be trembling. James was sympathetic: when was the last time this fellow had seen canoes full of strangers arriving from the interior? Who could they be

"Running rapids on the Doobaunt River." (TFRBL, J.B.T. papers, P10293)

but the Inuit's traditional enemies, the bloodthirsty Chipewyan? The Tyrrells' own men pulled into shore with trepidation.

"Halloo! Halloo! We are white men, glad to see the Inuit!" James shouted in Inuktitut. *"Chimo! Chimo!"* the Inuit man replied, and broke into a grin. "The doorway of the topick was thrown open," James writes, "and with great rejoicing and excited gestures all the inmates scrambled out to meet us at the shore as we landed. The Eskimo himself was a tall, well-built, stalwart man, with a shrewd, intelligent face. With him were his two wives, and six children, and all joined in extending to us a hearty welcome.

"Their lodge was a large, well-formed, clean-looking one, made of deerskin parchment, and supported by stout spruce poles, which must have been brought from some distant place. Seats of deerskin were offered by the hostesses and venison was placed before us, while we in return handed around presents of beads, tobacco, matches and such things. About us were to be seen evidence of communication with traders, such as a large tin kettle, two old guns and a pair of moleskin trousers. Upon inquiry, I was

"Eskimo at head of Baker Lake, September 2, 1893." (TFRBL, J.B.T. papers, P10372)

told that they had received them in trade from other 'Innuits' (Eskimos). We satisfied ourselves that this family were accustomed to meet with the Eskimos from Hudson Bay, who trade at Fort Churchill or Marble Island, and for that reason the Dubawnt must in all probability flow into the bay." The Inuit obligingly drew a map of the river's course to salt water. He estimated the journey would take twenty days, and James's own calculations put them at least eight hundred miles from Fort Churchill.

They set off in haste, but the weather turned cold, and for the next five days, still running north, they fought freezing rain, headwinds, and high waves that nearly swamped their canoes. "It was heartbreaking work," Joe confesses. His hands were so cold he could hardly write, yet still they were bitten raw by blackflies; their food, tents, and clothes were wet, and they had no wood or moss for a fire. At a deserted Inuit campsite they came across a cache: some tools and a wooden sled, or *komatic*. The men were gleefully breaking it up for firewood when the Tyrrells intervened: this was an Inuit family's livelihood, a matter of life or death. The sled was repaired and replaced, and a plug of tobacco was left as an apology. The Tyrrells and their canoemen gnawed on dried caribou and boiled their tea over an alcohol burner.

They had reached the same latitude, 64°, as Baker Lake, but where was it? The Doobaunt River's habit of spilling into shallow, sprawling lakes had cost them frustrating hours searching for the outlets. Perhaps they had made a mistake. Were they on the wrong river?

"Throughout the day we have been keeping a constant course toward the northwest," Joe writes on August 25, "our hearts sinking as the river continued on and on in that direction."

They were heading away from Hudson Bay, straight towards Back's Great Fish River and the Arctic Ocean. Would their bones join those of Franklin's men at Starvation Cove? By evening, the clear water became shallow and turbid, then a cry went up: "Du bois!" "Du bois!" Driftwood! Not mere willow twigs, but whole trees, as big as two men could carry. A few miles farther on, the dark waters of another broad river joined the Doobaunt from the west. Numerous sandbars were strewn with driftwood and flocks of geese fed on the grassy shores. The men quickly camped, built a roaring bonfire, and feasted on roast goose.

The plentiful driftwood meant that this new river must have come from a forested area to the southwest. To the Tyrrells' relief, it seemed that they had reached the legendary Great Northern River that Joe had been seeking, the Thelon. The next morning, the river bent to the east, then southeast, and at sunset the canoes swept out on to the calm, deep water of a lake Joe named in honour of Canada's new governor general, Lord Aberdeen. The sparse vegetation on the shore was turning shades of brown and ochre, and the hills to the north were covered with snow; their supplies were running low, the flour almost gone. On August 27, Joe admits, "It is absolutely necessary for us to make all possible haste."

Still, Joe couldn't resist investigating an interesting hill or outcrop, especially if it showed signs of glaciation. The men

"Eskimo at Baker Lake." (CHP, James W. Tyrrell Collection, no. 489)

smoked while James searched for plants and Joe scampered up and down measuring striations and filling his bag with rock fragments: his rock samples more than made up in weight for the food they had eaten. The weather deteriorated after they left the lake at its eastern outlet: they were stormbound for two days before, to their great relief, a flotilla of Inuit in kyaks ushered them into a sprawling encampment. James bartered an empty butter crock, telescope, pocketknife, and an old shirt for some caribou clothing and prime musk oxen hides. And on they hurried.

On September 2, Joe and James Tyrrell gazed out over Baker Lake with mixed feelings of triumph, relief, and apprehension. They weren't home yet, but they were *here*, and since leaving Black Lake on July 8, without local guides or hunters, they had crossed the Barren Grounds, charting a route of 810 miles through an inhospitable country previously shunned by man. They had accomplished their mission, and they had come through without illness or injury, thanks primarily to brave Pierre's unerring skill in navigating whitewater. Yet, they had still to paddle another 250 miles to the mouth of Chesterfield Inlet, and 500 more down the shore of Hudson Bay to the nearest habitation, Fort Churchill. They would be running smack into violent September gales and dangerous tides; from here on, they would be paddling for their lives.

CHAPTER SEVEN

September 10, 1893, Chesterfield Inlet

Squinting through his field glasses, James studied a small, greyish object floating near the horizon. He expected it to disappear, swallowed by the waves, but no, it came closer, drifting, tacking, the eerie ghost of old Henry Hudson himself.

A ship!

From the Tyrrell brothers' perch on a hill, the phantom ship appeared to be a large, two-masted schooner, its square sails set, beating hard to the westward. Soon James could see tiny figures moving about on deck, but it was impossible for him to tell who they were. It was extremely late in the season for whalers or traders, and unusual for them to be heading inland.

"Halloo! Halloo!" James waved his red handkerchief; Joe fired his revolver into the air. A commotion on board told them they had been spotted, but the ship stayed its course. James and Joe clambered down the hill and ran along the beach, waving and firing frantically. This ship might be their salvation! For a week they had laboured down the inlet's monotonous, barren shore, battling riptides, rain, and harsh winds. The water was too salty to drink; they had no moss or wood for fire and no game to cook.

"Halloooo!! Halloooo!" The ship's sails luffed, slackened, then filled again as it veered towards them. "We could see that there were Eskimos on board," James writes, "and a moment later their anchor was cast out, and several of them, making a sort of raft with three kyacks they had in tow, paddled in to the rocky

"Camp on west shore of Hudson Bay, October 5, 1893." (TFRBL,
J.B.T. papers, P10404)

shore where we stood. In vain did we look for the face of a white
man. They were all natives, and as we gazed at each other in mutual
amazement, I broke the silence with the question, *Kudloonah
petehungetoo?* (Is there no white man?) *Petehungetoo* (There is
none) was the reply, so the whole party, which consisted of several families, men, women and children, were Eskimos, and with
them in their boat they had their dogs and other necessary hunting and camping equipments. They informed us they were
moving up into the interior from the coast to spend the winter,
so it was not surprising that nothing we could offer would induce
them to consider the question of taking us down to Churchill or
of selling their boat to us. We offered what to them would have
been fabulous wealth, but to no purpose."

The Tyrrells did consider an alternative: to accompany the
Inuit on their way inland, find the brown, driftwood river that
flows into the Doobaunt from the west, and ascend it. James was
almost certain that it was the Thelon, and that it would lead them
into the forest, possibly even the verdant valley Samuel Hearne
had described in his *Journey*; from there, with plenty of fuel and
caribou to sustain them, they could make their way back to Fort

Chipewyan or to Fort Rae on Great Slave Lake. The route, how-ever, was utterly unknown; they were running low on ammuni-tion, and if winter caught them, they would have to walk. Would the Inuit, or the Chipewyan for that matter, welcome eight desti-tute strangers into their winter hunting grounds? Sir John Richardson, the veteran of three British Barren Grounds expedi-tions, had observed: "Active philanthropy is not an attribute of the Eskimos and little or no effort would be made by them to prolong the lives of strangers perishing on their lands." And how would their Iroquois and Metis canoemen feel about being at the mercy of the fearsome Inuit?

These Inuit were suspicious. They stayed close to their kyaks, their eyes darting over the rocky hills where the Tyrrells' canoemen were hiding. They peppered James with questions: Where did you come from? Did you see our people there? James answered in Inuktitut as best he could. In their place, he'd be curious too. Hairy faced white men in fancy Indian canoes had never before been seen on this barren, windswept seacoast. Small wonder if they were taken for spies, sorcerers, castaways, pirates, lunatics.

The Inuit paddled back to their ship, hoisted anchor, and sailed away. The Tyrrells dejectedly put away their gift offerings: the last of their tea, Joe's briar pipe, their only bottle of Jamaican rum, saved for medicinal purposes, the Hawkeye camera, Joe's Winchester rifle. Laughing and cavorting with relief, their canoe-men packed up for an early start: the next morning, they pushed off for Churchill before daylight.

The days were growing short and the winds were fierce, but the weather was clear when they reached Hudson Bay and started south on the last long leg of their journey. On September 13, they camped off Marble Island, a gleaming hump of white quartzite rising out of the sea like Moby Dick. James had visited the island in 1886 on the *Alert* expedition. It was a favourite rendezvous for whalers, but to his great disappointment, no masts were visible in the little harbour.

Not many years earlier, whaling ships wintered there, but so many men died of scurvy that it had become a melancholy graveyard. The Inuit believed it haunted: the first white men they had met had been shipwrecked on Marble Island. In 1719, two Hudson's Bay Company ships, the *Albany* and *Discovery*, had sailed from England in search of the Straits of Anian, a northwest passage rumoured to lead to shining mountains of copper and gold. Commanded by James Knight, an aged trader who had built the company's first post at the Churchill River in 1715, the expedition carried bricks and lumber to make a sturdy shelter, coal, and enough provisions to last a winter. When the ships did not return, it was speculated that they had reached California, possibly China, but in 1722 a company boat from Churchill found a broken mast, sails, iron, and other wreckage on Marble Island.

Forty-five years later, a more thorough investigation of the island uncovered the ships' sunken hulls, guns, anchors, and other debris left undisturbed by the Inuit. Samuel Hearne, a regular visitor to Marble Island, tells the story of the wreck:

> In the Summer of one thousand seven hundred and sixty-nine, while we were prosecuting the fishery, we saw several Esquimaux at this new harbour; and perceiving that one or two of them were greatly advanced in years, our curiosity was excited to ask them some questions concerning the above ship and sloop. The account which we received from them was full, clear and unreserved, and the sum of it was to the following purport:
>
> When the vessels arrived at this place (Marble Island) it was very late in the Fall, and in getting them into the harbour, the largest received much damage; but on being fairly in, the English began to build the house, their numbers at that time seeming to be about fifty. As soon as the ice permitted, in

the following Summer, the Esquimaux paid them another visit, by which time the number of the English was greatly reduced, and those that were living seemed very unhealthy. According to the account given by the Esquimaux they were then very busily employed, but about what they could not easily describe, probably in lengthening the long-boat; for at a little distance from the house there is now lying a great quantity of oak chips, which have been most assuredly made by carpenters.

Sickness and famine occasioned such havock among the English, that by the setting in the second Winter their number was reduced to twenty. That Winter, some of the Esquimaux took up their abode on the opposite side of the harbour, and frequently supplied them with such provisions as they had, which chiefly consisted of whale's blubber and seal's flesh and train oil. When the Spring advanced, the Esquimaux went to the continent, and on their visiting Marble Island again, they only found five of the English alive, and those were in such distress for provisions that they eagerly eat the seal's flesh and whale's blubber quite raw, as they purchased it from the natives. This disordered them so much, that three of them died in a few days, and the other two, though very weak, made a shift to bury them. Those two survived many days after the rest, and frequently went to the top of an adjacent rock, and earnestly looked to the South and East, as if in expectation of some vessels coming to their relief. After continuing there a considerable time together, and nothing appearing in sight, they sat down close together, and wept bitterly. At length one of the two died, and the other's strength was so far exhausted, that he fell down and died also, in attempting to dig

a grave for his companion. The skulls and other
large bones of those two men are now lying above-
ground close to the house.

Marble Island was indeed an evil omen for the Tyrrells and
their six paddlers. Struggling against gale-force winds as they
made their way south, they were often trapped ashore by heavy
surf, or, at low tide, forced a mile or more out into the bay to
avoid the shoals and mud flats. After being stormbound for two
days on a sandbar, with no fresh water, they risked a run to the
mainland. "The wind had been rising higher and higher," Joe
writes, "and the waves were running very high, every moment
threatening to break over us. One wave just caught the back of
my canoe and almost sank us but I managed to bail out most of
the water, and at last we reached the land in safety but drenched
with the salt water." On September 18, their flour ran out (their
sugar was long gone); to conserve the last of their bacon, corned
beef, and dried caribou, they lived on ducks and gulls cooked
over fires of driftwood scavenged from the rough, boulder-
strewn shoreline.

Their location was uncertain. Constantly overcast skies and
fluctuations in the magnetic fields made their instruments almost
useless. As they travelled farther south, however, a little scrub
juniper appeared in the hollows, and, hiding in it, a few hares and
ptarmigan. Then, on September 22, a blizzard struck from the
northeast. Huddled with James in their tent, Joe writes: "As we
both had a little chocolate and a can of alcohol left, we managed
to get a hot drink, and a can of corned beef supplied the two of
us with all that we had to eat for the day. We are having the heav-
iest storm of the season, while our tents are on a low exposed
point, and our provisions are about done."

The storm, with wet snow, sleet, rain, and fog, continued
for four days; when they could leave their tents, the men struggled through the snow to hunt small game and gather juniper
twigs for their fires. "We have been able to travel only three days

out of the last 12," Joe writes on September 27. The next morning, he and James shared a ground squirrel for breakfast.

"We determined to make a start," James says, "for to remain where we were meant that we must soon starve to death. We were already much reduced and weakened from the effects of cold and hunger. Churchill was still fully three hundred miles distant. We had not one bite of food. The country was covered with snow, the weather piercingly cold. It was difficult to be cheerful under such circumstances, but we kept up courage and pushed on."

They were scarcely underway when a few caribou were sighted on the shore; they hurriedly landed, and Joe and James ran after the fleeing deer with their rifles. They chased the animals for hours across an open, desolate plain, but the caribou, aware of their pursuers, remained out of range. Plodding back, faint with exhaustion, the Tyrrells found that the ebb tide had left their canoes high and dry. Collapsing in the shelter of a rock, they handed their rifles to Pierre and Louis French: perhaps they would have better luck.

"We had done our utmost and had failed," writes James. "If they also should fail it was too apparent what must soon be the result. Then anxious hours of waiting followed. No shots were heard, but towards evening Pierre and Louis, and afterwards the other men, could be seen returning in the distance. None of them appeared to be bringing any game, so far as we could see, and at the sight, I confess, my heart grew sick. As they came nearer, however, Louis, holding up something in his hand, exclaimed, 'I got him!' It was the claw of a polar bear, and we soon learned with joy that, sure enough, he had killed a bear, which he had unexpectedly come upon at the edge of a lake while following the deer."

The bear turned out to be fairly small and scrawny – Joe measured him at six feet, five and a half inches – but to the starving hunters the rank meat was worth its weight in silver. They built a fire beside the carcass, tore off strips of meat, toasted them, and gulped them down half-raw. The carcass was butchered –

every scrap was saved, even the hide – and carried back to the canoes. They spent the next day feasting as they boiled the meat in their kettles to carry with them. "A strong east wind, driving a wild surf in upon the shore, made it impossible to launch," writes James. "The gale increased in fury until it became a terrific storm, accompanied by sleet and snow, and this continued for five long days."

Clinging together in their tents for warmth, the men chewed on bear meat and boiled their tea over alcohol burners. James suffered a severe attack of gastroenteritis after eating some bear liver, but their greatest enemy now was the cold. "One night," James writes, "the tent occupied by my brother and I was ripped up the back by the force of the gale, and with difficulty kept from being carried away. We were already numb with cold, but in the midst of snow and darkness I managed to find in my bag a sail needle and some twine, and then having lowered the tent to the ground, while my brother held it, I stitched up the rent. When the tent was again raised, our bedding was buried in snow, but the blankets being our only comfort, the drifts were shaken off, and in a half-perished condition we again crept beneath them."

On October 4, they struck off again, desperately pushing ahead through the new ice that was forming near the shore. In two days they made barely twelve miles. Paddling would soon be impossible. Should they walk? This too was impossible: even if they were strong enough, and this was doubtful, how would they cross the swift, open rivers lying between their present location and Churchill? Yet, as Joe admits, "It is clearly quite hopeless for us to reach Churchill with all the canoes and our present load."

All eight men agreed to cache everything unessential on the shore under an overturned canoe. It was, says James, "a sad and lonely task." Joe's treasured bags of rocks were first into the heap, followed by the heavy brass surveying instruments, camera, bales of caribou and musk oxen skins, the polar bear hide, a spare tent, and extra clothing. Joe noted the location: 61°30' N, marked by "a rather high island off a low, stony point and a prominent bluff on the shore behind." Then, Joe writes: "James and I sorted over all our stuff, took some extra socks and an extra shirt in the valise along with our notebooks, exposed photographs and the collection of plants, put our blankets in a bag, put the field glasses on our backs and took our guns and ammunition for we had now nothing to eat but a few pounds of bear's fat. We then broke up the grub box and made a fire and had a hot cup of tea, the first that we had had for a couple of days."

For eight days they struggled on, four men in each of two canoes, paddling with all their ebbing strength. Chunks of floating ice gashed their canoes, water froze on their paddles, and a ghostly rime of spray coated their beards and clothes. Their hands were numb, and to reach shore they had to haul their canoes and baggage over a mile or more of ice and mud; they lived on ducks, and warmed themselves beside fires made of driftwood. James and Joe grew too weak to walk any distance, and Joe's hands felt so dead he could no longer keep his daily journal.

James writes: "On October 14, as we advanced, the ice became so heavy, and extended so far out to sea, that in order to clear it we had to go quite out of sight of land. Towards evening we began to look about for some opportunity of going ashore, but nothing could be seen before us but a vast field of ice, with occasional protruding boulders. We pushed on, hoping to find some bluff, point or channel of water by which we might reach the shore. We stood up in the canoes or climbed upon boulders, vainly hoping to at least get a glimpse of the land.

"Soon the shades of night began to fall about us, our canoes were leaking badly, and the weather was bitterly cold. Failing to reach the shore, we resolved to wait for high tide, about ten o'clock, hoping we might with it do better. The tide came, but left us still in the same condition, no more able to penetrate the ice or gain the shore than before. It had become intensely dark, and we were in great danger of being smashed on the ice or rocks.

We were utterly helpless and could do nothing but remain where we were, or go where the tide chose to carry us, until the return of daylight.

"The hours of that night were the longest I have ever experienced, and the odds seemed to be against our surviving until morning; but at last the day returned and found us still alive. My brother was nearly frozen, having been obliged to sit or lie in the water all night. Poor little Michel had both of his feet frozen, and the rest of us were badly used up. Still we were in the same position as on the night before. We could not hold out much longer; we must gain the shore or perish. At the time of high tide, the ice being somewhat loosened, our canoes were thrust into the pack, and by great exertion, as well as much care, we succeeded about one o'clock in reaching solid ice, upon which we were able to land, and, for the last time, haul out our noble little crafts. We had been in them just thirty hours, battling with the ice, exposed to a chilling winter blast, our clothing saturated and frozen, and our bodies faint and numb with starvation and cold."

They climbed out on to the ice, stretched their cramped limbs, and dragged their gear to shore. While the men made a fire, James wrapped Joe in blankets and revived him with the last of their Jamaican rum. "As for launching our canoes again," says James, "that was entirely out of the question. If we would reach Churchill at all, it must be by land."

They figured the distance at no more than fifty miles, but only the three Metis – Jim Corrigal, John Flett, and François Maurice – were strong enough to walk that distance. On October 16, Joe gave Corrigal and Flett a note to the Hudson's Bay Company manager at Fort Churchill, with a reward of ten dollars each if they returned with food and transport, and sent them off. François Maurice built a snug camp near a creek in a grove of spruce trees; their ammunition was nearly gone, but they had ample firewood and enough seal meat to last a few days. Michel suffered agonies from his frozen feet, but Joe, who had no patience with complainers, ignored him, and there was nothing the rest of

"F. Matheson, Churchill." (TFRBL, J.B.T. papers, P10413)

his companions could do for him. Joe and James, dry and warm at last, fell into an exhausted, semi-conscious slumber.

"Halloo! Halloo!" They were roused the next afternoon by Corrigal and Flett, followed by four dog teams pulling empty sleds to carry them and their belongings the twenty miles to Churchill. The post clerk, F.W. Matheson, had sent them meat and flour, the latest newspapers, and a welcoming letter, and when they arrived at the decrepit old post on October 19, Matheson gave the Tyrrells his own bed, lent them his clean underwear while theirs was washed, and expertly treated Michel's rotting toes. Yet Joe could only find fault: "As the men were all in rags, I tried to get a few clothes for them from the store but even what was necessary to keep them warm was furnished with the utmost reluctance. I then endeavoured to obtain food for them but though they were almost starving I was unable to obtain more than two or three days rations of corned beef and pork four years old, flour and a little tea. It was a poor lookout for proper food for any of us in our present worn out condition." Matheson had a different point of view: "The men of the Expedition seem endowed with astonishing appetites," he writes in the post journal on October 21. "They have done away with 41 lbs of meat & a considerable quantity of grain between the night before yesterday & this forenoon – or actually eat [*sic*] 4 days rations in one & a half, so that I am compelled to reduce their allowance if I don't want to be masticated out of house & home."

Joe seemed oblivious to the fact that he and his famished men were devouring food that had to last the post's employees until the arrival of the company's ship, the *Eric*, the next summer. Joe had neglected to send a box of food and clothing to Churchill in advance, and his men had left all their spare clothes in the cache, yet he loudly resented the fact that Matheson was charging the expedition for every scrap the company provided. Joe blamed his own cramps, indigestion, and heartburn on his scanty meals of tough ham, hard cheese, boiled ptarmigan, porridge, and water, although he knew very well that severe discomfort could be expected after eating anything in his emaciated, semi-starved state. The Anglican missionary Joseph Lofthouse, with his wife and daughter, cheered the Tyrrells with tea, scones, and sympathy in their cozy Victorian cottage while the men went out hunting and trapping to earn their keep.

Matheson couldn't get rid of his hungry, ungrateful guests soon enough: on November 6, they were equipped with snowshoes and assigned to a company dogsled train heading south to Norway House via York Factory and Oxford House. The Tyrrells, their legs swollen and joints inflamed, suffered such agonies walking on snowshoes that they, like Michel, rode on the sleds. On November 14, they came to the broad, swift Nelson River; here they camped in the snow for ten days waiting for the ice-choked river to freeze sufficiently for them to cross. "We must be content with our bleak open camp surrounded by 9 half-breeds and Indians where there is no possibility of employing one's time usefully," Joe writes in frustration on November 18. "Men out hunting all day. They got nothing."

The prospect of starving again was horrible, but the hunters proved to be resourceful, if scanty, providers, and the camp, a bonfire surrounded by snowbanks and spruce boughs, was tolerable. By November 26, they had crossed the river on ice floes and Joe was able to buy jam and canned fruit at York Factory. Here Michel was left in the care of the company's doctor. The Tyrrells arrived at Oxford House on December 7, "tired and footsore" from having walked on snowshoes most of the distance, but now they were able to buy their own dog teams and two covered toboggans, called carioles, to ride in. They reached Norway House on December 21. "I have arranged for Jim, John and François to go up the Saskatchewan with my team of Huski dogs which I have sold to them for $25," Joe writes, and, on the next day: "Today I paid off Jim, François and John, the former two by order on H.J. Moberly at Île-à-la-Crosse, the latter by Survey draft."

What did Joe say to these stalwart, loyal companions who had saved his life? His notes, the official report of the expedition, and James's memoir contain not one word of thanks, praise, or appreciation. Of the French brothers, Joe's only observation was critical: "Michel complained to me of his frozen feet, but thinking that he was picking up his brother Louis' whining I paid but little attention to him." When Joe finally saw Michel's feet, he confessed that he was pained with remorse.

With fresh dogs and new drivers for their carioles, the Tyrrells made a mad dash down Lake Winnipeg to Selkirk; Pierre and Louis French ran behind. On December 28, Pierre dropped from exhaustion. He was left at a small outpost, Flathead Point, to be carried the rest of the way by wagon. On December 31, Joe writes: "Louis played out and we were obliged to leave him at Icelandic River to be brought on by a team." The Tyrrells reached the telegraph station at Selkirk on New Year's Day, 1894. Joe telegraphed Dollie: "Happy New Year. All Well." The

Map of Doobaunt and Kazan rivers and north-west coast of Hudson Bay.

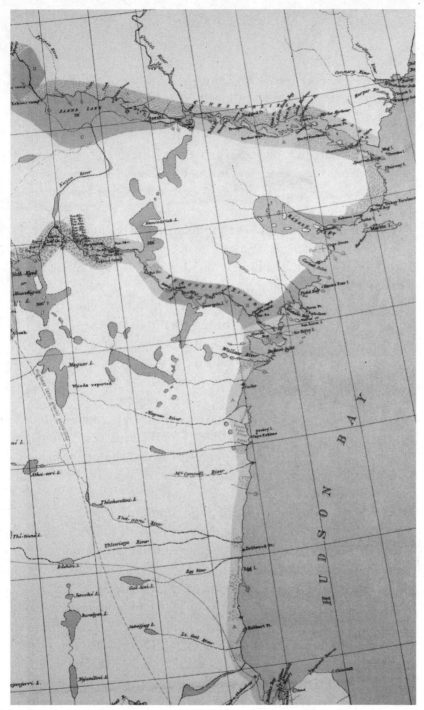

(TFRBL, J.B.T. papers, M10047)

second telegram went to T.M. Daly, the minister of the interior: "Expedition very successful. All well." The third was sent to Dr. Selwyn: "Complete success. Crossed Barren Grounds. Explored Chesterfield Inlet and West Shore of Bay."

By the time Joe and James arrived in Toronto a week later, newspaper reporters were clamouring for interviews. "It ranks in interest and peril with the greatest explorations that have been made in this or any other country," trumpeted the Toronto *World*. The Tyrrells' adventure had everything to excite the imagination: a weird, frightening landscape, Indians, Eskimos, caribou – A HUNTERS' PARADISE, headlined the New York *World* – canoes, a polar bear, suffering, endurance, and survival. It had been a close call; when Joe was rescued he was so weak he'd had to be carried from his tent: "The suffering through want and anxiety for the safe return of the men was indeed a terrible experience," he told reporters. The Tyrrells had been lost, and now were found, "exuberant in the health and vigour of youth," rejoiced the Toronto *Globe*. The *Globe* praised Joe as the "ideal explorer," tall, ruddy, with "a splendid physique," and Joe played along, tramping in for interviews in his voyageur outfit of blue blanket coat, multi-coloured sash, and moccasins. James provided the newspapers with a striking studio photograph of himself in Inuit dress. Telegraphed around the world, variations of the Tyrrells' story appeared in the London *Times* and the *Illustrated Saturday News*. New York's *Once a Week*, ranking the Tyrrells with Columbus and American Robert Peary, recently returned from Greenland, proclaimed: "Now it is Canada's turn to produce a hero of this type."

The Tyrrells' predecessors in the Barren Grounds had all been British or American, that is if you ignored the host of Canadian and aboriginal canoemen, guides, interpreters, wives, and children who had accompanied them. (Or had the explorers accompanied *them?*) Now, the Tyrrells' own Native canoemen were ignored. When, rarely, the newspapers mentioned them, their names were carelessly misspelled and their stories were left untold, although the reporter for the Montreal *Herald* could have

"James Tyrrell in Eskimo dress." The clothing appears more characteristic of Hudson Strait, where James had spent the winter of 1885-86,
than Baker Lake. (CHP, James W. Tyrrell collection, no. 218)

found Pierre, Louis, and Michel French in reasonable, if less than exuberant health, back at home across the St. Lawrence River in Caughnawaga.

The "nauseating flatulency in the daily press," to quote the *Mining Review*, inspired an anti-heroic reaction against this "modern Gulliver" and his new-found land, "Tyrrellania." The Buffalo *Express* had caught Joe in an honest, but politically indiscreet comment: "The expedition was entirely successful; we have proven that but for what minerals may be found among the very varied rocks of the Barren Lands, it is of small value." Yet the expedition had been extremely expensive. Why, asked the critics, had the Geological Survey forked out almost seven thousand dollars from a sixty-thousand-dollar annual travel budget for such "extravagant junketings"? Prime Minister Sir John Thompson quipped that the critics should be grateful – think what it would have cost had the men not starved!

At home, Joe was a black sheep. His elderly parents had feared both sons dead, and Dollie had been weepy since receiving Joe's last letter, from Fond du Lac, dated June 29. The Careys had had quite enough of this knight-at-arms alone and palely loitering; Joe and Dollie were married on February 14, St. Valentine's Day, in a quiet ceremony at her home. Their matrimonial home was a two-room suite in Joe's boarding house, and Joe was already making plans to cross the Barren Grounds again that spring.

Joe knew that, given his haste, his claim to have explored Chesterfield Inlet and the western shore of Hudson Bay was an exaggeration tantamount to falsehood, and his rock specimens, with the Survey's valuable instruments, were under a canoe on that shore. He badly needed to retrieve his cache and finish his work, but the Canadian government adamantly refused to finance another expedition. Joe had overspent his estimated budget by more than $2,500 (the exact total, according to the Survey's accountant, was $6,569.28). He'd had to pay James and his canoemen for seven months, not the three or four months he had anticipated, as well as cover the costs of their maintenance, medical care, and transportation home after they reached Churchill. In retrospect, Joe's conduct looked dangerously irresponsible. But he angrily rejected all criticism as inspired by ignorant, mean-spirited envy. How on earth could anyone expect him to predict the weather and travelling conditions in an unexplored area of the world? He had *crossed the Barren Lands! By canoe!* And what did he get? Blame!

Joe found unexpected and influential allies in the governor general and his wife, Lord and Lady Aberdeen. On January 27, 1894, Ishbel Aberdeen notes in her journal: "Mr. Tyrrell just come back from expedition to Northern Territories where he had discovered new large river & seen extraordinary herds of thousands & thousands of caribou all together." Only a year older than Joe, Ishbel Aberdeen was an enthusiastic traveller and photographer, and both the Aberdeens were eager to encourage all kinds of worthy, if controversial, enterprises. Shortly after Joe's return, they invited him to dine *en famille* at Rideau Hall and to speak to the Haddo Club, a regular gathering of their children and staff for the purpose of self-improvement. One of the aides-de-camp in attendance at Joe's lecture was Robert Munro Ferguson, a young sport always keen for an outdoor adventure. Ferguson, due to go on leave, proposed that he go north with Joe as his assistant, and pay half the expedition's expenses.

At least that was the official story. The Ottawa *Evening Journal* alleged that the entire expedition was to be privately funded, largely by Lord Aberdeen himself. It was customary in Great Britain for wealthy aristocrats to contribute generously to scientific ventures, and Canada, unlike the United States, did not have a geographical society, or merchant princes, however prosperous, willing to underwrite the costs of exploration. Canada's Royal Society was a club of aged professors, the universities were impoverished, and Canadian newspapers, unlike the New York *Herald*, saw no profit in sponsoring sensational expeditions. It could be convincingly argued that had the Survey given the Tyrrell brothers $10,000 to $20,000, and two or more years to do their work, everything would have turned out satisfactorily in the first place.

Public-spirited and anxious to promote Canadian sovereignty in the North, Aberdeen was no doubt eager to set an example for the short-sighted, penny-pinching colonials. However, he made a diplomatic blunder: he wrote to the government advocating the expedition, and spoke directly to Dr. Selwyn. For the Queen's representative to interfere personally in a government department was shockingly inappropriate. Selwyn could hardly tell Aberdeen this, nor could he reject his offer without causing offence, and that wouldn't do. Again, Selwyn stalled while the embarrassed politicians agreed on a compromise. On May 15, 1894, Ishbel Aberdeen writes in her journal:

"His Ex. [Lord Aberdeen] saw Mr Daly Minister of the Interior about Bob Ferguson's proposed expedition up to Hudson's Bay with Mr. Tyrrell – there are obstacles to be overcome, but probably these will be surmounted if both H.E. & Bob subscribe to the funds. It will take three months & be rather a rough piece of work, recovering the collections etc. left on the shores of Hudson's Bay last year by the party too exhausted to carry them, surveying certain parts of Hudson's Bay & exploring some rivers. Bob is very keen on it, & thinks from what he can hear, that H.E. showing an interest will stimulate the development of all that part of the country."

The expedition was approved, in spite of Ferguson's complete lack of scientific interests or expertise. The Survey committed to only $1,200; the rest of the cost would have to be covered by Ferguson, by private subscription, or by Joe Tyrrell himself. Nor was there room for James Tyrrell on this trip, although James had shyly written his brother, "I would enjoy going with you again." And what of Dollie, a new bride sent away to live with her family for many more anxious months? If Joe felt guilt, or sympathy, he did not express it in writing, and he was unconcerned about his own stamina. He had developed the manic obsessiveness characteristic of explorers – a virtue, or weakness, that made him admirable and at the same time exasperating.

Aberdeen's negotiations had wasted a precious month, yet Joe still had only the vaguest idea of where he and Ferguson were going once they reached the Barren Grounds. He was gambling on finding an unexplored river known to fur traders and Indians as the Kazan, south of the Doobaunt, then descending it to Hudson Bay near his cache, and from there paddling a relatively short distance south to Churchill. They would be travelling through country described by Samuel Hearne in his *Journey*, and visited in 1868 by a Catholic priest, Father Alphonse Gasté. There were many troubling questions, however: Would they take longer than three months? Where would they find a guide and an interpreter? Would they again encounter pack ice and snow on Hudson Bay? How could Joe alone manage the topographical survey in addition to geological and botanical exploration? To skeptics, it seemed idiocy to tempt the storm gods of the Barren Grounds a second time; to scientists, this expedition looked like nothing more than a rich man's shooting holiday.

"I have nothing to do with Tyrrell," Ferguson begins his diary. "He is on his usual trip – under gov't orders!" They set off from the shore of Lake Winnipeg on June 16, 1894, following a ceremonial presentation of two caged homing pigeons by Joe's enthusiastic friend, Manitoba's Lieutenant-Governor John Christian Schultz. The pigeons, intended as an experiment in long-distance communication between the Barren Grounds and Winnipeg, rode in state strapped to the top of Ferguson's baggage, but when his canoe capsized tracking up the first rapid on the Saskatchewan River, the pigeons, along with Ferguson's camera and two rifles, sank to the bottom. Soaked yet unharmed, Ferguson blamed Bell, their cook, "a picayune little cuss with one eye who went on the dead drunk for several days," for dropping the tow rope. "Why the devil didn't I take a rational and comfortable, if not luxurious, trip elsewhere," Ferguson complains to his

"Our Party at the Shore of Theitaga Lake, 1894." Bob Ferguson is on the left, the guides and canoemen are unidentified. (TFRBL, J.B.T papers, P10460)

diary, "(instead of sticking my ugly great nose into this country. It's only a desert anyway!)."

Fortunately, Ferguson's northern baptism thawed his frosty relationship with "T," as he called Tyrrell, and as soon as he dried out, he swallowed his pride, got to know the mosquitoes, and became a cheerful, observant camper. At Cumberland House, Ferguson was touched to meet two doughty old fellow Scots, James McDougall, who had surrendered the Hudson's Bay Company's Yukon post to the Americans when the Alaska boundary was drawn, and Roderick McFarlane, the indomitable Nor'wester immortalized by William Francis Butler in *The Great Lone Land*. Ferguson bought a new Winchester rifle, and Joe replaced the "disreputable scullion," one-eyed Bell, with an Indian cook and steersman named David. Pierre French had sent a note, via the Hudson's Bay Company, offering his services, but only John Flett from the previous year's crew was included, with two Indian canoemen Joe knew from Lake Winnipeg, Roderick Thomas and

John Harper. Their route would take them through familiar territory to the Hudson's Bay Company outpost, du Brochet, at the
north end of Reindeer Lake, then, with Chipewyan guides, they
would ascend the Cochrane River before heading northeast into
terra incognita.

On July 3, McDougall and McFarlane saw them off in style
with a two-gun salute fired from the post's ancient brass cannons,
Thunder and Lightning, and they sped up the old fur trade route
to Reindeer Lake. Their canoemen laughed and called out to each
other in a *patois* of Cree, French, English, and Ojibwa, delighted
to be in charge of the two rich *aventuriers* with their precious
cargo of ammunition and tobacco. Ferguson, calling himself
"the Scottish Adventurer," shared their high spirits, and he was
charmed by "gentle David," who made moss poultices for his
insect bites. Ferguson tried to repay the kindness by helping out
with the cooking, but he was tactfully told that David preferred
to do things his own way, even if it meant they ate everything
fried or boiled.

At du Brochet post they hired two young Chipewyan guides,
Thebayzie and Xavierseese, to take them up the Cochrane River
to Kasba (White Partridge) Lake and then down the Kazan River
to Ennadai Lake, the northern limit of Chipewyan territory. On
July 27, they left the Cochrane River and entered an eerily beautiful landscape of white and golden sand hills, eskers sculpted like
Greek temples, and coulees clothed with dwarf jack pines, wildflowers, and white moss – the banks of ancient glacial rivers. Old
caribou trails criss-crossing the sand dunes made it hard to follow
the innumerable portages from one stream, pond, or marsh to
another, but while they had started late enough in the season to
catch the autumn migration, they saw no caribou.

Ferguson wanted to linger beside the blue Aegean beauty of
Kasba Lake, which they reached on August 5. He noticed with
pleasure how much the scenery, with its delicate white, silver, and
grey lichen, resembled Greece, or his own native Scottish
Highlands, and he was fond of sleeping naked under a little tent

"Roman Catholic mission at DuBrochet Post, 1892." Photo by D.B. Dowling. (LAC, PA-038193)

of mosquito netting, snug in his Hudson's Bay blankets, lulled by the thrum of nighthawks' wings. Yet they had no choice but to hurry on. On August 7, Ferguson writes: "The shoot (chute!) down the river from Partridge to Cree (Ennadai) Lake was one giddy whirl. I could scarcely keep track of the canoe at all & dared not stop. For the 'Chips' brooked no delay . . . they didn't care a hang for surveys and didn't or wouldn't understand them – only wanted to get rid of us as soon as possible & hie back to the rest to make ready for the hunting."

The Chipewyan, led by a powerful chief, Kasmere, had already gathered on Ennadai Lake for their fall hunt. Joe paid off the guides and instructed Kasmere to watch for a smoke signal in case the expedition returned. Ferguson sat gazing out over the lake as the sun set in a blaze of copper, violet, and blue, longing "to live along that sandy ridge among the spruce groves and witness peaceful sunset calm like this – to see the camps of wigwams with their spires of blue smoke curled upwards – follow the

savage to the chase & look on the countless herds of caribou . . .
and here it was so near at hand, but we must hurry on."

Paddling down the Kazan River on August 15, they sighted
a caribou on a nearby hill, then another and another until the hills
and beaches were covered with waves of caribou running towards
them and plunging into the water. They shot twelve, to Ferguson's
delight and Joe's relief. Joe was worried. Once again, they were in
the middle of nowhere without a guide: the weather had turned
cold and stormy, and the Kazan River was flowing due north, away
from his cache on Hudson Bay and Fort Churchill. The river's
unexpected direction, contrary to Joe's rudimentary information,
forced him to consider turning back. There was time to return to
du Brochet, even Cumberland House, before freeze-up.

"It seemed as if nature was chilled to the bone & would
never smile again," Ferguson writes. "We felt pretty much that
way ourselves." They paddled on, hoping at least to reach Samuel
Hearne's Yathkyed Lake before giving up and heading home. On
August 16, they were startled to come across rows of decoy caribou, artfully made of sticks, stones, and moss, positioned on the
shore, and, in the water, freshly killed caribou carcasses. Rounding
a bend in the river the next morning, Ferguson spied "two odd
waddling skin figures with some dogs and carcases on the shore."

"*Chimo! Chimo! Kabloona! Kabloona Chimo!*" Standing in his
canoe, Joe shouted greetings in fragmented Inuktitut and waved
a fistful of needles and tobacco. The Inuit women squatted
calmly in the underbrush and waited for the canoes to land. As
soon as Joe held out plugs of tobacco, the women, Ferguson says,
"were convulsed with sudden joy, danced and shouted and wad-
dled back to their bundles, dived inside parchment bags, brought
out tin boxes, stone pipes. . . ." Joe produced matches and lit the
pipes, and they all sat around having a friendly smoke. The Inuit
men, it appeared, were downriver spearing caribou, and the two
women hopped in the canoes to guide them there. "A little way
down the river," says Ferguson, "they began to shout *Kabloona
Oomyak-O-Kuk*, 'the White Man Canoe is All Right,' in the

"Eskimo kyaks on Kazan River, August 24, 1894." (TFRBL, J.B.T. papers, P10505)

intervals beginning to think of barter and gain from the white man – the older asking for needles & thimbles & beads – opening all the pots & pans & asking also for them."

As they made their way downriver, twenty or more kyaks darted out from the shore, dancing around them like a swarm of water beetles. They passed several clusters of caribou-hide *topeks* before they were ushered ashore at the main camp to a jubilant, open-hearted welcome. "They offered us food in their tents," Ferguson writes, "trooped out to fetch brush for our fires – carried the baggage ashore & ministered to all of the wants they knew how to supply . . . they laughed and chatted with us – towed our canoes with their fish lines. . . . Some old women soon joined them & when they heard the joyful news of tobacco they simply danced in their enormous baggy skin trousers & long-tailed hooded coats shouting strange cries, with babies & all on their backs."

The apparent head men in this sprawling camp were two brothers – Hallo and Ahyout – and Ahyout's son Kakkuk. They paid Tyrrell and Ferguson the compliment of assuring them that they were indeed the first white men to venture down the Kazan

"Aiyout and Kakkuk, our two guides, at camp on Angikuni Lake, August 24, 1894." (TFRBL, J.B.T papers, P10499)

River; the Inuit knew the river well, since they traded at the Hudson's Bay Company's du Brochet post. They seemed to know exactly who Joe was and where he was going, and after a brief palaver, Ahyout and Kakkuk volunteered to act as guides. "Ahyout says that he has four times seen white men," Joe notes, "at Churchill, du Brochet post, and at the posts to the west, probably Forts Rae and Resolution. He has travelled over all the country from Doobaunt Lake to Churchill. The other, Kakkuk, his son, saw white men once when he was a little boy. He thinks they came from Churchill overland to here in the spring. They all knew of my trip down the Telzoa (Doobaunt) river last year, Ahyout introducing me everywhere as the man who went down that river and left the plug of tobacco at the commotic [sled]."

The sled may well have belonged to Ahyout himself and Ahyout may have been in the crowd who had greeted the Tyrrells at Baker Lake. Ahyout was obviously exceptionally well informed, and Joe got out his drawing paper and pencils so that Ahyout could make a map of the Kazan River. Ferguson, meanwhile, bartered with the women for skin clothing, robes, and waterproof

parchment boots for the cold, wet days to come. Ferguson enjoyed
the ladies' company as much as they enjoyed his:

"In trying some fur 'mits' for winter ahead a pair of old
white kids [gloves] (used for keeping off blackflies in the long
portages behind) were shown to the ladies in comparison – the
softness of their leather & thinness, the fine stitching and the
wonderful black backs quite overcame their feelings, in regard for
which the young man gallantly presented them to one – the belle
of the camp, with a brass band around her forehead & her hair
done up in two long clubs on either side of her head, hanging
downward, twisted in cloth with windings of cloth and beads.
The lady was quite overcome – hot with emotional feelings – but
merely because she had nothing to give at the time in return, so
she finally borrowed a cake of lard from one of her companions
& with fearful hesitation, knowing it could never be accepted as
payment in full, offered it. . . . For the rest of the time, she sat
chanting and singing by the camp fire like one possessed."

Ferguson doesn't say if the beauty did offer more, but he lost
all interest in hunting. He watched through his field glasses as the
Inuit expertly speared the swimming caribou from their kyaks:

"Kakuk, the son of Ayoot, shot away in his kyack and managed to catch the last one. He headed the buck from the shore
and seemed to play him to tire him, for the sake of the sport!
Then let him go to the land & struck him just as he was rising to
his feet in the shallow water. He seemed to hold the deer down
with his spear on the further side of the kyack, leaning right over
upon him. Then laid the body across behind his 'hole' and paddled home triumphant – chanting across the water – It was a
beautiful evening & night and the scene full of a novel charm –
the three great white pyramids of topecks – with their circle of
dogs tied round them – each growing fat on his carcase – the heap
of slain deer on the shore; some drawn up out on the brown
rocks, some half immersed in the water – their antlers swayed by
the current & ripples. A goose floating close to the shore & flocks
of white gulls – some wheeling round with their cries of warning

against the deep red frosty sunset – there were bands of deer in clear outline looking round from the tops of the ridges – on the other side was a golden full moon & the opal mist rising over the willows & across a bay full of islands – in the glow of the camp fire sat a circle of skinclad gypsies – their garb a deep russet brown in the ruddy light of the embers & Kakuk's chant resounded more clearly as he neared the shore in the pale mist."

Ferguson made himself at home, and was treated with courtesy by the Inuit: "They crowded into our tent, of course, and sat in a hot, pervasive circle while we ate, but never touched things without our leave and were only good-naturedly inquisitive." Joe, on the other hand, was impatient to get away from "the swarm of dirty, inquisitive Huskies who have surrounded us for several days." As they loaded their canoes on the riverbank, Ferguson noted "a murmur of discontent & a mother's moaning and sobbing": Kakkuk's mother strenuously objected to his leaving. The surrounding crowd sighed and groaned in sympathy as Joe attempted to placate her first with a tin kettle, then a flannel shirt, and finally, when those were rebuffed, a red cotton handkerchief. After much hesitation, she accepted the handkerchief. With sighs of relief, the expedition pushed off. "The deal was closed and sealed," Ferguson notes, "but the mother & wife & small brothers & sisters set up a most heartrending outcry & the others joined in the wailing . . . with the dogs in chorus."

Ahyout and Kakkuk whizzed ahead in their kyaks, cheerfully reassuring Joe that, although the broad, swift Kazan River was still flowing north, the journey to Hudson Bay would be quick and straightforward. Information was communicated largely in pantomime. Writes Ferguson: "For instance, a rapid ahead: the guide makes a fearfully hideous face, pretends to froth & sputter & foam at the mouth – waves confusedly with hands and fingers with a sudden downward dip – Ayoot acted for us the most abstract ideas – portraying the human (Eskimo) passions, senses, seasons, weights & measures, natural objects, weather, time of day, space & colours, animals, numbers, sexes & the universe – an extraordinary jumble of ideas collected finally in one which seemed to signify 'Now here!'"

On August 25, they stopped to camp in a little sandy bay below a rapid; Ahyout and Kakkuk paddled on ahead to consult Pasamut, an elder whose family was camped downriver.

"This morning we brought the rest of the things over the portage," Joe writes that night, "and as we were about to start Pasamut came to us from the Eskimos just below us and drew a map of the river for us, showing that it ran into Chesterfield Inlet. This at once decided us not to go on, as we would have no chance of getting to Churchill in open water that way." Ferguson's response is blunter: "A very stunning blow indeed. It would take us eight days or so to get there & the same old racket that T. went thro' last year so direfully and narrowly with life wd have to be sustained again – perhaps less fortunately than then – and that meant 'cold Kabloonah' for the little white foxes' breakfast and tea."

Their chances of getting back to Lake Winnipeg before freeze-up didn't look any better, and neither Joe nor Ferguson relished the prospect of spending the winter with the Inuit living on putrid meat from the stinking caribou caches that lined the shore. If Samuel Hearne had travelled overland from Churchill to Yathkyed Lake, only a short distance northeast of their present location, Joe was certain that there *had* to be a more direct route, and these Inuit knew it: "Mr. Ferguson and I went down in a light canoe to the Eskimo camp and there got Pasamut to draw a map of the country. We found that there is a route by a portage out of this river into another which flows into the Bay opposite Sea Horse Islands. We decided to try that."

Ahyout rebelled, angrily protesting that Joe's proposed route, via Kaminuriak Lake, involved long, arduous portages and a series of impassable rapids. But Joe placed his faith in Pasamut, who had just returned from trading with the whalers at Marble Island: shouldn't he know something of the Hudson Bay coast? Joe knew something about barter too: after he and Ferguson offered guns, ammunition, many pounds of tobacco, knives, hammers, nets, trading tokens on the Hudson's Bay Company posts, needles, thimbles, beads, and their pick of Joe's cache on Hudson Bay, Ahyout relented. He provided more deerskin clothing and several hundred pounds of caribou meat to see them through the cold weather ahead, and found five friends to help them over the portages.

By now, Joe and Ferguson felt almost members of this extended Inuit clan: judging from the number of *topeks* Joe could see along the riverbanks, he estimated the total population at between one and two thousand. Ferguson listened, fascinated, to women chanting in a nearby *topek* as one of them gave birth, and he and Joe sorrowfully visited a young hunter dying from a gangrenous wound in his arm, unable to help. Lying awake on the shore of Yathkyed Lake, Ferguson had a spiritual epiphany: "In addition to the almost three-quarter moon shining across the lake & above a range of hills, the splendid glow of the frosty sunset still shone with crimson & purple & gold all over the lower western sky. Down to the south and east, at first were glimpses of northern lights which late in the night broke forth in the north in a glorious crystal circle & fringe, rising & falling in shimmering folds up into the highest heaven – or a wondrous scroll outspread – blazoned and lit with the flashing streamers – telling the truth that we cannot yet understand – the waters rippled their glad assent & the darkened islands & rocks lay wrapped in deep contemplation."

On September 1, they trekked off from the northeastern arm of Yathkyed Lake into a dismal frozen marsh. Winter set in the next day: a cold, relentless east wind, sleet, and snow. Lakes, when they came to them, were icing over; they had no wood for fires, and the moss was covered with snow. On September 13, south of Kaminuriak Lake, they were stormbound for two days. Ahyout said the storm was caused by a woman's spirit angry at white men going down the river. Joe notes, "If I would give him a plug of tobacco he would take it up the hill and give it to her,

and tell her that we were only making a map of the country . . .
and that we were not taking anything out of the country and that
we would not drive away the deer. I gave him a full sized plug of
tobacco to take to her. He at once went up the hill in the face of
the storm, and for a long time we heard him shouting a speech
of some kind to her. Then he came down and said that he thought
that she would let us travel the next day."

She did, possibly because Joe had forgotten his field glasses
on a hill upriver, and the weather was so cloudy that he was
unable to survey the entire distance from Yathkyed Lake to the
mouth of a rapid-strewn river he named for Ferguson "as a tribute to him for his splendid contribution and assistance." On
September 18, he and Ferguson parted from Ahyout and Kakkuk
on the stony shore of Hudson Bay; it was snowing and ice was
forming near the land. From here on, their lives would be in the
hands of their four faithful canoemen, Flett, Thomas, Harper,
and David, men so dependable and self-effacing that neither Joe
nor Ferguson had remarked even on their presence for many
weeks. Joe's field notes give the impression he and Ferguson were
travelling down the coast alone:

"September 21, Friday

The point at which we were camped appeared to be north
of my cache of last year, so leaving Mr. Ferguson to launch the
canoes and bring them on as soon as the tide should rise high
enough, I started walking down the shore. The little ponds were
all frozen over and many deer were feeding on the soft grass near
the shore, but I could see nothing of the cache. The tide was now
ebbing fast and it was necessary for me either to get into the
canoes and travel on, leaving the shore altogether, or to land the
canoes for the day. The season was so far advanced that it seemed
very unwise to lose a day's travel, especially as we should have
been unable to take the stuff even if we should have found the
cache, for it is all we can do now to paddle our canoes against
the seas. Besides this, the Company or Mr. Lofthouse may have

taken the things or the wolverines may have destroyed them. I therefore continued the journey. . . ."

They arrived safely in Churchill on October 1. This time they were expected, and Joe had sent ahead sufficient supplies. Nonetheless, Ferguson suffered from "constant, insatiable hunger, a greedy ravening," and Reverend Lofthouse, with whose family Joe and Ferguson lived for the next eight weeks, dryly commented that their appetites had "a devastating effect on one's winter stock of provisions." Waiting for freeze-up, Joe spent many pleasant hours hobnobbing with Captain John Hawes, stingy Matheson's welcome replacement as the Hudson's Bay Company's post manager, and, when the weather was mild, tramping along the shoreline trying to ascertain if the land had risen since the ice-sheet's retreat. Climbing across one smooth, granite ledge, he found, chiselled as crisply as if it had been engraved only hours before, the name SL. HEARNE, YR. 1767. All Joe had to do was shout "Halloo!" and conjure up in his mind Sam Hearne, his heart's companion during so many harsh months on the Barren Grounds, striding out from behind a boulder in his blue frock coat and ruffled shirt, his gaze penetrating, his manner frank, but reserved.

Hearne had been stationed at Churchill for the better part of twenty years, and he had spent the first fifteen years at the company's Prince of Wales Fort. Joe often visited the fort's massive stone ruin, overgrown with scrub willow, sedge, and gooseberry bushes, which loomed through the mist on a windswept, rocky flat five miles north of the present post. He had investigated numerous derelict fur trade forts throughout the North-West, but even whitewashed Fort Chipewyan, and that Gothic ruin Rocky Mountain House, were matchstick miniatures compared to this melancholy folly. The walls of Prince of Wales Fort were forty-two feet thick. *Forty-two feet!* And nearly seventeen feet high. With a five-foot parapet and embrasures for forty cannon. Many of the cannons were rusting in the grass, and Joe scavenged some cannonballs to take back to the museum in Ottawa.

"Fort Prince of Wales, October 11, 1894." Interior near south-east bastion, showing the walls of the old dwelling house. (TFRBL, J.B.T. papers, P10523)

The English had begun to build the fort in 1733, and finally gave it up forty years later. Inside, the walls were rough granite rubble, with scarcely space enough left for a common dwelling house that had measured about one hundred feet by thirty. It was hard to imagine that in the time of young Hearne's master, Moses Norton, this house, sumptuously furnished with tapestries and books, even an organ, had been the steamy cesspool of vice and debauchery Hearne portrayed:

> Mr. Norton was an Indian. . . . He kept for his own use five or six of the finest Indian girls which he could select; and notwithstanding his own uncommon propensity to the fair sex, took every means in his power to prevent any European from having intercourse with the women of the country. . . . Among his miserable and ignorant countrymen he passed for a proficient in physic, and always kept a

box of poison, to administer to those who refused him their wives or daughters.

His apartments were not only convenient but elegant, and always crowded with his favourite Indians: at night he locked the doors, and put the keys under his pillow; so that in the morning his dining-room was generally, for the want of necessary conveniences, worse than a hog-stye. As he advanced in years his jealousy increased, and he actually poisoned two of his women because he thought them partial to other objects more suitable to their ages.

An inflammation in his bowels occasioned his death on the 29th of December, 1773; and though he died in the most excruciating pain, he retained his jealousy to the last; for a few minutes before he expired, happening to see an officer laying hold of the hand of one of his women who was standing by the fire, he bellowed out, in as loud a voice as his situation would admit, "God d—n you for a b—h, if I live I'll knock out your brains." A few minutes after making this elegant apostrophe, he expired in the greatest agonies that can possibly be conceived.

Hearne, handsome, virile, and unabashedly fond of women, leaves little doubt that he was one of the aggrieved officers. His published journal says nothing about his own sexual relationships, but his emotional tribute to Norton's daughter Mary, paragon of every "good and amiable quality, in most eminent degree," suggests that they were lovers when Governor Hearne surrendered the fort to the French, without a fight, in August 1782.

"The ghost of Hearne must surely haunt its broken battlements in shivering penitence for his cowardice," Bob Ferguson argued, but Joe countered that Hearne had wisely learned to compromise, and to accomplish his purpose by politic and peaceful methods: "He had acquired the stoicism of the Indian and he

"James Westascot and friend." (TFRBL, J.B.T. papers, P10569)

suffered quietly just as an Indian is prepared to suffer." Within a year of Hearne's surrender, the shifting winds of diplomacy had returned Prince of Wales Fort to the English. It had been shattered by the French gunners, and Hearne learned that during his absence as a prisoner of war, Mary Norton had starved to death among her Cree relatives.

What of Dollie, then? Did Joe miss her? Worry about her? There was no mail, and field notes were no place for reflections on intimate matters. Ferguson's diary gives one hint about Joe's feelings: "T. said that one of the Eskimo maidens he saw last year was as pretty as any girl he ever had seen – almost." Joe was in no rush to go home. Instead of hitching a ride with the Hudson's Bay Company's southbound dog teams, as he had the previous year, Joe hired the company's best driver, Jimmy Westascot, to break a new shortcut trail for him via Split Lake. Westascot recruited a friend, David Dick, but they didn't have enough dogs to haul provisions for the six men; Joe waited nearly two weeks for some Chipewyan to come in with more dogs, but then the dogs were too weak and mangy. Captain Hawes, furious at Joe's stubborn insistence on going his own way, reluctantly rented him a team of company dogs. The expedition set out on its homeward leg on November 28.

The trip to Split Lake was tough slogging through deep, soft snow at –40 Fahrenheit temperatures; when the dogs floundered, the men had to break trail on their snowshoes or haul the sleds themselves.

Ferguson suffered the pain of blisters, sore knees, and a frozen toe in good spirits, and they made Norway House in time for Christmas. On January 7, 1895, Dollie at last received Joe's blessed telegram from Selkirk – "Happy New Year. Snowshoes from Churchill. All Well."

CHAPTER EIGHT

January 8, 1895, St. John, New Brunswick
  "My own dearest Joe,

  "How can I be thankful enough for your return! I have been very anxious and had about given up hope of seeing my own dear husband again. Everyone has been so good to me, and I do not know what I should have done without dear mother and father and the girls. They made my sorrow theirs and in every way took care of me for I have not been well lately, have been fainting and all that sort of thing but I am all right now, for it was only you I wanted dear. Oh, how I have missed you!

  "Do write and tell me Joe dearest where I am to meet you, for I cannot wait. I do want to see you so and kiss your dear old face. Do come quickly to me dear, for your wife is nearly wild."

  Dollie dashed this letter off as soon as she received Joe's telegram. It crossed in the mail with his letter written the next day from Winnipeg:

  "My dearest Dollie,

  "Again our long separation is almost at an end and how anxiously I am counting the days and hours until I can again fold you in my arms and kiss your sweet lips. . . .

  "I cannot tell you when to meet me dearest, for I have used up every cent of money I have in helping to pay the expenses of this trip and I cannot send you any to bring you up until I return to Ottawa. I have been obliged to draw all my summer's salary to pay the wages of the men.

"With my fondest love, from your own true Joe."

Dollie's father paid her train fare to Ottawa. Reverend Carey had returned to his old church in St. John, and Dollie had been living with her parents and sisters for the nearly seven months of Joe's absence. She'd had enough of it. When not lying awake at night picturing Joe starving or sleeping in the snow, she had kept busy making curtains and tablecloths for the lovely red-brick house they were planning to rent in the village of New Edinburgh, across the Rideau Canal from Ottawa, trusting, she wrote to Joe, "that we shall not have to part for a long time again. You know I shall try not to stop you in your work, but oh, I do want you home."

Joe arrived back in Ottawa in mid-January, and in the spring he and Dollie moved into their first home at 52 Alexander Street. They furnished it with gifts from their parents and Joe's explorer memorabilia: bearskin rugs, photographs of the Barren Grounds, Native beadwork and embroidery, and the snowshoes Joe had worn to walk the seven hundred miles from Churchill to Winnipeg (he didn't mention, when he showed them off, that he'd ridden part of the way on dogsleds or in carioles). Joe's fame, together with his socially prominent Aberdeen and Ferguson connections, brought a host of visitors, from missionaries to millionaire trophy hunters, and encouraged by Dollie's flare for the dramatic, Joe's adventures grew more astonishing with every retelling. Louis French's fight to the death with a gigantic polar bear rivalled the exploits of folk hero Davy Crockett, even legendary Paul Bunyan.

According to tradition, it might have been anticipated that Joe would follow in the footsteps of Hearne, Franklin, Back, Richardson, and other Barren Grounds explorers and publish a popular narrative of his journeys, illustrated, in his case, with dramatic photographs. He would be in distinguished company, and, more practically, a book would bring him an international reputation, money, possibly a knighthood. But Joe faced an awkward obstacle. His brother James was writing his own book about their 1893–94 Barren Grounds trip. Customarily, an expedition's subordinates were required to turn over all their notes, memoranda, and collections to their commander, and to waive their right to publish independently, but the Tyrrell brothers had made no such agreement. James had done all of the expedition's topographical surveying and botanical research, as well as serving as Inuit interpreter. He had submitted his notes and specimens, but he kept a private diary; moreover, he was asking the Survey for permission to include in his book a selection of the photographs they had both taken.

Joe, meanwhile, hadn't yet written his official report. His first excuse had been that his rock specimens were in his cache on Hudson Bay; well, one year and another expedition later, his bags of rocks were still cached on Hudson Bay, or they had been irretrievably scattered. The humiliation of explaining this to the Survey's new director, Dr. G.M. Dawson, was hard to bear. Old Selwyn, in Joe's absence, had been pushed into retirement, and Joe no longer had a browbeaten boss who would allow him to do much as he pleased. "He will be strict," Joe had written to Dollie about Dawson, "but he will be rational and if I cannot get along with him it will be largely my own fault."

Dawson absolutely refused to cooperate with any book project until Joe had finished *all* his reports, starting with his 1892 expedition to the south and east of Lake Athabasca; as a Survey employee, Joe's primary responsibility was to produce thorough, accurate accounts of his expeditions based on his geological observations. He was, after all, mapping an unknown land. Other scientists could not evaluate his work from his conversation, or sensational stories in the daily newspapers, nor could the government, stung by accusations of "expensive junkets," justify spending thousands of dollars on his explorations without maps and data to show for it.

Joe had some explaining to do. Rushing against time and the weather, he had only partially surveyed enormous areas of the territories he had been assigned to examine, and had omitted some regions altogether. He didn't have a map of the entire Kazan River because he hadn't followed it to its mouth, nor had he surveyed more than a fragment of Cree, Doobaunt, Kasba, Ennadai, Yathkyed, and Baker lakes, or the entire area between Yathkyed Lake and Hudson Bay. So how was he going to justify this claim, reported in New York's *Once a Week* magazine: "Mr. Tyrrell's survey will have the effect of completely changing the shape of the Hudson's Bay shore as at present seen on the maps. Being the first to come down the coast in a canoe, he was enabled to make observations which show that the existing information supplied by sailing vessels was wholly inaccurate." Joe's field notes from both expeditions record no such shoreline survey. In 1893, storms, snow, darkness, and debility had made it impossible; in 1894, following only a short stretch of the coastline, the men had paddled so quickly that Bob Ferguson believed they had passed Joe's cache in the dark. On both trips, low tides and mud flats had forced them long distances off shore.

Had Joe panicked? Ferguson's diary reveals "T" to be more nervous and hesitant than Joe admitted in his own journal, but James Tyrrell maintained a loyal, discreet silence about his brother's conduct and personality. Was Joe ever despondent? Elated? Scared out of his wits? The dominant emotion Joe's terse notes reveal is angry impatience: with Dawson, with his perfidious guide, Moberly, with Louis and Michel French's whining, and with the "dirty, inquisitive Huskies." His rare praise was reserved for those who, like Ferguson and Ahyout, exceeded his expectations. Of Ahyout, Joe later writes:

"I told him where I had left the field glasses and asked him to pick them up when he was going back up the river, and he at once asked me how much I would pay him for doing it. I asked him how much he wanted, and he said a carrot of tobacco (such as the sailors had at Marble Island). I explained to him as well as I could that the H.B.C. did not keep that kind of tobacco, but he would get blackstrap instead. He said that he would get it [the field glasses] on his way back if a wolverine had not found it, but if a wolverine had found it, it would carry it away and hide it so securely that even he could not find it. All this was agreed to. This would be a severe test of honesty, for telescopes of any kind were a very precious article to these people living on those vast open plains of the north. However a year or two later in Ottawa I got a letter from Mr. Des Chambault at Du Brochet with the field glasses which had been delivered to him and an account for three and a half pounds of tobacco. Quite a wonderful record!"

Joe was a generous, if demanding, boss, and a good judge of men; he listened attentively and respectfully to people he trusted, and while he could look hostile and humourless, especially in photographs, he had a disarming, ear-to-ear grin when he was amused. His success, his very survival, proved that he inspired loyalty, confidence, and dedication in independent and diverse crews of Chipewyan, Cree, Iroquois, Metis, and Inuit. Joe may have modelled himself on Sir George Back, who advised in his *Narrative of the Arctic Land Expedition*, "Squeamishness is little heeded in such travelling as this, and shirking is quite out of the question. Pity for temporary ailments might be felt, but was not to be expressed; the restraint, however painful, being absolutely indispensable. Action, if it had no other effect, would at least keep up the spirits of the men and divert their thoughts from the privations they were suffering." Joe's sang-froid may have given him the ability to endure weeks of extreme suffering without breaking down, and to forge ahead into the perilous unknown when a more excitable, or empathetic, leader would have turned back. Joe's only admission of weakness, apart from having to be carried into Churchill after their rescue on Hudson Bay in October 1893, was his inability to write his notes during the final few days; he filled them in from memory (and probably from James's memory) in Churchill.

Now, married and comfortably settled in Ottawa, Joe couldn't write his reports. Physically, he was in the pink of health, but psychologically he showed symptoms of having become "bushed." Earlier, Joe had tried to explain to Dollie, in half-joking ways, his feelings of alienation from society after half a year in the wilderness. Barren Grounds traveller P.G. Downes, who, in the 1930s, followed part of Joe's 1894 Kazan route, gives in his memoir, *Sleeping Island*, a more complex analysis of the "consuming restlessness" that he found possessed every man in the North:

> It is as if he were in self-protection forced to share the unseen movement and the rhythm of the natural world about him. It is almost as if he felt that should he remain inactive for even a few hours the deadening, gray impact of the world of raw nature would crush him. He is constantly fleeing an unknown, a subconscious enemy. Once he surrenders, he is lost; he is engulfed in a gripping prison of apathy, the space, the crushing power of a world of nature too big to struggle against; it breaks the spirit, it leaves his body to be swallowed up in the immensity. This world of insatiable restless movement seems to possess everything in the Barrens and lastly it is communicated to man himself. The living world, the animals, the birds, the very winds, storms, and lastly the ground itself, seem in a state of flux and movement. The caribou are ever wandering over the country, day and night. The wolves, the foxes, even the tiny lemming roam and migrate and pass, it seems, never resting. . . . The weather is never constant for a day – sunshine, storms, and always the winds are blowing and herding the distraught clouds across the sky. The gray rocks crack and crumble; the land flows and creeps; the greater the depth into the earth the slower the rhythm and the movement but always it is there, inexorable, mighty, timeless. The coasts are slowly emerging from the sea, but the evidence is perceptible; the great glaciers far to the north grind down to the

ocean. The lakes are retreating, and the trees and muskeg follow them. The rivers eat and groan in their labors as they devour the banks and with their moving boulders grind away at their rapids and falls. In this macrocosm of change and flux is man. He too must catch the strange beat or perish.

In the Barrens, Joe's impulsive, intuitive way of doing things had caught the beat, but not in Ottawa, where his inability to knuckle down to geological analysis and map-making made him seem undisciplined, arrogant, and lazy. Psychologically, Joe may have needed to block traumatic experiences and to invent or exaggerate others, but Sigmund Freud was still an unknown, unpublished doctor in Vienna, and in Canada there was little sympathy or understanding for people who were irrational, visionary, or even unconventional. At the best of times, the public tended to think explorers were "off their nuts," as indeed many of them were, and no medical vocabulary as yet existed to explain the adrenalin rush, the addictive, compulsive "high" that adventurers experience in situations of extreme danger and physical stress. The downside was more familiar: depression, boredom, and irritation with the mundane routines of everyday life. Always thin-skinned and resentful of criticism, Joe developed a fixation that Dawson was persecuting him, and that his Survey colleagues were jealous of his popularity. Celebrity Joe gloried in his acclaim, but Geologist Joe was hurt at being criticized as a vulgar "publicity-seeker."

Soon after his return, Joe posed for a studio photograph dressed in his Inuit caribou-skin clothing and moccasins, holding his snowshoes. His expression is faintly embarrassed, and his plump face and round glasses give him an appealing, but unheroic, White Rabbit look. Snapshots of Joe hamming it up with a furry Ferguson on the steps of Rideau Hall capture Joe's sense of fun, but unhappily he tended to hide this virtue beneath a pompous, stiff-necked public persona. Joe poured a great deal of time and

Joe in his caribou parka. (TFRBL, J.B.T. papers, F0656)

Tyrrell and Ferguson hamming it up on the steps at Rideau Hall, 1894.
(TFRBL, J.B.T. papers, P10575)

money into making lantern slides of his Barren Grounds photos with the idea of giving public lectures, but he was a slow, serious speaker, and after a lecture or two, no stage tour materialized. Parka-clad Robert Peary had already stolen Joe's thunder with an American lecture tour following his first Greenland expedition, and Peary's show had featured a team of husky dogs that howled in a most thrilling, blood-curdling manner.

Certainly Joe could provide huskies, sleds, kyaks, *topeks*, tipis, and Inuit and Indians to boot. There were popular precedents: real cowboys and Indians performed across North America in Buffalo Bill's Wild West Show, which Joe loved, and in 1893, the Chicago World's Fair had displayed several Inuit families, including children, who had lived on the fairgrounds, with their *topeks*, kyaks, and skin clothing, in a make-believe Arctic encampment.

In Canada, this kind of show might do well in winter, with dog-sled and snowshoe races, igloos, Inuit women with babies in their hoods cooking caribou tongues over their campfires, chanting, conjuring, and drumming, sharp-shooting and harpoon-throwing contests, maybe even a few live caribou. Either the possibilities of such a spectacle escaped the theatrical impresarios, or the logistics of employing Native performers were too daunting: Sioux chief Sitting Bull had quit after only one season with Buffalo Bill, and Inuit brought to Europe or America almost invariably sickened and died. As it was, Tyrrell of the North couldn't hope to compete on stage, lantern show and all, with a young Mohawk princess, Pauline Johnson, who declaimed her dramatic poetry in a revealing deerskin dress.

On the other hand, if Joe went back to live with the Caribou Inuit as an anthropologist, he could become a world authority on the Barren Grounds and its people. Joe knew that he had stumbled upon an exotic, even unique culture – Inuit who lived off the land, not the sea – but their history, beliefs, and customs did not arouse his curiosity. Bob Ferguson's observations in his private diary, which has never been published, were more perceptive than Joe's field notes, and James Tyrrell included two studious chapters on the Eskimos in his book *Across the Sub-Arctics of Canada*. Joe Tyrrell's attitude towards Native people was unusual for his time: he treated them like everybody else. He did not regard Natives as an inferior, "savage" race, doomed to extinction, or as children in need of paternal protection, education, and Christian salvation; they were not freaks to be examined, collected, and exhibited at carnivals or in museums. Joe commissioned Native women to make moccasins and mitts for himself and as gifts; he did not buy or scavenge their clothing and personal possessions in the name of science. Joe liked and admired people who were honest, intelligent, and hard-working; professionally, he valued them in terms of their contribution to his work. If Joe could be callous, indifferent, and ungrateful towards his Native guides and canoemen, he could be that way to Dollie too. If he could wear stinking filthy clothes for months on end, were the Inuit's sanitary customs truly worthy of scientific study? Joe didn't appreciate people prying into his private affairs – why should he pry into theirs?

Had Joe possessed more aptitude for languages (he'd struggled hard with Cree and Inuktitut), or a shred of interest in Inuit cooking utensils, tools, or spiritual beliefs, he could hardly have taken Dollie north with him, or left her alone in Ottawa for a year or two. Peary's wife Jo had given birth to a daughter at their base camp in Greenland, but even if Dollie were strong and daring enough to risk living in a *topek*, such radical behaviour would embroil them both in controversy. The Caribou Inuit would have to wait more than a decade for a scholarly visit from a Danish Greenlander, Knud Rasmussen, and Denmark's Thule Expedition. In the summer of 1895, Joe, his reports still unwritten, returned to Lake Winnipeg for a three-month geological survey of the northeastern watershed, and Dollie, happily pregnant, again went off to stay with her parents and sisters.

"June 27, 1895, 242 Princess St., St. John, New Brunswick

"My own dearest Joe,

"The sun is shining in the window on me as I write and there is a cool breeze blowing from the water. How I wish you were here with me! Ada, the girl, brought up my breakfast this morning before I was awake. I missed my dear husband who calls me a 'rabbit' and a 'cat.' I do want to see you so much darling, but I pray for you every night and think about you. I sleep alone in a big bed where if I am ill I can lie and see the water. I sleep alone but I think I'd rather have you with me. I wish you could just see this lovely sparkling sea and the little rocky island with its lighthouse and foghorn. This sea air ought to make the little baby so strong and well. I am not going to make an invalid of myself at all.

"You will come to me soon and hold me tight in your arms again, won't you, darling?"

Dollie, recuperating from a bout of diphtheria that winter, seemed content to snuggle into the bosom of her close-knit family: "They are all very fond of you and father is so delighted to hear that are good to me. He says he is thankful and very proud of you. Love from all, and most and best from Dollie." Then, less than a week later, came two consecutive postcards with an identical troubling message:

"July 4th

"My dear J,

"I am feeling perfectly wretched as I told in my yesterday's letter. I was never so sick as I was yesterday and today. Mother is afraid I am going to have bilious fever. She is going to have the doctor come and see me tomorrow if I am not better. It isn't because I have not been out because I have had a long walk every-day since I came. I don't tell you to worry you but just to let you know how I am. The sea air is delicious & so refreshing. . . .

"Yours with best love, M.E.T."

Dollie's initials meant trouble. Mary Edith Tyrrell was Dollie's assertive self: Dollie could be petted and played with, imperious Mary Edith demanded attention. What was Joe to do? He had closed up their Ottawa house for the summer and was busy in Winnipeg hiring men and buying provisions for a trip into an unexamined labyrinth of rock, water, and muskeg; there, he would be a week or more away from the nearest Hudson's Bay Company post office, and mail, including telegrams sent to Winnipeg, travelled slowly by steamboat and canoe. He and Dollie were to write to each other every Sunday, but they could expect their letters to arrive in batches, late, and far apart. Was he to spend his summer sick with worry?

"My own dearest Dollie," Joe writes on July 17 from a steamboat chugging up Lake Winnipeg. "It was not pleasant to have to go away thinking that you were very sick, perhaps in the midst of a raging fever. It is not nice to know that you are ill, darling, but it is even worse not to know at all how you are. . . . Loving you always and all the time, your own true loving husband, Joe."

Dollie was already feeling better: "It is so lovely being at home," she writes on July 7. "No place else could I be as happy or comfortable. Mother seems to know just what is good for me."

Her next cheery letters are full of domestic news about picnics and boat trips on the Bay of Fundy and the St. John River, putting up jars of jam, sewing baby clothes, reading Shakespeare, eating fruit, and growing fat "for the sake of the baby." Joe too writes about homely details: his shorn hair and lengthening beard, the rivers he is exploring around Norway House, the lovely weather. "The days are perhaps a little monotonous," he assures her, "and the country is rather dreary and uninteresting." In their letters, they called to each other over echoing distances from different worlds. Joe did not ask about Dollie's pregnancy; she never mentioned his work. Joe wrote about where he was, Dollie about how she felt:

"September 1

"My dearest Joe,

"It is Sunday again and such a long, long week as this has been, and then too dear I have been worried about receiving no letter from you for it will be seven weeks on Tuesday since I received your last one. Surely you are not going to die and leave me too. . . ."

Six days earlier, Lissie, Dollie's married sister in Michigan, had died suddenly after a lingering illness. It was a terrible blow for her parents, and for grieving Dollie, her distraught family was no longer a peaceful sanctuary:

"Do come home soon dear Joe. My heart is just aching for you and when day after day passes with no letter I grow sadder and sadder. I am afraid dear this letter is very dismal but I must write you just as I feel and I think anyway that you would rather your wife would trust you enough to feel sure of your sympathy so that she can write you exactly what is in her own heart. I do hope you will come home soon to me for I cannot stand it much longer having you away. You know, dear that sorrow of this kind has never touched our hearts before. Ever your own Dollie."

By September 30, however, Mary Edith had reasserted herself, and sends a frosty postcard:

"Dear J. Thought it hardly worthwhile to write a letter this week as I expect you to come in this week some time. I received your letters written on the first and eighth of this month and am glad to hear of your welfare. We are all well. . . . Hope you will come soon for I want to get settled at home before the cold weather sets in.

"Yours, M.E.T."

Joe did not reach Selkirk and open Dollie's package of letters until October 8; he responded by dawdling for ten days with Lieutenant-Governor Schultz in Winnipeg and at his parents' home in Weston. In retaliation, Mary Edith brought her sister Ellie to live with them in Ottawa, because, she admonished Joe, "you are with me so little."

After their daughter Mary was born on January 29, 1896, Dollie had plenty to occupy her time, but Joe, having to share a small house with a convalescent wife, a crying baby, and a sharp-tongued sister-in-law he disliked, retreated into a cloud of pipe smoke and grumpy silence. He laboured to finish his report on his 1892 Lake Athabasca expedition, and the arrival in March of the remnants of his Hudson Bay cache, located by Inuit the previous fall, meant he had to get to work on his Barren Grounds report. As for his unexciting last summer's work on Lake Winnipeg, well, who knew when that would get done. Joe was overburdened, and distracted by money worries: he was mired in debt.

Joe was hopeless with money. When travelling, he carried wads of cash in his pocket. Sometimes he lost it in the bush, or blew it on things like sled dogs, sailboats, and other fancies not covered by the Survey budget (he was always overbudget anyway). He bought the latest German field glasses and microscopes, subscribed to journals, and collected valuable books, including a first edition of Samuel Hearne's *Journey*. He didn't gamble, drank sparingly, and cared nothing about clothes, but he had joined Ottawa's elite, expensive Rideau Club, and, as an officer, he contributed substantially to the maintenance and entertainment of the Governor General's Foot Guards.

These necessities, as Joe saw them, strained his annual salary of $1,800, but a more serious drain was paying the interest on his own and his father's mortgages. Over eighty and in poor health, William Tyrrell was bankrupt. Having devoted most of his time to county and Conservative politics, he had not developed his construction business into a profitable enterprise. Moreover, he had speculated recklessly in farmland, oil wells, sawmills, general stores, and all sorts of investments that had never paid off, and he had difficulty renting out houses he had built in Toronto and Weston. He had subdivided his own Weston farm into lots he'd sold to his sons, but the rows of city houses and stores they had envisioned on streets named after themselves remained pipe dreams. Nevertheless, the Squire of Weston, in appearance and manner a dead ringer for Mr. Micawber in Dickens's *David Copperfield*, lived like an Irish country gentleman on his estate by the railway tracks. The sixth, landless son of County Kildare gentry, William Tyrrell had spent his life avenging his exile to the backwoods of Upper Canada, and now his family's honour and reputation were at stake. Rather than lose their family's property, the Tyrrell brothers scraped together hundreds of dollars a year to keep the creditors and tax collectors at bay, and they paid their father a regular $5 allowance to keep his own household afloat.

Luckily for Joe, Dollie kept their household accounts, and she was, as Joe gratefully joked, a "sharper." Dollie could pinch a penny until it screamed, but they were always behind on the rent, the coal bill, the snow shovelling, the butcher, and everything else. Dollie wasn't embarrassed to keep chickens and sell eggs – she even thought of keeping a pig – and she enjoyed access to a private income: her mother Mary's Killmaster inheritance. Dollie's mother was generous but tactful in her gifts: clothes, furniture, barrels of oysters, and other treats, and of course all Dollie's and the baby's living and travel expenses while Joe was away. The Careys had such complete faith in Joe that they had lent him the money to buy David Thompson's *Travels*.

Nobody else wanted it. Although Joe had returned Thompson's handwritten manuscript to Charles Lindsey in 1891, he had been annotating his typed copy as he traced Thompson's routes throughout the North-West, anticipating that his updated interpretation would find a publisher and make his fortune. Yet in June 1894, while Joe was on his way to the Barren Grounds, Lindsey had offered Thompson's manuscript for sale for $1,700 through Toronto book dealer Albert Britnell. It didn't sell, so in March 1895, Lindsey included it in an auction of his entire library in Boston. When it failed to sell there, Lindsey let Joe have it for $400.

Joe had no contacts in Canada's nascent literary community, no special talent as a writer or editor, no experience in publishing, no time to market the manuscript, and no money to publish it himself. After offering it to several publishers without response, he grasped at a dour reply from the Macmillan Company in New York. "There is altogether too much matter," the editor wrote. "The style in a number of instances requires correction and altogether the book should be thoroughly worked over before being submitted to a publisher."

Dollie enthusiastically took on the "working over" job. She was good at spelling, and as eager as Joe to get the book published. She'd already been typing up his annotations and arranging the narrative into chapters; now she got to work cutting out "those ugly descriptions of animals and uninteresting ways of trapping them." Dollie's uncomprehending, dismissive attitude towards Joe's idol was characteristic of the miscommunications in their marriage. Dollie delighted in lighthearted company and conversation; Joe spent the evenings reading or writing in his study. Dollie would join him with her own book, as she had done with her father, and pretend to sit quietly, while doing her best to entice Joe off to bed. But the more Dollie/Mary Edith provoked, pestered, cajoled, sobbed, teased, complained, flirted, or tried to help, the deeper Joe shrank into his snapping-turtle shell. Their main battlegrounds were religion and illness.

"You will help me, won't you, to make a happy Christian home for our little child?" Dollie pleaded. "I do think you are a Christian, though you say you do not believe." Praying to God was as natural to Dollie as breathing, but Joe would only promise to make "a good, kind home," and "to live as true a life as possible." Joe agreed to rent a pew at St. Andrew's Presbyterian Church (a fashionable compromise among the Baptists, Methodists, and Anglicans) but he ridiculed the old-fashioned theology and scoffed at all religion as "cant." Nor would Joe sympathize with Dollie's chronic ill health: he countered her every symptom with his own moans about indigestion, constipation, and lumbago, and he reminded Dollie repeatedly that *quiet and solitude* were *absolutely necessary* to his well-being.

By the spring of 1896, they had agreed that spending six months a year apart was probably a good idea. By May 1, Dollie, her sister Ellie, and baby Mary were in Port Rowan on Lake Erie to spend the summer with a crowd of Killmaster cousins. Joe remained alone in Ottawa, finishing his reports and happily eating out of tin cans heated on his kerosene stove, before he headed off at the end of June to continue his geological survey in northwestern Manitoba. Their letters are friendly and diplomatic; Dollie writes pages praising baby Mary's every smile and gurgle, Joe assures her that he is mowing the lawn and collecting the eggs. Dollie's manner is timid: "Do just what you like yourself," and when Joe ends his eagerly awaited one-week visit to Port Rowan after two days, she is grateful that he came at all.

On his way west, Joe instructed Dollie to write only to Cumberland House, a post he would not reach until at least the end of September. That way, he would be spared her letters pleading with him to come home, and, as it turned out, he read Dollie's frantic descriptions of Mary's nearly fatal fever long after she had recovered. If Joe preferred not to know what was happening back home, Dollie didn't want to know what he was doing either; she professed not even to know, or care, where Cumberland House was, although she had closely followed Joe's earlier journeys on a map, and when it came to geology, she laughed that it was all "beyond me."

Ignorance was an approved, even required, feminine attribute in most circles, but not in the Carey household, and Joe himself had offered to pay his youngest sister Lizzie's way through medical college before their father had forbidden her to enroll. Sequestered in a virtual harem as she was, Dollie was up-to-the-minute on political intrigues, and she was perceptive enough to pick up the hurtful hints, passed along by her catty sister Alice, about why it really was that Mr. Tyrrell never took his young wife along on all those long, lonely trips.

Was Joe a "squaw man"? Did he have Native girlfriends, a wife, another family, in the North-West? It was well known, almost taken for granted, that Hudson's Bay Company men, even those of the highest rank, had "country wives"; Joe visited frequently with many of them, and didn't Joe's Chipewyan guide Moberly have the same name as the veteran trader at Île-à-la-Crosse? It was said too that Indian men never went anywhere without their women to cook and sew for them. Did Joe's Indian canoemen bring a woman along for Joe? Even missionaries had Indian wives and nobody thought anything of it. Everyone knew about Lieutenant Peary's Eskimo wife and baby, even though his own wife had gone to Greenland with him. Dollie had read about the Yellowknife *femme fatale* Green Stockings, in Sir John Franklin's narrative, and in Sir George Back's book too, and the gentlemen seemed to be doing a lot of winking and nudging between the lines. Dollie had laughed at Bob Ferguson's stories about the Eskimo belle offering him the cake of lard, and how he and Joe had enticed the waddling little skin-clad women into their canoes with tobacco – but didn't Eskimo men offer their wives to visitors? And wasn't it rude to refuse?

Yes, the Geological Survey had assigned Joe to explore the Lake Winnipeg basin, but had Joe requested this assignment, as he had others, and did he insist for personal reasons on returning to his same old haunts year after year, although he had made no significant mineral discoveries there since he had identified the gypsum deposit near Lake Manitoba in 1888? This summer, Joe hired the same men, Roderick Thomas and John Harper, and, as usual, posted his letters from Selkirk and Norway House. Joe's letters were always addressed to "My dearest Dollie," and signed, "Your own loving husband, Joe," but the repetition seemed mechanical, and his days almost too boring: "Someway or another I have not yet taken any interest at all in this trip," Joe writes from the Nelson River on July 12, 1896. "The country is an uninteresting rocky wilderness and the summer appears to be merely a time to pile up work I cannot get through in the winter. I would sooner be home with you than roaming here, worse than alone in this dreary country. . . . After the year's roaming is over, nothing seems to come of it but vanity and vexation of spirit, but after all others have had the same experience for thousands of years past. I must try to do the work that is set out for me, at most it will be only for a few more years and then can come quiet rest."

Did Joe and his crew really get up at 4:00 a.m. and go to bed at 8:30 p.m. every day? Why did Joe take pains to point out that he slept in a tent by himself, and ate his meals alone? If they were all in one canoe, as Joe said, did another, with their women, follow behind? A great deal could be read into Joe's dry, reticent letters: extra days spent in Norway House refurbishing his boat *Pterodactyl* for resale, calls paid on missionaries in Indian settlements, weeks laid up with a burned hand at the Nelson House Indian reserve, although Joe wrote that the burn wasn't bad enough to leave a scar.

Joe's life in the field, celibate or not, was part of Dollie's own, like it or not, and she accepted their marriage with a statement of faith he could take or leave: "Every year you and I are growing to understand each other better, and are growing more to each other," she writes to him at the end of August. "You know you are a great deal fonder of me now than you were when we were first married or when we were engaged, and I am of you, though we know each other's little failings more, yet we know the nice parts better too."

Mother Earth, sensuous, capricious, elusive, was herself a seductress, but if Joe were enchanted by anyone, she was a sea of ice he now named Keewatin, the Cree–Ojibwa word for "north," and Canada's geographical name for the district where she had been born during the Ice Age. Joe had been tracing Keewatin's sensual curves since 1883, when he had come across the strange, out-of-place granite boulders he now believed she had carried to the foothills of the Rockies. During his past thirteen years with the Survey, he had mapped her across the North-West, through the Eagle Hills, the Hand Hills, and the valley of the Battle River, charted her claw marks on the shores and islands of the Lake Winnipeg basin, and clambered up and down her pale sand eskers in the Barren Grounds. There, in the area of Doobaunt Lake, Joe believed he had located her *névé*, or birthplace. Much of the time that he was supposed to be writing his reports for the Survey, he'd been making diagrams of the hundreds of the glacier's moraines, eskers, and striae that he had recorded over the years, and he chose to publish his results in independent journals, *Geology Magazine*, the *Geographical Journal*, and, in 1896, the prestigious *Journal of Geology*.

In this article, Joe identifies Keewatin as "a great glacial center or gathering ground lying comparatively close to the west coast of Hudson Bay, from which the ice radiated in all directions; eastwards into the basin of Hudson Bay, which was probably an open body of water then as it is now, and furnished the moisture for the immense precipitation of snow a short distance to the west of it; southward towards Manitoba and the Great Plains; westward towards the Athabasca–Mackenzie Valley and the Rocky Mountains; northwestward and northward toward the Arctic Ocean." Moreover, he adds provocatively: "I would suggest that Dr. Dawson's name, 'Laurentide Glacier,' be restricted to that great *mer de glace* centering over the country north of the St. Lawrence River and the heights of Labrador."

Joe had feared that Dawson, as Survey director, might suppress his discovery of Keewatin, or co-opt it as his own. Although Dawson advocated for a Laurentide glacier in the east, and an

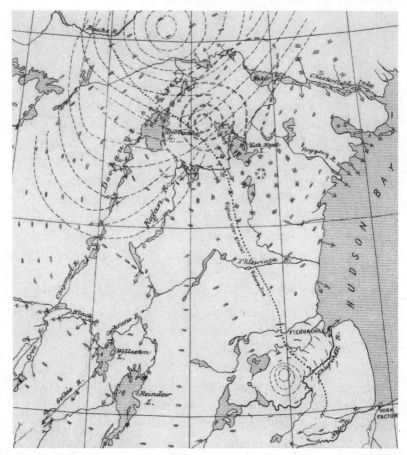

Centre of the Keewatin Glacier, 1897. (GSC, Natural Resources Canada, Map 621)

ice-sheet he called the Cordilleran in the Rockies, he still clung to the obsolete theory that the landscape of the Great Plains had been shaped by oceanic and iceberg activity. Ill will, however, seems to have been almost entirely on Joe's side; Dfawson approved all his articles for publication, including a paper on Keewatin, "The Glaciation of North Central Canada," that Joe was to read in August 1897 to the annual meeting of the British Association for the Advancement of Science in Toronto.

A gathering of the "who's who" of British science in Canada was a rare opportunity for ambitious young colonials to be noticed, and Joe was to deliver a second paper, "The Natural Resources of the Barren Grounds of Canada," based on his report, at last completed, of his 1893 and 1894 expeditions. Contrary to his earlier opinion that the Barren Grounds were of no value, Joe now confidently claimed to have located an extended area of potentially rich mineral-bearing rocks similar to the gold-, silver-, and copper-bearing Laurentian rocks north of Lake Superior and Lake of the Woods. His hopes of recognition were so high that he insisted Dollie come in from Port Rowan to help him make a good impression at the banquets and receptions. His papers, however, failed to create a ripple of interest, and he had been excluded from the association's railway excursion to the resort of Banff in the Rocky Mountains: Joe had to leave the train in Winnipeg to continue his survey of western Manitoba.

His last chance was to buttonhole an influential patron in the conviviality of the smoking car as the train threaded its way along the north shores of the Great Lakes, but when Joe boarded in Toronto, he found himself alone: everyone had retreated to their compartments. The next morning, however, he was warmly greeted by Byron Edmund Walker, general manager of the Canadian Bank of Commerce and an amateur paleontologist who often consulted the Survey about his fossils. Walker, a host of the excursion, was responsible for entertaining its most eminent participants, Lord and Lady Kelvin, and they were bored to tears. Would Joe go to their private car and talk to them about the country they were passing through?

Had Joe felt less forlorn, he would have been struck dumb at the prospect of conversing with the inventor of thermodynamics and the absolute scale of temperature; as it was, he spent a pleasant afternoon with elderly William Thomson and his wife, describing the geology and resources of the starkly beautiful landscape outside the windows, and chatting about his research and adventures in the North-West.

"I actually believe that they were rather sorry to leave me behind, as I was sorry to say goodbye to them," Joe writes plaintively to Dollie after the train had pulled out of Winnipeg. "If it had been possible for me to have gone west to Banff today to cultivate the acquaintances made yesterday it would have been fortunate."

The disappointment was one of many. In June 1896, the Liberal Party had won the Canadian election. With old Sir John A. Macdonald and the last of Joe's trusty Conservative government contacts gone, his father's letters to well-placed political friends would no longer push his career ahead. Competition from younger men with Ph.D.s put his job itself at risk, and he could expect neither promotion nor a raise in salary: the Liberals were even stingier towards the Survey than the Conservatives, and Joe's achievements had been eclipsed by his colleague Arthur Peter Low's sensational discovery. In the District of Ungava, north of Quebec, Low had found enough iron ore, he claimed, to supply the world.

Joe's work in the summer of 1897 took him back to Lake Manitoba, the same swampy area where he had nearly died of typhoid nine years earlier. Nine years! Sixteen years with the Survey, and what did he have to show for it? The Sir George Back Award from the Royal Geographical Society – a silver tankard and fifteen British pounds – in recognition of his two Barren Grounds expeditions. Where was he to go now? He had covered all of Manitoba, and most of the Great Plains, on foot and horseback, by wagon and canoe. There wasn't much white space left on the map, and what chance did Joe have of being sent on another "extravagant junket" to the Far North? All the new jobs in the universities were going to younger men. Joe was nearly forty. What was he going to do for his next thirty years at the Survey? Joe was feeling like a fossil himself; in his letters to Dollie that summer he repeatedly refers to himself as "your old husband." Was he doomed to suffer the same poverty and oblivion that had engulfed David Thompson, whose unedited, unpublishable,

"Dollie with Mary, Ottawa, circa 1897." (TFRBL, J.B.T. papers, F3590)

unsaleable *Travels* hung like an albatross around Joe's neck? Even Dollie said: "Our difficulties began with that wretched thing."

Joe and Dollie quarrelled constantly, even by mail. "You do not care to hear about people so there is nothing to tell you," she writes from Port Rowan. "I used to write you about everything – even my family – but I know now that you are not interested and there is nothing left but Baby and I have about finished her for today." Joe accuses her in turn of disliking "scientific people" and being uninterested in his work. She complains that he has sent her away and is glad to have her out of the house: "I do wish you would let me come back. Would you like to have me with you or are you happier without me?" Joe counters: "I want to have you with me, dear, more than you want to be with me. You would very soon tire of being here alone with a stupid old fool like me." Even their efforts at conciliation have a ring of wishful thinking: "You do love me, don't you Joe?" Dollie writes, "And are not cross any more, you and I must not be cross at each other must we, dear, for we belong to each other, don't we?" Joe responds: "We are both quick-tempered. We will both try not only to control our own tempers but to avoid those things which annoy the other. I am sure we can be very happy in our own little way."

Joe was away, as always, for Dollie's birthday, September 11, 1897; at twenty-seven, she too was feeling decrepit – she wanted friends, fun, *life*! "I do not want gay times for I do not enjoy them," she had written him apologetically in July, "but just quiet happy times with my loved ones and friends near one." Joe offered a vision of domesticity that must have terrified them both: "We are going to have a lovely time at home this winter," he writes from Stonewall, Manitoba, on October 28. "It will be a great pleasure to help you with your history studies, and we shall work together, first at one thing, then at another. I shall work hard at the office, and take my lunch uptown, or come home to it, just as you like, or as we think best, and after a hard day's work we shall be able to feel that our evenings belong to ourselves, and we will spend them as we think best. Your husband's prosy ways may get to be tiresome, but you will not tire of Mary's ever-changing activities."

Was this a letter written by a man about to desert his family?

CHAPTER NINE

July 19, 1898, Big Skookum Gulch, Yukon Territory
Joe lies half-awake in his tent, listening to the rapids . . . no it's a harsher sound, gravel rattling and crunching as the rushing water from the creek pushes it down the sluice. It's nearly midnight, eerie green twilight here on the upper reaches of Bonanza Creek. He's dead tired after his tramp from Dawson City, but his heart is pounding; Joe Irvine, foreman of this claim, has invited him to watch the sluice being cleaned up in the morning. Only hours ago, Irvine had panned out a few shovels of gravel that Joe had dug randomly out of the dump; as Irvine's deft hands tilted and twisted the pan in the stream, the lighter sand drifted away and nuggets of gold gleamed through the coarse, dark grit at the bottom of the pan. Irvine nonchalantly picked them out and put them on his scale: forty and one-quarter ounces of gold out of fifteen to twenty pounds of muck. Worth more than $600, Joe's entire summer's wages.

Whenever Joe closes his eyes, he sees the glossy lumps of gold nestled in the grimy tin pan. It is possible that he has been played for a fool, and Irvine, knowing he was a Survey man, had planted the nuggets to boom the value of the claim for a quick sale. Yet Irvine, a gruff old geezer, didn't seem too happy to have Joe poking around. Was Irvine being honest, or was it all a con?

Joe sits bolt upright, head cocked, eyes open. Silence. The sloshing noise has stopped. Men's voices, calling instructions. He gropes for his glasses and peers at his watch: 12:10 a.m. Morning! They're cleaning the sluice! Joe pulls on his boots and runs down the hill to the creek. The men grunt greetings, then turn back to the delicate work of picking out the gold caught in the crossbar riffles lining the bottom of the sluice. The sluice is a crude thing, built of boards hand-sawn from the nearby spruce trees, but gold sticks to the rough wood like butter to bread. In less than two hours, the men fill six pans with coarse gold, each pan weighing, Joe guesses, forty to fifty pounds. Total value: $60,000 to $75,000. Irvine dumps each pan into a gunny sack and stows the sack in a log shanty belonging to the claim's owner, Dick Lowe.

As Joe watched the sorcerer's apprentices perform their dawn ritual, common sense told him that gold was not likely to be this dense throughout the claim, and the pie-shaped claim itself, a fraction left over when the original staking was corrected, was, at most, ninety feet wide. Still, blind luck or not, drunkard Dick Lowe stood to be a millionaire by the summer's end, and if a standard five-hundred-foot creek valley claim yielded only a tenth of Lowe's pay dirt, it would make its owner a wealthy man. The real risk lay in the streaky nature of the gold – a claim only a stone's throw from buckets of free gold might be pure muck – and the hard truth was that all the creeks were already staked.

Joe had no business being in the Klondike: he was supposed to be far to the south surveying the headwaters of the Yukon River. A month ago, he'd come in to the Yukon territory over the Chilkat Pass and up the Dalton Trail with fourteen emaciated pack horses, three hired men, and a motley mob of fortune seekers. It was the first time Joe had seen women wearing trousers, or loggers' boots and short skirts that barely covered their knees. One woman, in farmer's overalls, wearing a fancy hat, carried a canary in a cage as a precaution against mine gas. The Dalton was called the "rich man's trail" because Jack Dalton charged $250 a head, and promised to shoot anyone who tried to sneak by, a threat he was rumoured to carry out. Joe was more worried by the number of gaunt, staggering men he met coming the other way

"Pack Train climbing out of a gulch, 1898." (TFRBL, J.B.T. papers, F3599)

with nothing but the threadbare clothes on their backs; they said they had spent their grubstake, or lost it gambling.

Joe had dutifully spent five weeks exploring the beautiful Klehini and Tatshenshini rivers in the mountainous southwest. The purple meadows were carpeted with rare flowers, *Parrya macrocarpa, Phlox richardsonii, Gentiana frigida,* but no river maidens trilled of gold there. When Joe reached the Five Finger Rapids on the Yukon River on July 14, he should have turned upriver, but as he climbed the bank overlooking the rapids, he was astounded to see that an armada of small boats choked the river from shore to shore. The craft were of all shapes and sizes, from cockleshell skiffs to scows, rafts, and lumbering blunt-nosed houseboats; a few had blankets rigged up as sails, others had oars, but they all seemed to be cobbled together from raw, unpainted wood. Laden with passengers, top-heavy with baggage, they were drifting en masse downstream to Dawson City, gateway to the goldfields.

Several boats had beached for repairs above the rapids where the mounted police had a lookout. The boats offered an irresistible invitation for Joe to hop aboard. It would be easy for him to spend a few days scouting around the Klondike, then find his way back; his horses needed a rest, after all, and his men would be happy to laze around. But Joe's offer of $10 for a ride had no takers; the boats were already stuffed to the gunwales. "Can you steer?" one black-bearded fellow asked in heavily accented English. Joe nodded. The fellow turned to his companions, and after much gesticulation and exclamation, they invited Joe to be their pilot.

At first glance, Joe had taken them for a religious order, with their ankle-length black overcoats, black felt hats, and long, pomaded hair curled into ringlets, but they were Russian Jews going to the goldfields with bales of clothes, tea, tobacco, thread, and needles to sell. How warmly Ahyout, Kakkuk, and the Inuit women dancing with their plugs of tobacco on the banks of the Kazan would welcome these Jews! Joe was charmed: the Jews might have stepped out of *Ivanhoe*, and the Yukon pilgrims' crude, handmade little boats spread out across the broad, blue river looked like a medieval tapestry depicting the Norman invasion of England.

On the third day, with Joe at the rudder, they drifted up to a city of tents spread out on a mud flat at the mouth of the Klondike River. This was Dawson City, named for Joe's boss. It was an incongruous honour; in Ottawa, Dr. George Mercer Dawson was known as "the fool who missed the Klondike." It wasn't entirely his fault. In 1887, Dawson, with Richard McConnell, had travelled the Yukon's major rivers for the Geological Survey, observing the picturesque landscape with its snow-capped mountains, lakes, and canyons, and buttonholing the territory's few traders and prospectors for information about minerals. Finding traces of gold dust, Dawson optimistically predicted in his "Report on the Exploration of the Yukon District" that since the many of the rivers' innumerable tributaries had not yet been examined, discoveries of placer gold "may be expected to occur at any time." Yet he had made no such examination or discovery himself, and the cautious, thrifty Canadian government, disillusioned by earlier, flash-in-the-pan gold rushes in British Columbia, decided to leave prospecting to the American drifters who were making their way in from Alaska. On August 16, 1896, one of these drifters, "Siwash" George Carmack, found a fistful of nuggets in Bonanza Creek that started a human stampede to the Canadian Klondike.

This summer, 1898, McConnell was assigned the humbling task of examining the Klondike's gold resources in the wake of that stampede. Joe remembered how ten years ago McConnell had chatted about the free gold he'd seen in the Yukon's streams, so unemotional you'd think the specks had been frogs' eggs, but then, get McConnell going on the synclinal of the eastern slope of the Rockies and he'd yak your leg off! McConnell was a true saint in the service of science: diligent, modest, brilliant, and self-reliant, on time with his reports, never overbudget, as good a man in the bush as Joe Tyrrell, or better. Money meant nothing to Richard McConnell. Good thing too, as government employees were not allowed to stake claims.

The Dawson City shoreline was so thick with boats that Joe and his Jewish mates had to tie up to one scow and clamber over half a dozen more to reach land, if ankle-deep muskeg could be called land. Joe shouldered his way through the throngs milling in the lanes that straggled in all directions through the maze of tents; if he could find the police headquarters, they'd tell him where to bunk down for the night. He was in luck: McConnell was here, and Joe knew his tent by the old Survey canoe overturned in front. McConnell was glad to see him. McConnell

"Dawson City, circa 1898." (TFRBL, J.B.T. papers, F3600)

was sharing his digs with a cocky young English schoolmaster, Arthur N.C. Treadgold, whom he and Joe had met on the boat to Skagway, Alaska. Treadgold, a direct descendant of Sir Isaac Newton, as he told everyone on first meeting, had come to the Klondike to write stories about the gold mines for British newspapers and magazines, but his boasting about his aristocratic connections hinted that he was scouting the ground for British financiers. Joe didn't mind: he had never met a newspaperman he avoided, or a rich man he ignored.

Joe sat up all night in front of the tent, keeping watch. McConnell scoffed: You can leave a sack of gold sitting on the street and nobody'll take it! Guns weren't allowed in Dawson either, but Joe had two loaded Colts in his valise. No one was attempting to search the mountains of luggage coming across the passes and up and down the rivers. Every second tent in Dawson was a saloon, and card sharks were operating right out in front. Joe'd had a close call getting off the steamer from Vancouver in that villainous hole, Skagway. He'd been befriended by a well-dressed young man who'd offered to guide him to his hotel. Before long, they were caught up in an agitated crowd gathered around a game of craps in a saloon doorway. One of the players was losing badly. Suddenly he held out the dice to Joe, saying, "Here stranger, roll for me. Bring me luck!" Joe rolled, and won. The crowd erupted in cheers, and the winner thrust a poke full of gold dust into Joe's hand. "Take this, friend, with thanks!" The crowd, murmuring now, shuffled closer. Joe figured that in an instant he'd be knocked down and robbed of his valise, which contained more than two thousand dollars in cash. He threw the poke in the gambler's face and pushed his way through the throng and into the street.

As the sky over Dawson shaded into amethyst and periwinkle, the tents glowed like fireflies. The sharp air was fragrant with woodsmoke, fresh-sawn spruce, horse shit, frying bacon, hot bread, and, underneath it all, the moist, earthy smell of the rivers. Voices carried like bells, especially the women's laughter and singing, and the tinny tinkling of pianos. The cacophony reminded Joe of the carnivals he had been forbidden to attend as a boy. He thought too about the fun they'd had singing around the piano at home, Minnie's strong soprano carrying the tune. But Minnie was dead twelve years now, and Joe was sitting here on a sweet summer night in a weird ephemeral encampment on the edge of the world.

Joe spent the next ten days tramping through the hills and valleys and gulches of the Klondike watershed. He had plenty of company: word of Dick Lowe's incredible strike brought a horde of prospectors to pan even the most unlikely swamps, and a lowly shoveller's wages at the sluices ran a good $15 a day and more. The creek beds were honeycombed with open pits and trenches, each mine marked by growing mounds of dirt and gravel, and sluices on rickety trestles, gigantic centipedes, crawled from pit to pit. In some pits, the men had to dig down twenty feet or more to reach gravel, then dig through layers of gravel to the bedrock where the heavy gold had nestled into crannies and crevices. Muddy workmen laboured like ants, digging, hauling, dumping, rocking dirt in rough cradle-like contraptions. Egypt! Treadgold exclaimed. They must have mined this way in the age of the pharaohs! Treadgold was an Oxford man. He called the gold-seekers Argonauts. Primitive as their methods were, the miners cheered whenever the washed gravel revealed flakes of gold, some of them the size and shape of rolled oats. Joe hefted one nugget as big as a potato.

Joe ignored the pit mines; he was looking up. The hillsides, stripped of their trees by the miners, were marked by white quartz terraces, or benches, shorelines of the ancient rivers that, over millennia, had carved these gullies. As the rivers cut away at the rock, chunks had plunged to the bottom, or had been ground into sand and pebbles on the banks. It stood to reason that if gold had been washed down to the present creek beds, more might be found in the old terraces, and, even more tantalizing, that all the gold may have broken off from a great motherlode still in place on the hills. The creeks of the Klondike watershed all seemed to flow from a central hill the prospectors had named King Solomon's Dome.

"We had no trouble determining the conditions under which the gold was deposited, in fact in making out the secret of the Klondike," Joe writes triumphantly to Dollie from Dawson on July 29. "We have seen too that the country is marvelously rich, and tho' gold to the value of many millions of dollars has already been taken out of the ground, many more millions will yet be taken out of it. It seemed hard to be poor where gold was scattered through the earth in such abundance, but of course it is just as much the property of others as the goods in the stores in Ottawa. One's geological knowledge, however, ought to be of some value in a country where such great riches are hidden."

Joe's head whirled with plans. First, he must stay in the Klondike. It would be dark and quiet in the winter, and he could tramp on snowshoes to out-of-the-way places without being seen. He'd ask the Survey for a leave of absence, and he was almost certain his brother James could not resist coming out. They would make friends with the Gold Commissioner, and pick up some government exploration work. Knowing the right people would give Joe a real leg-up when it came to setting up his operation, and, since Joe, as a civil servant, was ineligible, James could register their claims in his name. Joe had never wintered in the north, but log cabins were going up in Dawson and he had time to order in his provisions before freeze-up. How Dollie and two-year-old Mary would manage in his absence didn't cross Joe's mind.

"I know, dearest, that you want to do what is best for Mary, me and yourself," Dollie wrote to remind him as soon as she received his letter in St. John at the end of August. "You know, dearest, that I love and believe in you more than anyone else does in the world and I advise you to the best of my ability after praying over it. I lay awake all night thinking and praying. . . .

"1st. You may stay in there _if_ the Government would grant you six months leave of absence but otherwise it would be _madness_ I think to throw up a certainty for something so uncertain. . . .

"Now I must tell you the second thing I thought and this in my mind is the better plan – Come home as soon as you read this letter . . . come to Ottawa, resign, making them pay your salary until your reports are written. Frequent the Club. Get around that Englishman Coates and all the wealthy men there, and then start out backed up by these wealthy men. You have been in the country. You are an experienced man and a clever geologist. You can do this I know. . . .

"God guard and keep you, darling, now & always and help you to make a wise decision, Your own _Dollie_.

"My heart will just ache for you all winter, if you do not come back, but I can stand it, though I think you will really return."

Joe came home. After all, he couldn't leave his hired men and horses stranded at Five Finger Rapids up the Yukon River, and the Survey flatly rejected his request for a paid leave of absence. It was the latest in a litany of grievances that Joe now bore against "that hunchbacked dwarf," as he contemptuously called Little Doc Dawson. Impatient, easily bored, and unwilling to admit any fault of his own, Joe blamed Dawson for every imaginable slight and frustration, especially his lack of advancement. Joe had lost his temper in the spring when McConnell received a $200 raise, with promotion to technical officer, and he had not. "I'll make a recommendation," Dawson had promised him. "See me when you return." Joe saw Dawson on October 31, Hallowe'en: his raise and promotion had been rejected by the Liberal minister of the interior, Clifford Sifton. Joe quit the Survey the following day, his fortieth birthday, with the defiant cry "I am worth more than $1,800 a year!"

On January 19, 1899, Joe, now an independent, self-employed consultant, headed back to the Klondike with a light heart and a wad of cash borrowed from his friends and Dollie's mother. He stopped off in Winnipeg to pick up Roderick Thomas, his veteran canoeman and dog driver from the Lake Winnipeg and Barren Grounds expeditions, and four sled dogs that howled in the baggage car all the way to Vancouver. By the end of the month they were in Skagway, ready to start for Dawson City up the White Pass, a longer but easier route than the precipitous Chilkoot Pass, and much shorter than the Chilkat. Joe had worried that the trail, notorious for the thousands of dead and dying pack horses that had fallen, or been pushed, into the gulches the past summer, would still be clogged with Klondike stampeders, but he and Thomas were alone except for gangs of construction workers cutting a railway grade into the sheer sides of the mountains. The deep snow was heavy going, but the view was breathtaking and the weather so mild that Joe could trot behind the sled in his shirtsleeves; he felt healthier than he had in years, and he could do twenty miles without feeling tired. Thomas was expert at making an outdoor camp, but they usually found a comfortable roadhouse or police outpost every fifteen miles or so, and the climb was so easy that Thomas kept asking, "Where's the pass? Where's the pass?" They arrived in Dawson on March 4, having covered six hundred miles in twenty-six days.

In Joe's absence, the city of tents had shrunk to a ramshackle town of log and frame houses, with a gaudy waterfront district of

"White Pass Trail, March 1899." (University of Washington Libraries, Special Collections, Hegg 595)

saloons, gaming parlours, dance halls, and brothels, and a more respectable string of music theatres and hotels. Joe put up at the Fairview Hotel, owned by Belinda Mulroney, an enterprising coal miner's daughter from Pennsylvania, no older than Dollie, who was making her fortune selling liquor to miners. The next day, Sunday, Joe attended the Presbyterian church, one of five

"My Cabin in Dawson, April, 1899." (TFRBL, J.B.T. papers, F3601)

Christian missions in town, including the Salvation Army, and on
Monday he and Thomas moved into a one-room log cabin that
Joe rented for fifty dollars a month. They made furniture out of
boards and boxes, and Joe hung out his shingle: J.B. TYRRELL,
CONSULTING MINING ENGINEER.

Joe wasn't an engineer, and he knew so little about mining
that he'd brought a box of textbooks. No matter. No one in
Dawson City paid much attention to these niceties. The politically omnipotent commissioner of the Yukon, William Ogilvie,
had been an ordinary land surveyor, and Faith Fenton, the popular Klondike correspondent for the Toronto *Globe*, was a pseudo-
nym for journalist Alice Freeman. Old names and identities were
left behind on the Outside; everyone in Dawson, from Diamond
Tooth Gertie, dance hall queen, to Big Alex "Moose" MacDonald,
King of the Klondike, had a nickname, a costume, and a role to
play. Dawson City itself, with its false fronts, canvas walls, piano
players, and painted ladies, was a theatre. What was on the bill
today? *La Bohème*? *The Pirates of Penzance*? Or Dawson's charming
Oatley Sisters singing "A Bicycle Built for Two" at the Pavilion?

Joe took to wearing starched white shirts and bow ties. He shaved his beard, clipped his hair short, and waxed his moustache into two sharp points until he looked like an émigré count from Montenegro. He passed out handbills and advertised his services as a mine assessor in the local newspapers, but he had no takers. The first wave of prospectors who had failed to find gold in the Klondike had rushed on to Nome, Alaska, and wary speculators were waiting to see what the cleanup yielded in the summer. Before coming north, Joe had sent out notices to five hundred potential investors in Ottawa and Toronto, but he'd forgotten that they couldn't reply; Dawson had no telegraph or telephone, and in winter the mail, carried across the mountains by mounted police dog teams, took months.

Worse, his Klondike secret, the old gold-bearing river terraces on the hills, had been guessed by others, and now the hillsides were staked. Joe had one last card up his sleeve, an informal verbal agreement with two powerful Ottawa businessmen, E.H. Bronson and C.C. Ray, to obtain a government permit to mine a five-mile stretch of creek valley. The idea behind these concessions, as they were called, was to encourage efficient large-scale mining in low-yield areas where small claims had lapsed or been worked out, but the miners who already occupied these claims on the creeks correctly suspected a conspiracy to push them out in favour of big financial syndicates friendly to the Liberal government. Because of this heated controversy, no concessions had yet been awarded. Joe's mission was to obtain for Bronson and Ray the richest concession in the Klondike; Joe's payment would be a one-third interest.

For two weeks in March, Joe and Thomas travelled by dog team up and down Indian River and the Bear, Hunker, Eldorado, and Bonanza creeks. The extreme cold, as low as –60 Fahrenheit some nights, was invigorating, and Joe loved the deep blue sunless sky, with its brilliant stars and sometimes a dazzling aurora rippling and writhing overhead, the pole star a constant guide. It was an old, weathered landscape: the hills, uniformly humped and

J.B. Tyrrell in the late 1890s. (TFRBL, J.B.T. papers, F3608)

rounded, rolled off towards the horizon like billows on an ocean. There was always a miner's shack to stay in, with a stove and kindling, and the miners, blackened with muck and charcoal, were talkative. They might have been Satan's minions in Hell itself: plumes of smoke and steam rose from countless pits where flickering fires thawed the frozen gravel, sluices loomed out of the mist, and ghostly gargoyles worked windlasses that creaked like rusty hinges. Treadgold had been right. These mines *were* primitive, and Treadgold was promoting his solution: hydraulics. Joe didn't have a clue what hydraulics meant, except that it had something to do with using waterpower to blast, dredge, and sift the gravel, and the more Joe saw, the more he was convinced that while millions of dollars in gold had been taken out of Bonanza Creek, at least $50 million more remained.

Getting a concession for Bronson and Ray's hydraulic mining company, however, was pure politics. It had to be approved in Ottawa by the minister of the interior, Clifford Sifton, the same politician who had denied Joe his raise, then by Yukon commissioner Ogilvie. It was generally assumed that Sifton could be bought – he was already said to have a personal investment in A.N.C., Treadgold's British hydraulic syndicate – but Ogilvie was incorruptible; in the twelve years Ogilvie had been in the country since surveying the Yukon–Alaska boundary, he had turned aside countless bribes and resisted every temptation to rig a survey. Moreover, he was an old sourdough, a member of the Arctic Brotherhood, the exclusive club of Yukoners who predated the Klondike gold rush, and he was close friends with many of the small-claim miners. Ogilvie was in no hurry to do favours for cheechakos, as Yukoners called tenderfeet, or concession promoters like Joe Tyrrell, and now that Joe had left the government service, he was excluded from the commissioner's clique.

Joe didn't really belong anywhere. Dawson City was crawling with lawyers, accountants, and consultants of every stripe, and they were all fighting one another. Even Treadgold had become Joe's rival. Etiquette in Dawson society was complicated. Chinese were banned altogether, Indians lived outside of town, and prostitutes were confined to tiny cribs, or cabins, on Paradise Alley. Respectable people might tolerate a dance hall girl in church, if she were repentant enough to go. Modestly dressed, they danced primly with their partners for a share of the tab they ran at the bar, and the beautiful "variety artistes" in gossamer silk who sang and danced the hoochee-koochee on stage were secretly admired as much as actresses anywhere. Saloons were acceptable places to do business because the millionaire Kings of the Klondike congregated there, and the Kings were the crudest men in town.

"You would like Dawson very much if you were here," Joe writes Dollie on April 16, 1899, "for it is one of the most orderly, quiet places in the world." The shooting of Dan McGrew in the Malamute Saloon was a figment of poet Robert Service's imagination: Service, a reclusive clerk with the Canadian Bank of Commerce, didn't arrive in Dawson until 1908. Superintendent Sam Steele and the North West Mounted Police made and enforced the law: no gunfights, no cheating, no public disorder. Dawson City was safe, and on Sundays when the saloons and dance halls closed up tight, duller than Toronto. Steele and his Mounties gave troublemakers a one-way "blue ticket" out of town, or sentenced them to a stint of hard chopping in the police woodpile. The churches ignored the temperance crusade sweeping across North America, and their congregations behaved charitably towards the sinners who contributed so much to their prosperity.

Sam Steele had created this frontier Utopia with the help of his old whisky smuggler friend from Fort Whoop-Up days in the North-West, John Jerome Healy. Sheriff Healy, as he called himself, had learned the subtle difference between smuggling and the import–export business. Here he was, fifteen years after Joe had inspected his gang's fake silver mine in the foothills of the Rockies, the dapper, white-haired president and chief partner of the North American Trading Company, with warehouses in Alaska and Chicago, whose fleet of ocean steamers and riverboats supplied the Yukon with champagne and whisky, faro dealers, pimps, and girls, and took away sacks of gold. Healy didn't want competition any more than Steele wanted trouble, and Steele's one-way tickets to the Outside were more easy money in Healy's pocket.

Money was everything in Dawson, and Joe had none. Prices were astronomical, and his living expenses were rapidly eating into the small grubstake he'd brought with him, including the

$2,000 Dollie's mother had given him to invest. If only he had $50,000! He could buy a mining property worth twice that, or lend the money out at 10 per cent interest *per month*! Joe had no regrets at leaving the Survey. "To me it is a very great pleasure to be free from Government tutelage and to be able to work in a way I myself think best," he wrote to his former colleague Robert Bell on April 7. "The same old racket will continue to go on until the men are treated like men with well developed mental powers and not like children." Yet Joe was lonely. To Dollie he confessed, "Very few people attempt to be companionable in any way with anyone."

He was not alone in the doldrums. Another isolated cheechako, Martha Louise Purdy, lived in a cabin on a hill overlooking Dawson with her brother and a son she had given birth to, alone, in January. If this weren't scandalous enough, wealthy, refined Martha Purdy had come to the Klondike from Chicago, without her husband Will, the heir to the Rock Island Railroad empire, and her two older boys. A social outsider, to her satisfaction, Martha had compassion for others: "I have an infinite pity for the men of those days, many of superior breeding and education," she writes in her memoir, *My Ninety Years*. "They were lonely, disillusioned, and discouraged. There were so few places to go where it was bright and cheerful. They gathered with the others in the saloons and dance halls. They joined the party with the first round, and then they drank to drown their woes. The continued Arctic darkness contributed to the debauchery. Revellers lost all sense of time, and attuned themselves to the ever-present night until they passed out from sheer exhaustion."

Joe protested, untruthfully, that he never went to saloons, but after a spectacular fire burned Dawson's waterfront tenderloin to ashes on April 26, 1899, his fortunes took a turn for the better. The firefighters made only a feeble effort to quench the flames the icy river water froze in their hoses – and the crowd of spectators was more excited by the liquor pouring out of burning barrels, and gold melting in the vaults of the British Bank of

North America, than by any danger to themselves or the town. Dynamite stopped the flames from spreading, and the smouldering coals were profitably sifted for gold dust. On May 13, just as the ice was breaking up on the Yukon River, Joe got his first contract, a mine inspection worth $580.50. The advance payment of $145 was the first money he'd earned since quitting the Survey.

"I think you will have to come and live in here," he writes immediately to Dollie. "There is probably no healthier climate in the world than Dawson. . . . We could have a lovely home. There are plenty of good, well-educated gentlemen here who would love to come for a little while into a nice home. We would gain influence with the wealthy men, and I would do ten times the business it will ever be possible for me to do alone. Besides, you are such a sensible little body that you could give me plenty of good advice. . . ."

Then Joe bought himself a mine. He'd been ranting at the manager of the Bank of Commerce about the stupid people who were investing blindly and losing all they had, while with his knowledge he could secure mines worth a fortune if only he had $100,000. "I'll lend you the money," said the manager. Joe laughed aloud, but it was no joke. He borrowed $30,000, at 24 per cent annual interest, to buy a property on Hunker Creek. The seller had already taken out $80,000 in gold, but to Joe the mine was a bargain; he expected to have his loan paid off by fall. "We shall be rich yet," he assured Dollie, "only perhaps we shall have to wait a little while."

Joe moved into a new, bigger log cabin, eighteen feet by twenty-four, and told Dollie to bring her sewing machine, typewriter, pillows, quilts, china, and chairs: nobody in Dawson seemed to have chairs. He sent her detailed instructions about the best boats to take from Vancouver, their comforts, cost, and the names of friends to contact en route if necessary. Then: "Unfortunately, just at present I cannot send you out money enough to bring you in, but probably Mr. Ray could advance it to you, and

I could repay him on his arrival here. If not, we shall have to stay separated a little longer until I can send you out the money. It will hardly be possible for me to get out this year."

How dare Joe ask her to borrow money from Mr. Ray! Ray was their coal merchant. Dollie would die before she begged from a tradesman, and they still owed him for last winter's coal. Dollie felt unutterably sad and lonely. Her beloved father had died suddenly at the end of May, and Joe might not yet have received her letter with the news. *I have no one at all.* She knew it wasn't true, but her sisters Ellie and Alice had both recently married, and she envied them their husbands' strong embraces in their grief. The intimate, affectionate Carey family had disintegrated. Dollie felt she had to bear up, for her mother's sake. But she felt like an orphan, an outcast, and the prospect of moving to Dawson City, bag and baggage, filled her with dread. Did Joe want her to bring Mary? He didn't say. The Bonanza Creek concession had finally been approved; wasn't she supposed to stay in Ottawa to butter up Joe's partners, Bronson and Ray? Dollie made it a point to call on Mrs. Bronson and the wives of prominent Liberals, and to attend important debates in the House of Commons, to keep Joe's name to the fore. Mrs. J.B. Tyrrell's little dinner parties were fun, she had been pleased to overhear, and Mrs. Tyrrell was developing a reputation as a wit. It was whispered too that Mr. Tyrrell had lost his wits, it was the gold fever you know. They'd be ruined soon.

In her bleakest moments, Dollie feared that the harpies were right. What lunacy had possessed Joe to gamble so much money on that mine? For five years, she had tried her hardest to believe in her husband, and she believed in him now, but he had never found a speck of gold or silver or a diamond or anything really valuable at all! Stupid coal. And piles of dirt, eskers, drumlins, whatever fancy names the scientists wanted to give them, that's all. Shouldn't she be prudent, stay in Ottawa, keep their irons in the fire and her ear to the ground?

"You do not know how much I should love to be with you," Joe pleads, "and you do not know how much I need you, for I can be so much happier and better when you are with me." He had bought a new two-storey log house, close to Government House, for her: "We can soon put up some partitions, stretch cotton on the walls, then paper the inside. You could bring strong but cheap white cotton and paper enough with you to cover the walls and ceilings. There are eight windows in the house, and we can have four or five nice rooms in it. So you see everything is all ready for us to be as comfortable as we like and it is not likely that in the winter time I would be much out of town."

Elated by Joe's ardour, Dollie dashed about choosing fur- nishings for her new home. A number of young Ottawa men she knew, lawyers and civil servants, were going back and forth to the Yukon all the time, so she and three-year-old Mary would have escorts and protectors on their long journey. Living in the land of the midnight sun would be a grand adventure, wouldn't it? Then, in late summer, Joe's letters became scribbled, almost incoherent: he might be away on the creeks for several weeks when she arrived, no, he'd be going to the mines earlier, no, later, in September, no, he'll be coming out this winter. Did Joe want her to come or not? He didn't say. Dollie wept and worried and prayed. *Enough of this moping!* piped up her angry self, Mary Edith. *Go! Mother will pay your fare. If Joe's not there, turn around and come home.*

Dollie and Mary left Ottawa on September 1 en route to Vancouver, Skagway, the White Pass, Lake Tagish, and Dawson City. Ever since Dollie met Joe, she had fantasized about living with him in a little log cabin in the woods, and now as the train chugged west through those almost mythical places, Winnipeg, Calgary, Kicking Horse Pass, that had been so much a part of Joe's life, her excitement overcame her fear. Skagway, with its crowded board sidewalks, Indians, and Babel of languages, was the strangest place Dollie had ever seen, and she and Mary were among the first passengers to cross the White Pass on the rickety railway Joe had watched being hacked into the side of the mountains eight months earlier. "On one side was loose, shifting rock," Dollie recalls, "on the other was the deep chasm. It was a narrow-gauge line and the roadbed had not yet been properly ballasted. As the train began to climb, the conductor walked through the crowded car and asked the people not to move from their seats in order to look at the scenery, as too much weight, on the gorge side especially, might easily tip the train over."

Transferring to a paddlewheel riverboat at Lake Tagish, Dollie was astonished when the roughneck dockhands at the Whitehorse Rapids asked the brass band of the Yukon Field Force, on its way to Dawson, to play for a dance. She timidly retired to her cabin with Mary, but the officer in charge of the band, Colonel Evans, persuaded her to attend, promising she would never see another dance like this one:

"Men crowded in from the store, the warehouses and tents until it seemed as if there were hundreds of them. There were only four women besides myself. The men were great, strong-looking fellows, most of them unshaven, and they wore broad hats which they never removed even while they were dancing. Their long riding-boots had spikes in them, and a considerable number had revolvers in their hip pockets. . . . A man would come up to one of the women with his arms outstretched, saying, as he spat out tobacco juice, 'Dance, pardner?' One or two came up to me, but the Colonel sternly refused to allow me to dance with them, though I am sure, from my subsequent knowledge of these men, that I would have been treated with the utmost respect. The oil lanterns shining dimly, the music of the band, the wail of the Arctic wind, and the splash of the water against the boat, made a weird scene which I have never forgotten."

Nor would she forget the next: "We arrived at Dawson about eleven o'clock at night, and I stood at the rail looking eagerly for my husband among the crowds of men waiting on the wharf.

The other women on the boat with us were literally carried off by triumphant and happy husbands, but I was left standing alone. There was no one to meet me.

"One of my young Ottawa friends called out, asking for Mr. Tyrrell. Someone shouted back, 'He has gone outside,' which in Dawson language meant the outside world. Then another called, 'No, he's back on the creeks.' Was I not that night the most desolate and lonely person in the whole Yukon Territory?

"After consulting with the captain of the steamer and the Ottawa boys, I decided to go to the Fairview Hotel, kept by Belinda Mulroney. If, in the morning, no word was received from my husband, I was to return on the same boat. The hotel was a fire-trap, lighted with oil lamps, and as Dawson had recently had a serious fire caused by two quarrelling women throwing lighted lamps at each other, I was afraid to undress. I put Mary to bed, but I never was so desolate as in the first hour I was in that room.

"Then a party of men and women came in from the mines and took the adjoining room, which opened into mine by a door having no lock on it. They ordered up champagne and other drinks and soon the place was bedlam let loose. Furniture was being flung around and the language was such as I had never heard before. I buried my face under the pillow and prayed that I might not hear what they were saying and that Mary might not awaken. Soon the party became so uproarious that every moment I expected them to burst into my room.

"I took Mary in my arms and went downstairs to the office, almost too frightened to speak. The clerk tried to reassure me with such remarks as this, 'As safe as in your own beddy-bye, lady; we know your husband, and anyway we treat ladies on the square in the Yukon.'

"That was all the satisfaction I got. Then three or four of the Ottawa boys sitting around the hall came to me and said, 'We have a room on the top floor and the other boys are all around us. You take our room and we'll take yours.' I accepted gladly and felt much safer. This room had no pretence of a lock and the door would stay shut only when some furniture was put against it. The partitions were of wood, and any knots there were had been pushed out. Anyone walking along the hall could look in. Occasionally I saw an eye at a knothole, for the hotel was crowded and people seemed to be passing constantly through the hall. After putting Mary to sleep again, I sat on the side of the bed and determined to take the steamer out next morning. The only comfort I had was that I had money enough to take me home again.

"As the night wore on, the clerk got the notion that I might like to see a Victorian nurse. All four were busy when word reached their headquarters, but Faith Fenton was there and she volunteered to return with the messenger. What a surprise and comfort it was to hear a friendly voice and a knock at my door! I removed the luggage which I had piled on a three-legged stool – the only seat in the room – opened the door and instantly recognized the correspondent, whom I had met frequently in Ottawa.

"I did not think it was possible for me to shed any more tears. I was wrong, but these were tears of joy and relief. She soothed me and comforted me by her assurance that my husband was back on the creeks. She told me of the irregularity of the postal service and even made me laugh over some funny experiences of her own. She stayed with me for more than an hour and promised to come in the morning to see how I was. Then, fully dressed, I lay down beside Mary and slept in peace. The young men who had kindly exchanged rooms with me told me the next day that they had had a terrific night and not a moment's rest from the infernal din next door. They had amused themselves by throwing boots and furniture around the room when the noise became too uproarious."

A messenger was sent to find Joe, and Dollie and Mary moved in with the customs inspector's family. Joe turned up two days later. *Why are you here? I wrote you not to come!* Joe cursed the post office: hadn't he written to Dollie in Ottawa and Vancouver telling her he was leaving the Klondike for the winter? He was going to England to help a wealthy client sell a mining property, all expenses paid, and a $1,500 fee to boot!

Nine days later, the Tyrrells took the last boat out of Dawson before freeze-up. Nine weeks later, Joe and Dollie were in Great Britain. They spent Christmas with Joe's sister Lizzie and her family on the Tyrrell family estate in Ireland; Lizzie had married a cousin, Billy Tyrrell. Joe had time to make friends among the fellows of the London Geological Society, but his speech on the Klondike to the Institute of Mining and Metallurgical Engineers was tepidly received. Britain was at war with the Boers in South Africa, and his audience's thoughts were on the risk to their gold and diamond mines there.

Joe returned to the Klondike in the spring of 1900 with another Irish cousin, Garrett Tyrrell, as a partner. Dollie remained in Ottawa. She was pregnant, and while Dawson City had a hospital, with qualified doctors and nurses, she likely felt safer with her mother: Dollie had never really left home. She may not have been missed. Years later, Joe reminisced, "Among the passengers on the ship from Vancouver to Skagway were a number of sporting women, including Marion Tracey and Lucille Elliott, the Queen of the Klondike. Sobriety was at a discount even among the ship's officers, and the ship had to stop twice at least to replenish its supply of champagne. Very few of the bedroom doors were ever shut."

But the gold rush was over: the value of mining property was plummeting and prospectors were fleeing. There were no big new discoveries, and now that all the easy gold had been scooped up, many claims didn't pay for the cost and effort of working them. Joe was undismayed. He had high hopes for his own mine on Hunker Creek, and he was confident that the Bronson and Ray enterprise, called the Bonanza Creek Hydraulic Mining Company, a two-and-a-half-mile stretch up the Bonanza Creek valley, would make their fortune. *We shall be rich yet, only perhaps we shall have to wait a little while.*

Joe's Hunker Creek mine cashed out nearly $16,000 in gold that autumn, but his men's wages came to $5,000, plus $1,250 for Garrett Tyrrell. Supplies cost $3,000, then there was $4,000 in

"Looking up Bonanza Creek valley, 1900." (YA, Anton Vogee fonds, no. 54)

interest to pay on his bank loan, and a government royalty of 10 per cent on his gold production. Joe managed to send Dollie a few hundred dollars; it would at least cover the doctor's bill and a nurse for their son, George, who was born in Ottawa on July 30, 1900.

Joe and Garrett spent the bitter black winter of 1900–01 in Joe's shack on Hunker Creek. The temperature sank to –60 Fahrenheit, and lower, for weeks, and the air froze blue. Working hard, with plenty of books and magazines to read, they survived in good health, still friends, without succumbing to scurvy, frost-bite, or the hallucinatory "cabin fever" that destroyed many of their fellow sourdoughs. Joe's greatest handicap was that at –50 Fahrenheit his breath froze on his spectacles; he became so blinded during one trip that his companion had to lead him by a rope.

"Our Cabin, Hunker Creek, Spring 1901." (TFRBL, J.B.T. papers, F3603)

Joe had invested in expensive steam hoses to thaw the gravel efficiently, but for all their care and ingenuity, the Tyrrells took out only marginally more gold that summer than the year before. Fearing that the Hunker pay streak might be running out, Joe bought four more properties, and adopted the common Dawson practice of taking shares in mines in lieu of payment for his work as a consultant. Claims that fell open for lack of work or unpaid licence fees could be picked up for as little as $100; Joe even had a one-quarter interest in a concession owned by two of Richard McConnell's brothers. By September 1901, when his brother James arrived to run the business while Joe spent the winter in Ottawa, Joe was rich: in real estate. Unwittingly, perhaps, he was following his father's ruinous example.

Bronson and Ray, Joe's partners in the Bonanza Creek Hydraulic Company, had made it plain from the outset that they had no intention of mining their concession. They would sell it to

Joe's two story log house in Dawson. The second Tyrrell was his brother James or his cousin Garrett. (CHP, James W. Tyrrell Collection, no. 517)

the highest bidder. For the present, such sales were prohibited, but they were confident that the same well-placed Liberal friends who had granted them the concession would eventually meet their wishes, as they had already arranged to exempt the Bonanza Creek Hydraulic Company from the required five thousand dollars in annual mining investment. As manager, Joe's only task was to talk up the creek's potential value to increase the sale price. The company was incorporated in 1902 with a million shares valued at a dollar each; Joe received a one-tenth interest. Another tenth went to the company's lawyer, the Liberal member of parliament who had fixed things so favourably, Napoleon Belcourt.

Joe refused to believe his Ottawa partners could be such short-sighted fools. He had inspected every square inch of this property, on foot, and rammed in the survey stakes himself; he was convinced it would yield a fortune. Joe went to Toronto to talk to some of the big money men there, but they had all been sucked into new transcontinental railway schemes. Couldn't they see the Klondike's possibilities? Treadgold had already raised a quarter of a million dollars in London and New York, and Treadgold's syndicate, with Ottawa's blessing, had acquired a monopoly on the water and timber rights for the entire Klondike watershed: soon all of the miners, dependent on water and wood for their sluices, fuel, and camp buildings, would be at the mercy of "Treadgold's Octopus." The Klondike *Nugget* denounced the "malignant" Treadgold concession as "the blackest act of infamy that ever blotted the history of the country."

Joe was damned if he'd sell out to Treadgold, or anyone else, and as soon as he went back to Dawson City he hired men to start digging trenches on the Bronson and Ray concession. Once he found gold, they'd change their minds about selling! *We shall be rich yet, only perhaps we shall have to wait. . . .*

There were more than forty concessions in the Klondike, and they provoked a mass rebellion by the small-claim miners who were being bought out, or pushed out, to make way for steam shovels, hoses, and dredges that would strip the muck and gravel from their hills and dump it in their valleys. Sure, displaced miners could go to work as labourers for one of the syndicates, but hell, they had come to the Klondike to get away from wage slavery and big bosses. Years before the North West Mounted Police had arrived in the Yukon in 1895, prospectors were governing themselves effectively by an unwritten code of conduct. Disputes were debated and voted on at open meetings, and if consensus could not be achieved, losers and lawbreakers were encouraged to leave the territory. Theft was the greatest crime; men were far more likely to die of disease on the creeks than they were to be murdered, and the shared imperative of survival created a miners' fraternity bonded by trust, honesty, and generosity.

Dawson City's spacious saloons and dance halls lent themselves admirably to political rallies, especially when the organizers bought rounds, and the miners' loud, well-organized opposition to government patronage and graft, especially the Treadgold concession, was heartily endorsed by both Dawson newspapers. In 1902, the miners helped elect James Ross, a Liberal lawyer sympathetic to their interests, as the Yukon's first member of parliament. The Liberal government in Ottawa counted Ross's votes, and appointed a royal commission of inquiry, headed by Justice B.M. Britton, to investigate the concessions.

Joe found himself in an impossible conflict of loyalties. On the one hand, he was a veteran of the trail of '98, a sourdough who worked his own small claims; on the other, he was a shareholder and executive in a hated Eastern interloper, the Bonanza Creek Hydraulic Company. In between, he acted as an expert witness in court for clients from all factions in their disputes over property rights. Joe had friends nowhere. His own mines were proving worthless, the concessions were in limbo, and in 1903 the editor of the Dawson City *News*, W.A. Beddoe, sued him for libel.

Quick as ever to form a grudge against anyone who crossed him, Joe had been infuriated by Beddoe's stories in the *News* charging that the Bonanza Creek Hydraulic Company's concession had been obtained by fraud. In May 1903, Joe presented a sworn affidavit to the publisher of the *News* accusing Beddoe of blackmail, and agreed to have him publish it in the newspaper: Beddoe, Joe claimed, had offered to cease his attacks in exchange for the grant of a mining claim, for a friend, within the Bonanza Creek Hydraulic Company's concession. Beddoe vehemently denied the accusation. The Beddoe versus Tyrrell $10,000 libel suit only inflamed public opinion against the concessions, and Joe's self-righteousness melted away as his own reputation was smeared by Beddoe's many defenders. Joe won in court, but Beddoe was rewarded with a plum position as press spokesman for the Yukon government. Joe's legal fees were nearly $900. He sent the bill to Bronson and Ray, arguing that he was defending the company's honour. Pay it yourself, they replied.

Bronson and Ray were washing their hands of Joe Tyrrell. Joe tried repeatedly to collect from them the thousands of dollars he had advanced on a line of credit to improve their property, and $7,600 arrears he claimed in salary. In response, they accused him, with some justice, of working for their rivals, and putting his own mining interests ahead of theirs. Joe offered to buy them out, but their price, $100,000, was outrageous. On July 1, 1904, after months of quarrelling by mail and telegram, Joe was dismissed. It didn't matter; the concessions were being cancelled and the properties sold off.

Where had all the gold dust gone? "Sometimes in the quietness of his tent at night, camping out amongst the spruce trees beside a mining claim, Joe used to think the matter over," muses W.J. Loudon in his 1930 authorized biography of J.B. Tyrrell, *A Canadian Geologist*. "The banks got much, the saloons and stores got more, the painted ladies most. But where did it all go in the end? Did it travel in a circle or along a straight path? What was a gold mine? Not like the soil, which, when tilled, gives forth continuous food to man; but something set apart to urge him on to evil deeds. He was not sure."

Or he wasn't saying. Joe edited and published his friend Loudon's book, and this cryptic little meditation was his self-censored version of a confession. Certainly it reveals a childlike grasp of economics, and hints that Joe had been seduced into immoral, even illegal, conduct. In his romantic adventure novel, *The Trail of '98*, drawn from recognizable people and events, Robert Service gives a portrait of Dawson substantiated by memoirs, court records, and newspaper stories:

> For Dawson was at this time the Mecca of the gambler and the courtesan. It was only towards nightfall that the town completely roused up, that the fever of pleasure-providing began. Nearly everyone seemed to be affected by the spirit of degeneracy. On the faces of many of the business men could be seen the stamp of the pace they were going. Cases in court had to be adjourned because of the

"Klondike Kate." (YA, MacBride Museum Collection, no. 3795)

"Red Light District." (YA, MacBride Museum Collection, no. 3880)

debauches of lawyers. Bank tellers stepped into their cages sleepless from all-night orgies. Government officials lived openly with wanton women. High and low were attainted by the corruption. In those days of headstrong excitement, of sudden fortune, of money to be had almost for the picking up, when the gold-camp was a reservoir into which poured by a thousand channels the treasure of the valley, few were those among the men who kept a steady head, whose private records were pure and blameless. No town of its size has ever broken up more homes. Men in the intoxication of fast-won wealth in that far-away land gave way to excesses of every kind. Fathers of families paraded the streets arm in arm with demimondaines. To be seen talking to a loose woman was unworthy of comment, not to have a mistress was not to be in the swim.

Most of Joe's letters to Dollie during this period were lost
or destroyed, and for long periods Joe didn't write. And there are
no letters from Dollie to Joe for 1900 and 1901, although Joe
was in the Yukon most of this time. Dollie, Mary, and baby
Georgie lived in Ottawa in the winters, and spent summers with
her married sister, Alice Whitman, in Canso, Nova Scotia. They
were not welcome in Dawson. Joe adamantly refused to allow
Dollie to live with him there, with or without the children, except
for a few weeks' visit in the summer of 1903. "How I longed to
go with him," Dollie writes in her autobiography. "I argued that
it would be no harder for me than for many soldiers' wives who
went to India and left their children at home, but Joe feared that
the long darkness of the winter and the lack of home comforts
might make me ill, since I was not very strong. How little men
really understand!"

No longer did Joe praise the Yukon's bracing climate, or
winters in his cozy log house. Dawson might have suited Dollie.
No bigger than a village, it had electricity and running water,
telephone, telegraph, Turkish baths, a Swedish masseuse, and
boutiques with pretty Paris gowns and lingerie at shocking prices.
Prostitution had been cleaned up, although the ladies of Paradise
Alley had simply moved across the river to Lousetown, and elegant Government House, encircled by carved rococo verandas,
conjured up Singapore or New Delhi. Dollie was fascinated by
the local characters, with their slangy speech and fancy clothes
adorned with ropes of gold nuggets, and Diamond Tooth Gertie's
dazzling smile charmed Dollie out of her prudishness. Many of
the painted ladies had married decent men, and Belinda
Mulroney lorded it over Dawson as Countess Carbonneau, the
millionaire wife of a French champagne salesman, Count Charles
Carbonneau. The stigma of divorce did not prevent Martha
Purdy, manager of a gold mine and sawmill financed by her
father, from marrying an ambitious Conservative lawyer, George
Black; in due course, Black became commissioner of the Yukon,
then, followed by Martha, a member of parliament. With its tight

little coterie of civil servants, police officers, judges, lawyers, doctors, and clergymen, Dawson was a miniature Ottawa, and Dollie would have loved the year-long whirl of tea and card parties, charity bazaars, dances, concerts, and theatricals, with all-night tennis in the summer, curling and skating in the winter. "Dawson society is especially fortunate in having at its head women of more than ordinary culture and standing," Faith Fenton, now a doctor's wife, Mrs. J. Elliott Brown, wrote in the Yukon *Sun*. "Many of these are women of travel and taste who form a little social world quite equal in brilliance and intelligence to any of the monde in bigger cities." There were plenty of children for a kindergarten and school. Even back on the creeks, women, single and married, kept house, picked berries, grew vegetables, ran roadhouses, and worked as cooks, bookkeepers, and managers. It was a life Dollie had dreamed of since she had played California Gold Rush with her dolls.

Exiled in Ottawa, Dollie angled for a job for Joe in the civil service. The Survey's director, Dr. Dawson, had died suddenly in 1901; surely the Survey would be glad now to take Joe back. Her heart bled with envy and regret when she met Joe's old friend, McConnell, walking down the street holding his little daughter by the hand. Her own three-year-old Georgie had recently asked, "I never saw favver, did I, muvver?" Joe's rare, despondent letters gave no hint of coming back, and he sent no money; in one letter he said that if he left the Yukon, he'd be thrown in jail. What did *that* mean? Did they still have debtors' prisons? Dollie worried that Joe was starving, and had nightmares that he had been murdered. She wrote to him loyally, reassuring him, and perhaps herself, "my heart is full of love and longing for you, dearest."

In the summer of 1904, Dollie gave up their rented Ottawa house, put their furniture in storage, and moved in with her sister Ellie and her husband, Dr. Tom Gibson. She quietly informed Joe of her new status: "I have so much to be thankful for with kind friends to shelter me when I am homeless & love me & care for me & and my little children. . . . I am not treated as poor relations usually are." Generous and forgiving as her sisters were, Dollie was a frightened, humiliated single mother. Sleepless, she brooded about where she would go if, or rather when, she wore out her welcome. Should she find work as a secretary, or take in boarders? What if Ellie and Alice, both childless, were to take her children from her? *I could not bear that.*

Early in August, Dollie received a letter from Joe that sent her rushing to her mother's lawyer: Joe intended to mortgage their furniture! Mercifully, everything except Joe's books was in her own or her mother's name, and she took the precaution of putting their silver and the David Thompson manuscript in her mother's safety deposit box. On August 11, she writes Joe: "It is no disgrace to lose everything & have to start fresh, but to do mean things & put a chattel mortgage on one's furniture, the very beds our children sleep in, the way petty trades people do God helping me <u>I will not do it!</u> I and my little children will lie on the street on bare boards before I will stoop to such a proceedings. I know darling you would not either if you had thought of it & knew how much it would hurt me.

"Oh this old wretched Klondike. How miserable you and I have been ever since it was discovered. I have never had one moment's happiness. We did wrong, I not to hold out more strongly & prevent you from going. No good could come from our being separated & the children not knowing their Father. It is unnatural & wrong to give up a good position such as you had & go off there in the chance of making a fortune but there is no use moaning over the past. God help us darling we have yet the future. I am not afraid of poverty or work but I am afraid & always was of this separation. Suppose we grew that we could not love or trust one another. . . . You have done wrong to keep me away all these years. There is no use beating about the bush. I must say darling exactly what I think & you know I have always thought the same. . . . Oh Joe darling, do do listen to me now & don't continue to make money there and sink it. We will always just be as far off the goal as we are now. . . . I feel confident my own love that everything will be all right yet & this is the way God has taken of bringing us to our senses. Indeed we needed it. If you had made a little money there it would only be that you go in deeper and deeper all the time & never be able to get out at all. Now God has given us one more chance to retrieve what we have lost in six years & with His help we will my dearest one, but only, dear, can we retrieve by working together not in this awful way. . . . Your own Dollie."

Over the next weeks Dollie poured out her pent-up emotions in a barrage of letters culminating in an ultimatum: "There is no way out of having your wife with you except a legal separation. . . . If you do not come out this winter I will come in. I can get money someplace or other & go I will, so you can just make up your mind to it. I know you will not shut the door in my face if you saw me coming tired & cold off the stage would you dear? . . . I am coming to you over the ice. If you have to starve & have hardships, I have to have them too. I will not be able to live much longer like this. Anyway, now people are beginning to hint that you have left me altogether – of course I know it is not so but it is hard to bear. I feel so ashamed to be away from my husband like this & so miserable & lonely. I know you are too dearest. God bless you and keep you, my own dear one now & always, ever your own loving Dollie."

Joe did come Outside that winter. His eighty-eight-year-old father died on November 8, 1904, and after all old William's land was sold and his debts paid, Joe came into a small inheritance. The Tyrrell family too was dispersed: after the Weston house was sold, his mother went to live with her daughter Annie Lennox's family in Michigan. Joe spent several weeks in Toronto, Ottawa, and New England beating the bushes for investors, or buyers, for his mines, and launched a suit for $30,000 against Bronson and Ray. Early in the spring of 1905, he returned, alone, to his two-storey log house in Dawson.

After six years, Joe Tyrrell was part of the shrinking, fractious Klondike community. With honest, but ineffectual, Ogilvie long

Tyrrell's primitive efforts at hydraulic mining in the Klondike, 1904.
(TFRBL, J.B.T. papers, F3604)

since replaced as commissioner by a Liberal hack, Frank Congdon, claim jumping, bribery, theft, falsified records, and rigged elections were part of Yukon life. Joe had a host of creditors, clients, and business partners, including Countess Carbonneau, in a vipers' nest of unprofitable mines and real estate deals as shady as the shell games the con artists had played in the saloons during Dawson's heyday. Joe owned a piece of the Dawson skating and curling rink, served as a godless elder in the Presbyterian church, and relished exchanging vitriolic insults with his enemy, Beddoe. If Joe Tyrrell's private life didn't bear scrutiny, it wasn't scrutinized; how could a middle-aged mining engineer compete for notoriety with world-famous Skookum Jim, Klondike Kate, or Stillwater Bill's teenage wives? Joe's only discovery had been a new species of violet, *Viola tyrrellii*.

We shall be rich soon, but . . . At forty-six, Joe was in danger of becoming one of those dishevelled, bad-tempered outcasts that he'd seen hanging around the Hudson's Bay Company posts throughout the North, or a hollow-eyed spectre later immortalized by Robert Service in *Songs of a Sourdough* and *Ballads of a Cheechako*. The Bank of Commerce had seized almost all of Joe's assets when he defaulted on his loans, but he could not bring himself to sell out his last Hunker Creek claim to Treadgold's Yukon Gold Company for a miserable $20,000, even if, as people said, Treadgold was backed by the mighty Guggenheims. Joe's cousin Garrett was still working his property on a rental basis, and Joe got a share of Garrett's small take.

"Can't we bear a little humiliation together?" Dollie asked. Joe was unmoved by Dollie's "broken-hearted wails," as she called her letters, but then, at the end of October 1905, he received a sharp rebuke from his brother James: "I would be glad to hear that you had sold out your mining interests at a good price so that we could see more of you, and that you might come south and live like a white man."

James, who had spent the winter of 1901–02 in the Klondike overseeing Joe's affairs, may have been referring to a Native woman on Hunker Creek, or to Joe's own backwoods lifestyle; he was certainly describing the blackness of Joe's conscience. Perhaps not by coincidence, Dawson's Presbyterian medical missionary, Dr. A.S. Grant, was trying to achieve Joe's financial salvation by mediating a sale that would allow Joe to walk away with his debts largely paid off and his reputation intact. When his powers of persuasion failed on behalf of Treadgold, Grant, who speculated in mining properties, offered to buy Joe's Hunker Creek claim himself for $20,000, payable over ten years. Joe accepted.

In December, Joe put his possessions in storage and bought his train and boat tickets for Ottawa. Would he be back? Was the Klondike's treasure still waiting for him deep inside those ancient hills? Or was it a phantasm? Dawson City was dying, and the hills were as stripped and scarred as his own hopes. On December 8, Joe writes in his notebook: "Left Dawson at 2 p.m. on the stage with Hobo Bill as driver."

CHAPTER TEN

Summer 1903, Mile 103, Timiskaming & Northern Ontario Railway
Bonjour, mon petit. Ça va, eh? Est-ce que vous cherchez mon déjeuner?
Fred La Rose straightens up from his anvil and eyes the red fox
slinking towards his lunch sack, which is stowed in a rock cranny
at the side of the clearing. The fox pauses and stares back.

Shhttt! Phhtt! Vamoose! La Rose brandishes his hammer
and flings it towards the fox. It misses and clangs off the rock face.
The fox disappears, but when La Rose retrieves his hammer, he
notices that it left a shiny scar on the rock. La Rose knows it's not
mica, or quartz, and the rock here is different from the usual pale
grey and pink granites, darker – heavier looking, with fuzzy
patches, like lichen, or mould, in glowing shades of violet and
rose. He has kept his ears open to the talk around the bunkhouse
about how the construction workers blasting the CPR railbed
through Sudbury years ago found copper in rough rock outcrops
like these, and big New York money men had paid plenty for those
mines. Sudbury is about ninety miles to the southwest, but who
knows? When La Rose finishes his lunch, he fills his sack with
bright metallic fragments chipped from the rock face.

Uneducated, French speaking, La Rose has worked all his
life in the villages and logging camps on the Ottawa River watershed northwest of his home in Hull, Quebec. He is at a loss about
how to stake a claim with the Ontario government, and he has no
money to work a mine even if he's found one. La Rose shows his
sack of rocks to his bosses, railway contractors John and Duncan

"Fred La Rose, Cobalt, Ontario, 1907." (AO, B115978)

McMartin; for a one-half interest, they will stake a claim and register it with the department of mines in Toronto. A few weeks later, on his way home to Hull, La Rose stops off in the little lumber town of Mattawa and expectantly dumps his rock collection in front of the storekeeper, Noah Timmins. In his fifteen years as a backwoods merchant, Timmins has grubstaked plenty of trappers, shantymen, and so-called prospectors in the Lake Temiskaming area, but he gives La Rose's collection a quick once-over and a polite smile of dismissal.

No sooner had La Rose left on the eastbound train than Noah received an urgent telegram from his brother Henry in

Montreal: free silver had been found at Long Lake, a short distance south of La Rose's claim on the T&NO Railway. Two timber cruisers, Ernest Darragh and James McKinley, had been scouring the lakeshore for trees for railway ties when they noticed strange, sooty-looking stones on the beach. "We immediately got down to business picking up the loose pieces of rock," said McKinley. "In washing some of the gravel in the lake, there were flakes or leaves of a bright metal which we could bend. I immediately thought of the advice of the old forty-niners and placed a piece between my teeth, and I succeeded in marking it very easily."

Ore from the McKinley–Darragh claim was assayed in Montreal at a spectacular four thousand ounces of silver to the ton, and Henry Timmins, alerted by Noah, rushed to Hull to track down Fred La Rose. Hull was full of La Roses, and Timmins patiently went from house to house, knocking on doors, until he located the blacksmith. La Rose sold Timmins a quarter interest in his claim for $3,500.

The Timmins brothers were in the nick of time. In October 1903, lumberjack Tom Hebert staked two enormous, visible silver veins on the west side of Long Lake, and Ottawa valley entrepreneur M.J. O'Brien picked up adjacent claims for four thousand dollars. Prospectors literally stumbled over silver. W.G. Trethewey recalled, "As the bluff was traversed, I noticed an almost natural opening or pathway over one portion of the bluff, which at this point jutted out into a swamp. The other prospectors had evidently taken this easier way. The point, from the swamp side, was covered with fallen trees; underneath, there was room for one to pass round the point of the cliff by wading in the water. The writer was after silver, and a little water or brush had no terror for him . . . there, beneath this Nature's covering was Nature's prizes. The thing that men work and sweat and hope for – silver in abundance!" In 1904, the T&NO Railway built a station house at Long Lake: the station and the lake were named Cobalt in honour of the common mineral that gave the area's rocks their rosy "bloom."

The clang of Fred La Rose's hammer reverberated around the world. That sound, more than Dr. A.S. Grant's financial finagling, James's disapproval, or his own remorse, likely brought Joe Tyrrell back from the Klondike. In Ottawa, Joe had no intention of rejoining the Survey, even if a job were offered. He continued to advertise his services as a consulting mining engineer, and as the Cobalt silver rush gathered steam, "New Ontario," not the Yukon, was the hot, if improbable, place to be.

The discovery of any metal, much less silver, in that swampy wilderness had been a surprise. The Ontario government was building the T&NO Railway to facilitate agricultural settlement in a pocket of good farmland west of Lake Temiskaming near the villages of Haileybury and New Liskeard; ultimately, the railway was intended to connect Toronto to a new seaport at the bottom of James Bay. Ten teams of government surveyors sent to comb the area in 1900 had failed to find any minerals. They may not have looked hard enough. Although a 1744 map of New France showed a silver mine on the east side of Lake Timiskaming, less than ten miles away, and iron, nickel, and precious metals had been found in other areas of northern Ontario, the consensus held that Canada's Precambrian rocks were worthless, and many experts who first saw the surface veins of silver in Cobalt dismissed them as a fluke.

Joe Tyrrell was among the skeptics. Grizzled and roughened from seven years of hard outdoor work in the Klondike, Joe adopted the role of the wise old prophet, the honest, frugal man of experience who had learned, as he phrased it, the difference between playing a game with a walnut shell, and the arduous, costly toil of growing a walnut tree. Refusing to admit that his own greed or stupidity may have contributed to his failure in the Yukon, or to acknowledge personal failure at all, Joe cast himself as the victim of others' wicked machinations, specifically the politicking of E.H. Bronson and C.C. Ray. The courts found unenthusiastically in Joe's favour by awarding him only $5,000 in unpaid salary to settle his $30,000 suit against his former partners, and he didn't collect a penny from the ephemeral, defunct corporation. But Joe's attitude of aggrieved self-righteousness won broad sympathy among Ontario's puritans, who regarded mining speculation as a paradigm for vice of all kinds, and the thousands of common people who had been stung by get-rich-quick schemes. Canadian financiers too were in a bearish mood: Joe Tyrrell was walking proof that for every mine brought into profitable production, a thousand were sinkholes. Still, they hated to be snookered by small-town rubes like O'Brien and the Timmins brothers, who were already shipping trainloads of high-grade silver out of Cobalt; why not get some advice from cautious, conservative Joe Tyrrell?

In the spring of 1906, Joe received word that William Mackenzie, president of the Canadian Northern Railway and one of Ontario's plutocrats, wished to see him in Toronto. Joe was on the next train. Ottawa, his home base, was inhospitable. Joe and Dollie had reconciled (they kept the details to themselves), but Joe felt estranged from his old scientist friends at the Survey, although they were cordial enough, and the Tyrrells were pariahs in Ottawa society, where Bronson and all Joe's Klondike enemies held sway.

William Mackenzie, like Joe, had built his career in the North-West. With Donald Mann, his partner in Canadian Northern, Mackenzie had made a fortune building bridges, trestles, and construction camps for the Canadian Pacific Railway as it pushed through the Rockies; Joe may have encountered Mann, the straw boss, at the Kicking Horse Pass in 1883. A few years later, Mackenzie had promoted a rail line from Saskatoon to Edmonton across land Joe had surveyed by horse and wagon, and Joe had ridden on Canadian Northern trains between Regina and Prince Albert on his last expeditions to northern Saskatchewan. In 1895, Mackenzie had built a line west of Lake Winnipegosis to ship gypsum from the deposit Joe had discovered in 1888, and early in 1898, Mackenzie had offered Joe a job in his scheme to build a 150-mile railway and sleigh route to Dawson City in the

Yukon from the headwaters of the Stikine River on the coast of British Columbia. As compensation for Mackenzie and Mann's estimated $5 million in costs, the Canadian government promised them twenty-five thousand acres of free land per mile of railway, a total of nearly four million acres. Joe's job would be to assess the mineral value of this vast tract of land. He'd asked for an outrageous fee – $10,000 a year – but Mackenzie merely nodded assent. The House of Commons had approved Mackenzie's scheme, but the Senate, furious at this giveaway of Crown land believed to be knee-deep in gold nuggets, overwhelmingly rejected it.

Now Joe waited anxiously in Mackenzie's Toronto office. And waited. And waited. All day, day after day. It wasn't his fault: the invisible financier didn't make appointments. Drop in any time, Mackenzie would say to his most important business associates, but if they did, he might be inspecting a railway station in Saskatchewan, or be sailing to South America: Mackenzie owned interests in street railways and electrical companies in Canada, Cuba, and Brazil, and his biggest bankers were in London. Had Joe not been unemployed, with another baby on the way, he might have told the mystery man to go to hell. *Can't we bear a little humiliation together?* Eventually, on May 5, 1906, Mackenzie emerged from his office, all smiles, and hired Joe as his mining adviser for $3,600 a year, plus expenses. Mackenzie gave Joe complete freedom: "Use your own judgment entirely and look about and do what you think will be most likely to lead to good results." His only suggestion: "I think it would be well for you to look around the Northern district."

Joe began with a trip to the silver mines in Cobalt. No expedition could be more civilized: he could board a modern T&NO Railway sleeping car in Toronto in the evening and be in Cobalt, with a stopover in North Bay, after breakfast the next morning. With its first-class dining car, club car, and a library car, the Cobalt Special served as a mobile office, bar, restaurant, and hotel for throngs of financiers, engineers, and wealthy sightseers. The train made an indelible impression on the residents of Orillia,

Ontario. In *Sunshine Sketches of a Little Town*, a satire of the town, which he renamed Mariposa, Stephen Leacock notes, "On a winter evening about eight o'clock you will see the long row of the Pullmans and diners of the night express going north to the mining country, the windows flashing with brilliant light, and within them a vista of cut glass and snow-white table linen, smiling negroes and millionaires with napkins at their chins whirling past in the driving snowstorm."

Millionaires there were, all American, and a good number of Canadian soon-to-be millionaires, but because of Cobalt's proximity to Toronto and Montreal, with their universities and government offices, the Cobalt mine sites, a short walk from the train station, were overrun with professors, politicians, civil servants, and peach-cheeked students with bush outfits from Abercrombie & Fitch. They were a genteel, gentlemanly crowd. Cobalt, a straggle of shacks made out of scrap metal and dynamite boxes, was no Dawson City; this was a commuter stampede of bankers and bureaucrats.

Joe Tyrrell reinvented himself to suit. He grew a bushy walrus moustache, and on his trips to the mines he wore a tailored tweed jacket with a matching buttoned-up vest, shirt, tie, and prim, bowler-style felt hat. Sitting in a canoe, he looked like a city slicker, but standing tall and straight with a group of miners in shirtsleeves, he could be taken for the boss, while his prospector's knee-high leather boots signalled that Mining Engineer J.B. Tyrrell was still one of the boys. At forty-seven, Joe was twice the age of the young pups coming out of engineering school, and he walked and spoke with the solemn air of authority gained by long experience. As a mining engineer, however, Joe's education was nil; he had acquired his licence in 1903 with no formal training whatsoever.

Joe had no mine to run anyway. He hit it off well with Noah Timmins, a diffident and courteous young man, but Timmins had bought Fred La Rose's last quarter share for $25,000 and didn't intend to sell: income from the La Rose mine was already climbing to one thousand dollars a day. All around the lake, the thin covering of bush and soil was being ripped from naked rock patterned with silver like the veins on a pregnant woman's belly. "Here a perpendicular bare cliff, 60 or 70 feet high, faces west," Ontario geologist Willet Miller reported of one spectacular site. "The vein cuts this face at right angles, having an almost vertical dip. When I saw it first it had not been disturbed. Thin leaves of silver up to two inches in diameter were lying on the ledges and the decomposed vein matter was cemented together by the metal, like fungus in rotten wood. It was a vein such as one reads of in text-books, but which is rarely seen, being so clearly defined and so rich on contents."

Miller described Cobalt as a "poor man's camp." Men drilled and hammered and hacked at the ore with their bare hands, and carted it away in wheelbarrows. It cost one operator only $2,500 to extract $250,000 worth of ore, and half the value of the millions' worth of silver mined in the camps was distributed among the shareholders.

"So no wonder the town went wild!" Leacock writes of Orillia/Mariposa. "All day in the street you could hear men talking of veins, and smelters and dips and deposits and faults – the town hummed with it like a geology class on examination day. And there were men about the hotels with mining outfits and theodolites and dunnage bags, and at Smith's bar they would hand chunks of rock up and down, some of which would run as high as ten drinks to the pound."

Leacock, an economist by profession, astutely describes the stock market adventures of the town's barber, Jeff Thorpe:

> I never knew the meanness, the trickery, of the mining business, the sheer obstinate determination of the bigger capitalists not to make money when they might, till I heard the accounts of Jeff's different mines. . . . But perhaps the meanest case of all was the Northern Star. That always seemed to me,

every time I heard of it, a straight case for the criminal law. The thing was so evidently a conspiracy.

"I bought her," said Jeff, "at thirty-two, and she stayed right there tight, like she was stuck. Then a bunch of these fellers in the city started to drive her down and they got her pushed down to twenty-four, and I held on to her and they shoved her down to twenty-one. This morning they've got her down to sixteen, but I don't mean to let go. No, sir."

In another fortnight they shoved her, the same unscrupulous crowd, down to nine cents, and Jefferson still held on. "They're working her down," he admitted, "but I'm holding her."

No conflict between vice and virtue was ever grimmer.

"She's at six," said Jeff, "but I've got her. They can't squeeze me."

A few days after that, the same criminal gang had her down further than ever.

"They've got her down to three cents," said Jeff, "but I'm with her. Yes, sir, they think they can shove her clean off the market, but they can't do it. I've boughten in Johnson's shares, and the whole of Netley's, and I'll stay with her till she breaks."

So they shoved and pushed and clawed her down – that unseen nefarious crowd in the city – and Jeff held on to her and they writhed and twisted at his grip, and then –

And then – well, that's just the queer thing about the mining business. Why, sudden as a flash of lightning, it seemed, the news came over the wire to the Mariposa Newspacket, that they had struck a vein of silver in the Northern Star as thick as a sidewalk, and that the stock had jumped to seventeen dollars a share, and even at that you couldn't get it! And Jeff stood there flushed and half-staggered against the mirror of the little shop, with a bunch of mining scrip in his hand that was worth forty thousand dollars!

Cobalt did have a vein called "the Silver Sidewalk," and a similar mine, the Temiskaming and Hudson Bay, that paid out an astronomical dividend, but while Joe Tyrrell was treated with deference as financier Mackenzie's man on the ground, he found nothing worthwhile left to buy. Once more, it seemed, he had arrived at the birthday party after the cake had been eaten.

Joe spent the rest of the summer prospecting unproductively on Mackenzie's railway lands in northwestern Ontario between Nipigon and Rainy River, and in September 1906, he returned to the Yukon to investigate some mining properties to which Mackenzie had committed hundreds of thousands of dollars with no return. It was a miserable trip. The purple mountains brought back painful memories, and the mines' principal owner, J.H. Conrad, considered Joe a snoopy troublemaker. Joe quickly concluded that the mines were worthless or unworkable, and that the directors, including Conrad, were ignorant, unreliable, and extravagant. When Conrad realized that Joe was telegraphing his critical reports to Mackenzie in secret code, he threw Joe off his property.

Joe returned home to Toronto on December 6, but Dollie, expecting their third child momentarily, had gone to the maternity hospital in Ottawa; she gave birth to their son Tom there on December 8. Joe had been away from home almost continuously for more than seven months; the annual absentee pattern of his eighteen years at the Geological Survey had inexorably reasserted itself. He was earning about the same salary as he would as a senior officer with the Survey, and he began to quarrel with Mackenzie exactly as he had quarrelled years earlier with Selwyn and Dr. Dawson.

First, Joe complained that he didn't have enough work to do. Instead of going off on his own, as Mackenzie had instructed, Joe sat around his office at Mackenzie's headquarters, 9 Toronto Street, impatiently waiting to be assigned. It was a habit left over from the civil service, and a protective response to Joe's disastrous independent ventures in the Klondike, but Mackenzie, elusive, disorganized, and distracted by his multitudinous business interests, paid scant attention to him. Second, Joe griped that Mackenzie ignored his reports, and acted against his advice. But what concern was that of his? Joe was a servant in the court of a railway baron, soon to become Sir William, whose whims were arbitrary and absolute.

I am not a stable hand! Humiliated yet not humbled, jealous of others' success, Joe made a rebellious courtier. He brooded and fumed and grumbled for months, and then, in October 1907, he quit. His timing couldn't have been worse. A swift, severe financial panic in the United States had created an international economic recession, and quashed enthusiasm for any kind of risky investment.

Joe dropped his fees as low as $200 per contract, but work was hard to come by and his assignments took him to the most inhospitable and inaccessible parts of Canada and Newfoundland. As Dollie had predicted, they were starting all over again – and they were no longer young. The Tyrrells lived in a succession of rented houses in Toronto while Joe travelled. He was still borrowing money and paying off old debts, but any temptation that he might have had to go prospecting on his own, as he had in the Yukon, was rejected: Joe was determined to be whatever Edwardian Toronto society defined as "a white man."

Too bad. In October 1909, young Benny Hollinger, one of hundreds of scruffy prospectors who had fanned out from the T&NO Railway track as it crept north, tripped over a clod of moss in a swampy area known as the Porcupine. Looking down at the exposed rock, Hollinger let out a whoop and began scrabbling furiously at the moss: beneath it, he saw pure white quartz sprinkled with blobs and strings of gold. Prospectors working nearby, hearing the wild shouts of Hollinger and his partner, Alec Gillies, rushed over and staked adjoining claims. Word spread like wildfire, and around November 1, an enterprising prospector, John Gray, visited Joe Tyrrell in his Toronto office. According to Joe's account of their meeting: "John Gray, who had worked for me with William Mackenzie, told me that his friend Benny Hollinger had discovered rich gold-bearing quartz in Northern Ontario about a hundred miles north of Cobalt, and to the west of the new northern extension of the T&N.O. Ry. As evidence he showed me some rich specimens of gold ore, which, he claimed, came from the discovery which he himself had seen. . . . He then said that Hollinger wanted to sell the group of claims that he had staked, and that he [Gray] could get an option on them for me, with ten days free to examine the property, after which the first payment would be ten thousand dollars if I wished to buy the property. That Hollinger was at Haileybury, where he could be reached quickly, and that he had promised to wait until he would hear further from him [Gray]."

Joe quickly drafted an option agreement, and gave it to Gray with enough money for a return ticket to Haileybury on the next train. Several days passed, and Gray did not return.

"Then one morning he came into my office, and instead of bringing me the signed option agreement he told me the follow-ing story: He went into the Matabanick Hotel in Haileybury and got in touch with Hollinger, who, however, was drinking heavily, so that it was hard to get him to talk business or to agree to any-thing. However Gray, who never drank to excess, if at all, at last got him seated at the table with my agreement in front of him, and with the pen in his hand ready to sign it, when just at that moment Noah Timmins came into the room, walked up to Hollinger, and asked him where he had been and what he was doing now. He replied that he had been out prospecting, that he had discovered a rich gold mine, and that he was giving an option on it to Gray for some one in Toronto. At the same time he handed Timmins some rich specimens of gold ore and asked him what he thought of them. How much is he giving you for the option, asked Timmins. Not a cent, answered Hollinger. Well, said Noah, those specimens look good to me, and I will give you two thousand dollars cash for that option, so the option went to Timmins, rather than to me."

This story, recorded many years after the Hollinger gold mine had proven to be one of the richest in the world, may have been a tall tale, but Hollinger did sell his claims to the Timmins brothers for $330,000.

In the summer of 1910, Joe received, out of the blue, a letter from the Anglo-French Exploration Company of London, England, summoning him to London to discuss gold mining opportunities in Ontario. Anglo-French had large, lucrative gold mines in South Africa, and as much as Joe professed to value his independence, he signed on as Canadian agent for Anglo-French for a modest $2,000 annual retainer, plus $50 a day and expenses when he was working on company business. Since Joe liked to work every day of the year, including New Year's Day, he estimated his annual income at $15,000 to $18,000.

Joe remained so enthusiastic about the Hollinger property that he persuaded Anglo-French's chief mining engineer, William Frecheville, to visit the Porcupine in October 1910. Frecheville, accustomed to the open, semi-arid veldt of South Africa, found himself deep in the heart of the boreal forest. From the T&NO whistle stop at Kelso, nearly one hundred miles north of Cobalt, they jolted another forty or so miles by wagon over a bush road of stumps and boulders until they reached a clearing, with a crude headframe, on the shore of Porcupine Lake. This was the Hollinger mine – a two-hundred-foot hand-hewn pit in the rock with a sideways drift extending another two hundred feet. In an act of incredible confidence, or sheer idiocy, Noah Timmins and his partners had paid nearly a million dollars, the fortune they had made from the La Rose mine in Cobalt, for the Hollinger and adjacent claims. To raise the money to develop the mine, Timmins was offering six hundred thousand shares at five dollars each.

The price was absurd – shares in wildcat mines sold for pennies – and the whole area, some eight thousand claims, was dotted with the camps of rival companies. The costs of hardrock drilling, extraction, and shipping heavy gold ore were virtually prohibitive, and as yet there was no rail line into the Porcupine. According to Frecheville, glaciers had scoured all the mineral rock off the Precambrian Canadian Shield. Wasn't this gold merely the dregs? Doubtful as he was, Frecheville, at Joe's urging, recommended that Anglo-French buy twenty thousand shares, at a deep discount, and take an option to buy another fifty thousand a year later.

Then, in July 1911, a five-hundred-square-mile forest fire swept through the Porcupine, destroying all the mining camps, villages, and the station house for the newly built rail line. Seventy-three bodies were found in the charred wasteland, but estimates of the unknown dead ran much higher. The Anglo-French Exploration Company dropped its option on the Hollinger shares.

Exasperated with these pusillanimous British ninnies, Joe turned his attention to politics. With the election of a Conservative Ontario government in 1905, the first in thirty-three years, Joe was again able to profit from his father's old Conservative connections. In the summer of 1912, the Ontario government appointed him to lead an expedition to Hudson Bay to explore the possibility of developing the shallow, swampy estuary of the Nelson River into a seaport. As Joe writes to a friend in London, England, Dr. J.S. Keltie, on May 18, 1912, "As the Nelson River is a stream almost as large as the St. Lawrence, it is quite within the bounds of possibility that one of the great cities of America may grow up at its mouth, even if the climate and the approaches to the harbour are not ideal."

This was bullshit, and Joe knew it. In November 1893, returning to Winnipeg from Churchill, he had spent two cold, hungry weeks camped with the Hudson's Bay Company dog train on the banks of the treacherous Nelson waiting for enough ice to form to cross safely to York Factory. In 1612, Captain Thomas Button had named the river for Robert Nelson, master of his ship *Resolution*, one of many of his men who died there during a harsh winter, and in the two hundred years since the Hudson's Bay Company had established itself on the Bay, the Nelson River estuary, shrouded in fog during the summer shipping season, had become notorious for its mud flats, shifting sandbars, and riptides.

The Nelson River, moreover, was in Manitoba. However, since Manitoba wanted to build a seaport farther north at the mouth of the Churchill River, Ontario had been awarded a small strip of land for a port on the Nelson. Visionary as it was, the idea of building a Stockholm or Copenhagen on Hudson Bay was enthusiastically promoted by expansionist politicians drumming up investment.

From Joe's old haunt, Norway House, the little expedition paddled down the Hayes and Nelson rivers to Hudson Bay. While the surveyor and geological assistant did their work, Joe pored over old Hudson's Bay Company journals at York Factory, unearthed the cellars of the original post, and poked about for relics of Button's ships. In September, he headed south through northwestern Ontario from Fort Severn towards the railway town of Sioux Lookout. On Trout Lake and the Fawn River in the district of Patricia, Joe found traces of an Ice Age glacier he concluded had formed to the southeast of the Keewatin glacier he had earlier identified west of Hudson Bay. He describes it in his report:

"As the Keewatin glacier began to shrink, another great glacier formed on the higher level somewhere between Hudson Bay and Lake Superior and flowed northward, and doubtless also westward and southward, over the surrounding lower land. . . . For this glacier, which has now been definitely recognized for the first time, I propose the name Patrician glacier to distinguish it from the Keewatin glacier to the west and the Labradorean glacier to the east."

Joe's report, honestly negative about the Nelson estuary, included entries on agriculture, peat bogs, timber, fossils, and Indians, but no discoveries of iron or precious metals, and when he reached Toronto at the end of October 1912, he learned, too late, that he had been in the right place at the wrong time.

The right place had been Swastika, a hamlet on the T&NO Railway about halfway between Cobalt and the Porcupine. Joe had passed through Swastika many times, and during a stopover in the spring of 1911, he had been asked to examine some unusual mottled rock on a mining claim close to the tracks. Joe instantly recognized porphyry, a reddish, highly crystallized volcanic rock. To him it indicated a break, or fault, through which molten minerals from Earth's core might have penetrated the surrounding granites. The presence next to it of volcanic feldspar, quartz, and lavas, commonly called conglomerate and greenstone, suggested that the fault, which ran east under the train tracks, would be well worth investigating. Within twenty-four hours, the claim's owner had found threads of gold. The discovery caused such excitement that members of the Toronto Board of Trade on a northern excursion spent an hour in Swastika grubbing for gold among the gravel and cinders. Prospectors who had been burned out of the Porcupine swarmed into Swastika, and, as word spread, they were joined by trainloads of gold bugs from the south. Joe, who claimed credit for identifying the porphyry, paddled off to Hudson Bay to tramp around the worthless mud flats of the Nelson River estuary.

What had Joe been thinking? By the early spring of 1912, the entire area east of Swastika had been staked by men who had tramped through waist-high snowdrifts and camped out in blizzards at −40 Fahrenheit, and before Joe returned from Hudson Bay in October, rich gold-bearing ore was being shipped from a pit five miles east of the Swastika station, near Kirkland Lake.

The mine was owned by an irritable, dirt-poor American, Harry Oakes, and four brothers named Tough.

If Joe cursed himself for a fool, he bit his tongue. But at the first sign of spring, he hopped on a train for Kirkland Lake to investigate the Tough–Oakes mine. Joe recalled later: "It was the 17th of April, 1913, and the ground was still covered with snow. The vein, which was in a strong fault running east and west, had been stripped on the surface for 380 feet, and the shaft was down 100 feet, both walls of the vein being conglomerate, often coated with gold. The vein averages 4 inches wide." O'Connor, the manager, told Joe that the ore was running eighteen to thirty-five ounces of gold per ton.

Joe was staring at treasure he'd only dreamed of finding in the Klondike. Could it yet be his? On June 9, Joe returned to Kirkland Lake with another representative from the Anglo-French Exploration Company, John Dennison: "During the next two days we visited prospecting work that had been done on the Hudson Bay and Wright–Hargreaves claims. However, on the Tough–Oakes claim, on which most of the mining work in the district had been performed, the shaft had reached a depth of 160 feet and the ore was still phenomenally rich. While the wall rock was still conglomerate the vein would shortly reach the contact with porphyry, and in the Porcupine district, which was regarded as a guide, the ore-bearing veins became poor when they entered porphyry, so . . . the chances of workable ore at greater depth were very uncertain. Mr. Dennison, who was a mining engineer with a large experience in the valuation of mining properties in various parts of the world, was not greatly impressed with the value of these gold bearing veins, as he considered them too narrow, and of doubtful persistency."

Joe had been overruled again, but his visits to Kirkland Lake that winter seemed to prove Dennison right. "I sincerely hope people will not lose a lot of money on the place," Joe writes to Dollie on February 25, 1914. Again, on May 19: "I am satisfied that most of the Englishmen do not want to really know anything about this country anyway. At all events, I have kept our people out of this Kirkland Lake fiasco."

Within weeks, a new friendship changed Joe's mind: "I was walking on the trail south of Kirkland Lake on the Lake Shore claim when I saw a man standing by a hand windlass at a little shaft. I turned off the trail and went across to him and asked him if he had found a vein. He said, No, that he was not sinking on a vein but in country rock, that he and his partner, Tough [Ernie Martin] intended to sink a shaft by hand for 200 feet, after which they would drive a crosscut northward under the lake to find the vein that was there. I asked him if he thought that there was an ore-bearing vein under the lake and he said that everyone knew that the richest veins were under the lakes in this country. Their little shaft was then down to a depth of 20 or 30 feet. He made the remark that this mining was not like that in the Klondike, where he said that he had been. I told him that I was an old Klondiker and we introduced each other, he telling me that his name was Harry Oakes and insisted that I stay to dinner with him. As he was the cook, he went to his log cabin and started a fire, and then went to the shaft, where he hoisted his partner in a bucket with the windlass.

"At dinner I asked Harry about the Tough–Oakes Mine, and he said that they had staked it, but that he had sold an interest in it, had taken the Lake Shore property, and was using the money to prospect it. That he did not know of any vein near the place where he was sinking his shaft, but he intended to look for one under the lake.

"He was very cordial and asked me to come again."

Almost everyone thought that Harry Oakes was off his rocker, his brain addled from fifteen years of futile prospecting in the Klondike, Alaska, Australia, and Colorado. He had arrived in the fall of 1911, reputedly tossed off the train at Swastika for failing to pay his fare, and his clothes were so patched they looked like the biblical Joseph's coat of many colours. As Oakes joked himself, "I had to outrun rabbits, otherwise I wouldn't have eaten." A hardbitten cuss, even in good times, Oakes was left to his own obsessions.

What if Oakes were right? Harry Oakes secretly spent a good deal of time reading geological reports in the Ontario department of mines in Toronto, and Oakes may have welcomed Joe Tyrrell because it was the news about porphyry that had brought him hotfooting it to Swastika. For all his poverty, Oakes was the college-educated son of a New England land surveyor, and his decision to run a shaft under Kirkland Lake was based on his intensive study of the direction of the gold-bearing fault. After their conversation, Joe decided to keep a closer eye on Kirkland Lake, and one day to take Harry up on his invitation.

The outbreak of war in Europe on August 4, 1914, made no impact on Joe's life. At fifty-five, he was far too old for military service, and his sons, George and Tom, were only fourteen and seven. Mining was an essential war industry, and Joe was able to be patriotic by prospecting for molybdenum, nickel, and other minerals useful in the manufacture of munitions. From the perspective of mining camps in northern Ontario, Saskatchewan, or British Columbia, the battles in France and Flanders were extremely remote. Joe, a former militia officer, took no part in recruiting or Victory Bond drives; nor did he express hatred for the Hun, or agitate for conscription. His views, expressed to the Toronto *Star* in the spring of 1916, mildly echoed the Conservative party: "We haven't begun to organize, we haven't begun to appreciate what we mean when we say we are fighting for national existence. We need a few Zeppelin raids to wake us up."

Zeppelins or not, it was business as usual for the Anglo-French Exploration Company. Every year of the war, Joe was required to cross the North Atlantic to deliver a report in person to the annual meeting of the board of directors, even though his ship had to travel in convoy from New York for fear of German attack. As soon as he arrived in London, the company seemed to forget why he was there; he was left to cool his heels for weeks, sometimes over Christmas, before a date was set for the meeting. Although England was mobilized, and, as the grim years passed, the toll of Allied casualties grew more terrible, Joe's hotel was comfortable, the food good and plentiful. In his letters to Dollie, Joe never complains of shortages, inconvenience, or danger; he expresses no alarm, anxiety, jubilation, or grief, relays no political gossip, and expresses no opinions on the progress of the war. He makes no reference to the war at all. Joe attended meetings of the Geological Society and the Institute of Mining and Metallurgical Engineers, dined with Frecheville and other directors at their clubs, and spent weekends freezing at their unheated country estates. Bored, frustrated, and hypersensitive to slights, Joe felt alienated: "This stay of mine in London is getting very tiresome," he writes to Dollie on April 18, 1916, "for after all I am interested in Canada and the people here are interested in England and are not interested in the least in Canada. A Canadian is a new kind of monkey or Indian who is the best fighter in the world, but of course is not fit to associate with *English gentlemen*."

Joe's chippy attitude towards the English sounds not unlike David Thompson's tone in his *Travels*, and in London Joe was able to track down records of the orphaned Thompson's childhood at the Grey Coat school, Westminster, before the boy's departure for Hudson Bay in 1784 at the age of fourteen. Alone in London on Christmas Day 1917, Joe attended the morning service at Westminster Abbey, then, he writes to Dollie: "I walked over to the Church of St. John the Evangelist, where David Thompson was baptized, and found that a communion service was being conducted so I went and had communion with the rest. The Parson and choir had red cassocks and the parson seemed to conduct most of the service with his back to the audience, but I liked the idea of taking communion in David Thompson's church."

Unbeliever that he was, Joe was giving thanks for the publication in 1916 of *David Thompson's Narrative of His Explorations in Western America, 1784–1812*, by Canada's Champlain Society. Founded in 1905 by banker B.E. Walker, now Sir Edmund

Walker, the Champlain Society published limited editions of significant Canadian historical documents. Earlier, Walker had assigned Joe to write an admiring introduction to the society's 1911 edition of Samuel Hearne's *Journey* across the Barren Grounds, and David Thompson's manuscript, with Joe's introduction and footnotes, had been scheduled for publication the following year. Joe would receive no royalty (he requested an honorarium to cover the $400 he had paid for the manuscript), but he was relieved to see the work at long last in print.

Joe and Dollie had spent more than twenty exasperating years cutting, rewriting, and annotating Thompson's unmanageable opus for a popular market, with no success. The Champlain Society's editor, historian Stewart Wallace, simply transcribed the original manuscript, trimming and editing for readability, but it took five more years of hectoring and squabbling before Joe's extensive additions had been whittled into publishable shape. In recognition of his ownership and meticulous research, Joe insisted on receiving sole credit as editor; Wallace was cited only for "assisting in the revision of the introduction and notes."

The era of canoe travel was nearly over. In the fall of 1916, Joe travelled to northwestern Manitoba by train as far as The Pas. His destination was a little lake named Flin Flon, west of an area of jumbled, metamorphosed rock formations he had reported on for the Survey in 1896. Inexplicably, Joe had never returned to the region as a freelance prospector – he claimed that he had completely forgotten it – and in 1913, a group of local bushwhackers had used his report to guide them to mineral outcrops. By now, test drilling had located vast reserves of copper, with signs of zinc and gold, and Jack Hammell, an aggressive Toronto promoter, had rounded up New York investors. Joe advised Anglo-French that the ore would have to be smelted on site, and a smelter, with a rail link to The Pas, would cost $7 million to $8 million, plus the $3 million the claims' owners were asking: "These properties are exceedingly interesting. It is true that they are now under the control of strong American companies, but other properties may be discovered before long and I opened up communication with the few prospectors who are working in the district, in order that we may be advised of any discoveries that are made. However, any such copper properties demand very large initial investment and are hardly as attractive in a new and remote country as gold properties would be."

Joe couldn't compete with Wall Street or fast-talking young hustlers like Hammell, but he didn't need to: Harry Oakes had found his gold under Kirkland Lake, and after 1918 the Lake Shore mine, incorporated in 1916, was producing ore valued as high as $1,200 per ton. In 1919, Joe persuaded Anglo-French to buy fifty thousand shares in Lake Shore, and Joe became their representative on the board of directors. It was no sinecure. Oakes, crowing and strutting like a bantam rooster, became a caricature of the self-made millionaire: rude, boastful, ostentatious, and loathed. He was ridiculed for marrying Eunice McIntyre, a twenty-three-year-old Australian half his age, and for building an elegant log house, called the "Chateau," on the mine property, but Joe, who often visited the mine, admired Oakes: he was smart, and he had not sold out.

Joe's own prosperity depended on the success of Lake Shore, Hollinger, and all the other mines, good and bad, that he'd bought shares in, and on his continued employment. Manpower shortages had shut down many mines during the war, and after the war ended in 1918, the miners returned to work militant, better organized, and prone to strike. But post-war industrialization created a boom for Canadian mineral exploration, and by the time Joe turned sixty-five in 1923, he was well enough off to own a handsome red-brick house at 14 Walmer Road in Toronto, steps north of Bloor Street, west of the university. Dollie devoted her energies to bridge parties, her book club, and her flower garden; Mary was married to J. Arthur Dalton and living in Kingston, Ontario; George, a graduate of Kingston's Royal Military College, was an engineer; and Tom was at Upper Canada College in Toronto, where Joe had briefly been a student. Joe was not nearly

Kirkland Lake mine, 1924. (TFRBL, J.B.T. papers, F3605)

as rich or influential as his old Weston schoolmate, Jimmy Lougheed, now a Conservative senator from Alberta, but Arthur N.C. Treadgold, who had squandered a fortune investing in hydraulic mining in the Klondike, was bankrupt, and Sir William Mackenzie's Canadian Northern Railway had been swallowed by a quaking bog of debt. Yet old age pensions, skimpy as they would be, were still in the future, and Joe's contract with Anglo-French was year-to-year. In a move that made the mining community gasp in disbelief, Old Joe Tyrrell embarked on the most reckless gamble of his life.

This adventure began on February 11, 1924, with a chance meeting in a smoking car on the T&NO Railway clattering south from Kirkland Lake to Toronto. Joe fell into conversation with Bill Sixt, manager of the Kirkland Lake Gold Mine, one of the town's seven gold mines strung out cheek-by-jowl along the vein that ran east to west beside the lake. The Kirkland Lake Gold Mine was southwest of Oakes's Lake Shore mine, with the Teck–Hughes mine in between, but in that short distance the lode of gold that had made Oakes a multi-millionaire appeared to dwindle away. Sixt was depressed. At a depth of one thousand feet, the Kirkland Lake Gold Mine wasn't making enough money to cover costs, or to pay the interest on its $450,000 debt, and, in spite of his pleading, the owners, Beaver Consolidated Ltd., refused to invest another cent. Yet the Kirkland Lake Gold Mine had produced more than a million dollars in its ten years of operation, and Sixt was convinced that if they only kept drilling deeper, they would surely hit the rich vein again. But the mine's shares were virtually worthless, and Beaver Consolidated intended to shut it down.

Everyone says we're washed up, Sixt grumbled. Finished. Petered out. A hole with nothing in it. It's a damned shame, but there you are. What can you do about it?

Was closing the mine common sense or cold feet? Joe knew that Sixt was a smart manager, and Kirkland Lake Gold had an expensive modern plant. Acting on behalf of Anglo-French, Joe immediately took an option on the mine, and his own on-site inspection a few days later convinced him that Sixt was right. Joe confidently predicted that high-grade ore would be found at precisely two thousand feet, on the eastern side of the property.

What was Joe thinking? He was already comfortably fixed as a director and shareholder in Oakes's Lake Shore; did he need another, problematic venture? He was not gifted with second sight, or X-ray vision; his conviction, based on the contours of the rocks and his underground knowledge of the other mines, was purely a geological hypothesis. Joe had once more been gripped by an obsession. Too old and creaky now to climb hills and run whitewater rapids, he would journey to the centre of the earth.

Joe's excitement convinced Anglo-French to put up half of the roughly $450,000 required to buy a majority interest; Joe would invest the rest himself. He didn't have the money, but Toronto broker A.E. Osler took $150,000 worth in shares, and Joe arranged to be paid $77,777 in shares in lieu of three years' salary as the mine's new managing director. "On April 24th, 1924," Joe notes with triumph, "the management of the Kirkland Lake Gold Mine was handed over to me."

Not quite. Compared to his corporate partners, Joe was a small minority shareholder. As managing director, he had to report to Frank Culver, the president of Beaver Consolidated, who ran the mine's day-to-day operations as he had before, and to Anglo-French's own engineer, J.A.P. Gibb. Joe had permission to sink the shaft to twenty-five hundred feet. If he failed to fulfill his prophecy, he'd be fired, his shares would be worthless, and he'd be the laughingstock of the world's mining industry.

The Kirkland Lake Gold Mine halted production as the shaft was dug below 1,000 feet at the agonizingly slow rate of 100 feet per month. Winter turned into spring with no sign of the gold-rich fault, and critics scoffed that the exercise was a phony ploy to goose the worthless stock. Gibb grated on Joe's taut nerves by criticizing everything he did, and when the shaft reached 1,600 feet, Gibb demanded that Joe be ordered to stop. Joe blew his stack, and Gibb retreated to England, but by October 1925, Joe had become so irritated and annoyed by "accusing and misleading" letters from Anglo-French, he submitted his resignation, effective December 31, 1926.

"I was very emphatic on the point that I would make money for you whether you liked it or not," he rudely told them. "This implied clearly that though I might be your representative I was not necessarily at the same time your servant."

Then, on October 23, 1925, *The Market Despatch* in Toronto ran this banner headline: KIRKLAND LAKE GOLD MINES LTD. STRIKES RICHLY MINERALIZED OREBODY AT DEPTH. STOCK SKYROCKETS AS NEWS OF SENSATIONAL DISCOVERY REACHES MARKET.

> A few weeks ago, a rich and important discovery has [*sic*] been made along the 1,975-foot level by Kirkland Lake Gold Mines Ltd. Upon receipt of the first news of the strike, on Tuesday last, the stock bounded upward with rapidity, carrying the market price to above the 50-cent mark before profit-taking sales could check the advance. . . . The new vein, tapped in the crosscut at the lowest

depth yet opened up in the Kirkland Lake Camp, is four feet wide, and the gold content is expected to run from $50.00 to $100.00 to the ton. . . . THE DISCOVERY OF SUCH A SPECTACULARLY RICH OREBODY IS ALL THE MORE IMPORTANT, INAS- MUCH AS SUCH IS NOT BELIEVED TO BE THE DOWNWARD EXTENSION OF THE MAIN VEIN. . . . BUT AN ENTIRELY NEW ONE.

Too much credit for the success cannot be given to Mr. J.B. Tyrrell, the eminent engineer and geologist. . . . The mining fraternity of Northern Ontario is glad to extend heartiest congratulations to him, for his indomitable courage. . . . We desire to join in these felicitations to Mr. Tyrrell, whose name will emblazon the history of the Kirkland Lake Camp as the man who first reached a depth of 2,000 feet, to prove the productiveness of this horizon.

Joe was in high spirits when he spoke to a Toronto *Star* reporter three days later: "Mr. Tyrrell laughed heartily when asked how far the discovery was from the original point at which he calculated it would be found. 'If I had my original sketches here I could show you,' he said. 'It was within 50 feet of it. I've been badgered a good deal to change my original plan of campaign but thank goodness I didn't. I believe we now have a mine.'"

As *The Market Despatch* had noted, a sell-off had followed the sudden surge in Kirkland Lake Gold's stock. The biggest seller was the Anglo-French Exploration Company. Overnight, it unloaded 100,000 shares, then, as the stock's price rose to 93 cents in November, 300,000 more. Joe was livid: a sell-off by the mine's major investor was a devastating signal of no confidence. It appeared that Anglo-French was trying to cause panic selling, and ruin him and the mine. The company's cautious directors may have been spooked by Joe's determination now to dig down to 2,900 feet, or by worry that the value of his discovery was more wishful thinking than fact, but having made a tidy profit on its initial investment, Anglo-French was free to walk away from Kirkland Lake Gold at any time, with money in its pocket, leaving Joe, his brokers, and the remaining shareholders holding the bag.

Joe wasn't going to wait: if the British didn't want his mine, he'd find Canadians who did. Canadian entrepreneurs generally viewed British investors as perfidious cheapskates, and the market for mining stocks, fanned by unregulated brokers working banks of telephones in their "boiler rooms," was so hot that even the most fraudulent wildcats found gullible buyers. Anyone with a few loose coins in his pocket could buy a mining stock on margin, with only a fraction of the price down, and the fun of watching the tickertape alone was worth the risk.

Joe himself had been frantically buying up Kirkland Lake Gold Mine stock, and in October 1926, with the assistance of influential Toronto broker Frederick H. Deacon, he led a shareholders' revolt of friends, family, and wealthy Ontario businessmen that gained control of the board of directors. Anglo-French immediately sold all its remaining shares. David B. Hanna, a veteran railway executive, replaced Frank Culver as president, but it was understood that Joe Tyrrell, vice-president, managing director, and consulting engineer, made all the final decisions. It was his mine.

Rejoicing at Joe Tyrrell's "sensational discovery," however, had been premature: his miraculous vein of gold had disappeared into a wall of solid rock. Had it been an illusion? A hoax? The Kirkland Lake Gold Mine went back into production, milling ore that it had extracted during the past two-and-a-half years, but while the shaft was sunk deeper and deeper, the ore's persistently low value barely met expenses. Joe urged "patience and forbearance," but while he paid himself handsomely, his shareholders received no dividends. Joe's own one million or so shares made him wealthy, on paper. He had learned that it was easier to buy a mine with other people's money than to dig one yourself, and if you want people to think you're a rich man, act like one.

Joe Tyrrell with William Sixt, manager of the Kirkland Lake gold mine. (TFRBL, J.B.T. papers, F3606)

Gentleman Joe Tyrrell was as plump and pink as the millionaires with napkins at their chins that Stephen Leacock had observed in the dining car of the T&NO trains rattling north to the mining country. Joe smoked long Cuban cigars, and bragged that if he didn't own the richest gold mine in Canada, it was the deepest! He bought a big LaSalle car, and hired a chauffeur to drive him to and from his Toronto office, the York Club, and a farm, Maplewood, that he had purchased near the village of Agincourt, east of the city. Here Joe began to plant an apple orchard, a nostalgic recreation, on a grander scale, of the apple and pear trees his father had tended lovingly in Weston. Still, Joe didn't go in for racehorses or faux chateaux, and the orchard would be a source of income if the mine failed. He bought Dollie expensive jewellery, but she had grown stout in middle age, and almost defiantly asserted her plainness by pulling her straight, grey hair severely back from her face. The late 1920s were a time of wild living and hard drinking for Toronto's young mining promoters, but while they had friends, and enjoyed a laugh, Joe and Dollie were too old, prim, and battle-scarred to dance the night away. The joyous, carefree fun Dollie had so missed as a lonely young wife could not be had now for love nor money.

Dollie, thankful to have a home at all – the house on Walmer Road was in her name – was content to play Wendy to Joe's Peter Pan. She invested in the stock market profitably on her own account – Joe had sold $15,000 of her shares in an Alaska gold mine to pay off an old Klondike debt – and was preoccupied with her family and her health. She suffered from innumerable complaints, from rheumatism to heart palpitations to appendicitis, and Joe noted, without comment, that his gamble on the Kirkland Lake Gold Mine had caused her to have a nervous collapse. It may have been a Mary Edith temper tantrum: Dollie preferred to travel without Joe, and not to northern Ontario. She visited Kirkland Lake for the first time between Christmas 1924 and New Year's Day, as a guest of Harry and Eunice Oakes, and in her memoir, *I Was There*, she skips over this entire period of her life as if nothing eventful happened.

The Tyrrells did not vacation in Europe, the Caribbean, or even Muskoka. Their travels invariably involved meetings of the multitude of organizations that Joe had joined: the Royal Society, the Canadian Institute, the Champlain Society, the London Geographical Society, the American Geological Society, the National Geographical Society, the International Association of Mining and Metallurgical Engineers, and more. For a reclusive soul who professed to love solitude, Joe had always had an insatiable appetite for conventions, meetings, lectures, and banquets, and he worked diligently as a host, secretary, and organizer. The role of smiling public man pleased him more as he grew older, and he was still stubbornly shameless about promoting himself and his causes. As president of the Champlain Society, Joe Tyrrell stood proudly among the distinguished guests of honour at the unveiling of a monument to David Thompson in Montreal in the summer of 1927, the seventieth anniversary of Thompson's death, and Canada's Diamond Jubilee as a nation.

CHAPTER ELEVEN

Would admirers one day build a monument to Joseph Burr Tyrrell, or would he too be forgotten for generations, perhaps forever? It had horrified Joe to learn that Thompson died blind and so poor that he had been forced to pawn his astronomical instruments. Even the paper, pens, and ink he'd used to write his *Travels* had been charity, and although he had advertised for subscribers, he had been unable to finance the publication of his manuscript. Thompson's old partners in the North West Company had gone bankrupt, taking most of his savings with them, and both the governor general of Canada and the governor of the Hudson's Bay Company had refused his plea for a pension. In his old age, Thompson had managed to sell at least one copy of his great map of the North-West. Published without accreditation by Arrowsmith, it had guided the Palliser Expedition and, later, the Geological Survey; a second copy, appropriated with the rest of his late father's papers by Joshua Thompson, Joe had found, almost by chance, in the vaults of the Ontario land office.

Joe was getting old now too, nearly seventy, and he had accumulated boxes full of his personal notebooks, diaries, maps, and letters, as well as newspaper clippings and copies of published reports and articles dating back to his adolescence. But he had not begun to write the story of his own travels. Could he not decide how to begin, or which of his many identities to present to the world? Was Joe the Kid counting his steps across the Crow's Nest Pass the same man as Explorer Tyrrell shooting rapids on the

Doobaunt River, Sourdough Joe of Dawson City, or Engineer Tyrrell, president of the Kirkland Lake Gold Mine?

Time was not a constraint; over the years, Joe had taken time to write more than one hundred articles for a variety of scholarly and popular journals, and he dictated many long letters to his secretary, Myrtle Irvine. Then, in April 1928, a severe heart attack confined him to his house for the rest of the year. One of Joe's faithful visitors was William J. Loudon, an old schoolmate from the University of Toronto, and Joe, in a reflective mood, entertained Loudon with tales of his adventures. Over the course of two years, Joe's fragmentary reminiscences, buttressed by excerpts from his notebooks, grew into a short biography, *A Canadian Geologist*, published by Macmillan in Toronto in 1930.

Loudon, a mechanics professor who wrote entertaining stories about his university days, *Studies of Student Life*, recreates Joe as a fictionalized hero from a boys' adventure story, a combination of Huckleberry Finn, David Copperfield, and Ivanhoe, with an aged Ulysses thrown in at the end. Geology, Loudon writes, is "too technical" to be included, and his depiction of dinosaurs gambolling about the fertile valleys of the Red Deer River is a scientific travesty. Joe's pioneering research on Ice Age glaciers, for which he had been awarded Britain's Murchison Medal in 1918, is omitted, and the book ends with Joe's "most friendly" association with the Anglo-French Exploration Company, years before their nasty quarrel over the Kirkland Lake Gold Mine. The mine isn't mentioned.

Surely Joe must have been mortified by this juvenile misrepresentation of his scientific career? Not at all: he recommended *A Canadian Geologist* to everyone, and sent dozens of copies to friends and acquaintances. While Joe publicly claimed that Loudon had written the book entirely on his own, his correspondence with both Loudon and the Macmillan company reveals that Joe wrote some of the chapters himself, revised the entire manuscript, and published it at his own expense. His contract provided that he would be repaid in full once the one thousand copies were sold, and he and Loudon would share any subsequent royalties equally.

As Joe's sketchy self-portrait, *A Canadian Geologist* is characterized by boastfulness, distortion, vast areas of omission (including the entire history of Arctic and western Canadian scientific exploration), a mean, denigrating attitude towards the few colleagues he bothers to acknowledge, and a haphazard forgetfulness: Joe can't seem to remember the names of his Inuit guides, Ahyout and Kakkuk, his Chipewyan map-maker, Ithingo, or a host of companions whose assistance was essential to his success and survival. Like a colossus, Tyrrell of the North strides through the Great Lone Land of his imagination.

"I have endeavoured to paint this picture," Loudon/Tyrrell write in the introduction to *A Canadian Geologist*, "in the hope that my story of a scientist and pioneer may not only afford good reading but may prove an inspiration to the younger generation of Canadians who, with brave hearts and steady eyes, turn their faces ever to the North."

"The Call of the Wild," as American writer Jack London named it in his famous novel about the North, had seized the Canadian imagination. The phrase was used to even greater effect by Robert Service, whose novel, *The Trail of Ninety-Eight*, and three volumes of verse, *Songs of a Sourdough*, *Ballads of a Cheechako*, and *Rhymes of a Rolling Stone*, all published between 1907 and 1912, achieved international immortality for his lusty, macabre dramas of Everyman's life-and-death struggle against the wild. Writing his ballads in a rhyming, slangy vernacular, Service simplified them into fables by giving his characters familiar nicknames – Blasphemous Bill, Muckluck Mag, One-Eyed Mike – and pitting them against a living, humanized Nature. In "Clancy of the Mounted Police," Service writes:

> Said the Wild, "I will crush this Clancy, so fearless and
>   insolent;
> For him will I loose my fury, and blind and buffet and beat;

Pile up my snows to stay him; then when his strength is spent,
Leap on him from my ambush and crush him under my feet."

Clancy triumphs over Fear and Death, bringing a half-frozen, crazed prospector safely to barracks at the cost of his own frostbitten toes. Service's sometimes comic melodramas were as likely to feature lunatics, gamblers, murderers, and outcasts, but his message was Darwinian: only the strong survive. Service's and London's wilderness tales appealed to restless, well-fed city people by conjuring up a lost age of danger and adventure, and in Canada their tradition was carried on, in a gentler, more innocent voice, in the beloved and admired nature stories of Sir Charles G.D. Roberts, Ernest Thompson Seton, and, by the 1930s, Grey Owl, an Englishman, Archie Belaney, posing as an Indian.

The mystique of "the true north, strong and free" sprang from a practical, economic need to make Canada productive, and after the young Norwegian, Roald Amundsen, successfully traversed the Northwest Passage in 1906, the North became a more accessible frontier. Settlement of the prairies in the west peaked by 1914, and hopes of Canada becoming "the breadbasket of the world" faded into the unromantic reality of killer frosts, grasshoppers, and drought. At the same time, Canadian-born explorer and anthropologist Vilhjalmur Stefansson kindled enthusiasm for the North with his popular but controversial books, *My Life with the Eskimo*, published in 1913, and *The Friendly Arctic*, in 1921. Stefansson, an American citizen of Icelandic ancestry, claimed to have discovered "blond" Copper Eskimos, descendants of Norse migrants, in the Coronation Gulf, and to have lived comfortably off the sea and land by following the customs of the Inuit. Stefansson's Icelandic–Inuit Utopia was a fantasy, but the idea that the North could be colonized excited Canadians who for years had dreamed of railways to Hudson Bay – praised by geologist Robert Bell as "Canada's Mediterranean" – linking millions of people in prosperous farms and cities strung across the Barren Grounds.

In 1929, a railway intended to carry grain to ships bound for England was completed from Winnipeg to Samuel Hearne's old trading post at Churchill. The Ontario government, failing in its foolish attempt to build a seaport (against Joe Tyrrell's advice) at the mouth of the Nelson River, extended the T&NO line to the Cree settlement of Moose Factory on James Bay. Rail lines and rough roads brought missionaries, teachers, nurses, doctors, and city goods to previously isolated northern settlements, and bush planes, equipped with floats, began opening northern lakes and rivers to prospectors, sportsmen, traders, and tourists.

The Wild, however, was not easily tamed. In 1911, four mounted policemen froze to death on a winter patrol to Dawson City from Fort McPherson in the North-West Territories. In 1913, two Roman Catholic priests, Fathers Rouvière and le Roux, were murdered by Copper Inuit; the following year, eleven members of a Canadian scientific expedition, commanded by Stefansson, died after their ship, the *Karluk*, was crushed in Arctic pack ice. In 1927, an Englishman, John Hornby, and his nephew, Eric Christian, starved to death on the Thelon River in the Barren Grounds. The most successful inhabitants of the North were brown-skinned, black-haired aboriginal peoples, but Canada's northern vision was drawn from the British imperialist prejudice that only white-skinned, fair-haired Nordic or Saxon races were smart and strong enough to conquer the world. This view sat well with most Canadians, because it reflected themselves. Joe Tyrrell expressed it this way:

"Canada was settled by people from the British Islands and the nearer ports of Europe. They were not looking for lives of ease and idleness but were anxious to work. They were not afraid of personal inconvenience, hardship, suffering, starvation or danger from men or beasts. They had great determination and force of character (moral force) and were able to think for themselves, plan out their own work and their modes of life. Physically and mentally they were the strong and independent ones picked by a natural selection from the inhabitants of the countries that they left.

"In coming to Canada they came to a country of great natural resources, in which their abilities, both mental and physical, could be adequately nourished and fully developed. Such stock, well nourished in this land of abundance, should produce men and women of outstanding ability and power who will be leaders in the affairs of the world."

The moral of *A Canadian Geologist* was exactly this: barefoot blue-eyed boy travels far, works hard, strikes it rich. In 1927, Joe felt flush enough to donate $10,000 to the London Geological Society to encourage British geologists to study in Canada. The bursary, with its implication that the British were insular and ignorant of Canada, was a slap at the Anglo-French company, although Joe didn't name it in a December 9, 1927, story in *The Financial Post* headlined: 64 MILLIONS SLIPPED FROM HANDS OF BRITISH GROUP; TYRRELL FUND IS OUTCOME.

"Some years ago when I was in England," Joe told reporter Wallace Laut, "I presented them with a memorandum of what the options I had secured for them or the properties I recommended them to buy would have amounted to in cold cash. At that time their profit would have been $64,000,000. I have not figured out what the amount would be to-day, but I believe it will considerably exceed that figure.

"We should not go to England or any other country with hat in hand and beg for capital. We now are capable of providing the capital required for mining development from the wealth of our own people . . . we must not take the attitude of the suppliant. . . . Let us not go begging to England but turn to our own people."

Joe's $64 million estimate was an unsubstantiated and likely inflated hypothesis, but his message of patriotic independence was exactly what the *Post* wanted to hear. Laut praised Joe as "Canada's dean of geologists," "the outstanding explorer of new frontiers now living in Canada," "the discoverer of the great coal deposits on the Crow's Nest Pass" who "helped to get Canada's gold out of the Klondyke, and came through that mining welter with an enhanced reputation." Tyrrell of the North was a natural symbol and spokesman for the post-war, post-colonial "New Canada." In 1928, Joe presented to Canada's Royal Society a gold medal, named for himself, to be awarded for excellence in historical scholarship; on the reverse was engraved his portrait photograph in which he wore his caribou-skin Inuit costume.

Vain as it was, the Tyrrell Medal did enhance the prestige of the obscure and ignored field of Canadian history. Joe had thoroughly studied the history of the North-West, and had lived it; he had explored and surveyed blank spaces on the maps, traced many of the fur trade routes, interviewed countless traders and Native people, examined the sites of original trading posts, and, after years of banging loudly on the door, he had cracked open the Hudson's Bay Company's priceless archive of journals and correspondence. Joe's field work set a rigorous standard for on-site, feet-on-the-ground primary research – he was an archaeologist decades before the discipline was recognized in Canada – and young scholars like Harold Innis, whose classic history *The Fur Trade in Canada* was published in 1930, were deeply indebted to Joe Tyrrell's innovative work.

In August 1933, Joe accompanied Innis on a canoe trip down the Saskatchewan River from Prince Albert to The Pas to revisit some of the old forts he had located in the 1890s. At seventy-five, Joe had some trepidation about undertaking the trip, but he was in excellent health, and involved with numerous mining ventures. True to the adage that gold is the only safe haven, Canada's gold mines had easily weathered the 1929 stock market crash, and were sailing briskly through a catastrophic world-wide depression. Joe's Kirkland Lake Gold Mine – he was now officially president as well as managing director and consulting engineer – was a relatively poor sister, unable to pay a shareholders' dividend, yet

Joe blithely used Kirkland Lake Gold stock to underwrite specu-
lative adventures in his other mining properties.

One of these was the Brett–Trethewey Company, and on
October 17, 1932, Joe wrote to a partner, A.J. Brett: "We [Kirkland
Lake Gold] have been rather fortunate in finding a new gold mine
in a new district, 125 miles north of Sudbury. We, and the
Brett–Trethewey Company, have been working at it for a year
now and it has been looking better all the time with development.
. . . We have just incorporated it as the Kenty Gold Mines,
Limited, and the Kirkland Lake Gold Mining Company is finan-
cing it. If it turns out as good as it looks now, it will be a big thing
for both our companies."

Earlier, Joe had warned friends that Brett–Trethewey was a
"straight gamble," yet he committed nearly $1 million of
Kirkland Lake Gold Mine stock to the Kenty Mine. He had
another interest in a company named El Bonanza, and was enthusiastic about "very intriguing" ore discoveries by a rival company,
Eldorado, at Great Bear Lake.

"The public is frightened at the remoteness of the district,"
he writes to Brett, "but really it is very much more accessible
than the Klondyke ever was, for the McKenzie [sic] river, right
from the end of the railroad, is a great navigable waterway. The
Eldorado Company has undoubtedly got two very rich properties. We sent in a man by aeroplane last fall and he staked thirty-
five claims in as similar geological conditions as he was able to
find, but still several miles away from the Eldorado claims. Our
men started prospecting on the ground this summer and the last
word we had was that they had found two veins, samples from
which assayed from four to twenty ounces in silver. The men are
staying in at Great Bear Lake until next September, and we are
hoping that they will find something really good on our property
between now and then, but of course that is mere chance."

The intriguing mineral at Great Bear Lake was uranium.
Nearly forty years earlier, in the summer of 1893, Joe and James

Tyrrell had hurriedly paddled past an outcrop of pitchblende, uranium's host rock, on the north shore of Lake Athabasca. The ore, had they stopped to examine it, would have been unremarkable: Pierre and Marie Curie did not isolate radium until 1898, and while the magic of the X-ray was well known by 1932, experiments had not yet revealed practical uses for all the radioactive properties of uranium. Now, prospectors swarming over Great Bear Lake's rocky shores were innocently ushering in the Atomic Age, a hundred miles west of the valley where, in the Age of Enlightenment, Samuel Hearne and Matonabbee had followed the Coppermine River to the Arctic Ocean.

How could Joe resist a flying visit? On August 31, 1938, he writes to Dollie from Yellowknife on Great Slave Lake: "We had a very nice trip from here to the Eldorado Radium Mine on the shore of Great Bear Lake, a distance of 300 miles which our plane made in two and a half hours." At the mine, Joe shared a room with "a Mr. Jackson, an artist from Toronto, who is up north painting pictures of the grim scenery," and the next day he enjoyed "a splendid tramp" through the mine. He wasn't the only pilgrim: "A bunch of Freemasons had come up from the south, our pilot, May, being one of them, to hold a special meeting of a lodge at the mouth of the Coppermine river to initiate Mr. Walli (manager) into masonry, and they urged me to go along as it would cost me little or nothing. The day was perfect so we all went in the morning, held the meeting in the afternoon and came back before seven o'clock, the flying time being an hour and a quarter each way. I never expected to see the little village at the mouth of the Coppermine river, but nevertheless was glad to see it and on a bright, warm day which they tell me is rare up there."

It was characteristic of rich Joe Tyrrell to catch a free ride: in a time of desperate poverty and unemployment, he was as stingy as Scrooge. Ironically, Joe's fortune was made by government efforts to stabilize the financial free fall by pegging the price of gold at $35 an ounce, $15 higher than it had been since

the Ontario mines were developed early in the 1920s. The gold
standard meant a windfall for all the gold mines. In 1934,
Kirkland Lake Gold Mine began paying its first dividend, a
meagre three cents a share, but Joe's private investments in Lake
Shore and Hollinger, two of the richest gold mines in the world,
kept him in clover. Still, Joe clung to the high salaries he paid
himself for his three jobs at Kirkland Lake Gold until 1935,
when a long-smouldering shareholders' revolt, led by Frederick
H. Deacon, the Toronto broker who had financed and master-
minded Joe's takeover of the company in 1926, forced him to
step aside as managing director in favour of a young engineer,
Victor H. Emery. With the value of Kirkland Lake Gold's shares
stuck at around $1, about what they had been worth ten years ear-
lier, Deacon criticized both the management and the board of
directors (which he had recruited himself) as "deadwood," and
castigated their failure to develop or acquire profitable mines elsewhere. Deacon's coup failed, and Joe remained president, but to
pacify his critics, he fired Bill Sixt, the optimistic, hard-working
manager who had tipped him off about the mine's potential, and
who, for nearly twenty years, had overseen the drudging on-site
work that had kept the mine in business.

Joe had never lived in Kirkland Lake, a feisty, ramshackle
town built in classic "mine gothic" style – the picturesque lake
was buried by tailings from the mines – and he had bunked in at
the mine during his visits from Toronto. Unlike Harry Oakes,
who donated generously to civic projects, Joe gave nothing to the
community. But then Oakes infuriated Canadians by refusing to
pay his income tax. Oakes huffed off to the British Bahamas,
where he was knighted for his contribution to a Royal charity,
then gruesomely murdered by an unknown assailant. Joe unos-
tentatiously divided his time between his modest home on
Walmer Road and his Agincourt orchard, and grudgingly paid his
taxes, but he was coldly indifferent to the human suffering of the
Great Depression.

"Kirkland Lake, Main Street, looking east, 1927." (LAC, PA-043889)

"I disapprove of mass charity just as I disapprove of mass religion," he curtly replied to appeals for aid to the sick and destitute. Advocating "personal charity" to friends and family, Joe gave only to causes that bore the Tyrrell name: two student scholarships in honour of his parents, and, later, a scholarship for economic geology in his own name at the University of Toronto. At the same time, he paid journalist Arthur Hawkes $2,000 to write a biography of his father, *William Tyrrell of Weston*, that even Joe thought was sycophantic, and he financed the publication of Dollie's memoir, *I Was There*. Even so, there was no gift of a Tyrrell wing for the Royal Ontario Museum, no endowed university chair, and no Tyrrell Foundation to perpetuate Joe's name and further his work.

Miserliness seems uncharacteristic of a man who had been irresponsibly profligate with his own and other people's money. Yet Joe had usually spent money to further his own interests and reputation, and when he didn't get his way, he'd resorted to sulks, temper tantrums, and blood feuds with those who crossed him.

He had triumphed, but old age couldn't be bought or bullied; his brain was lucid, and his bad memory no worse, but his legs shook, his eyesight was failing, and he had become stone deaf. Irritable and despotic, his ego inflated to monstrous proportions, Old Joe had become *Tyrannosaurus tyrrelli.*

Supplicants brave or desperate enough to ask Joe for help usually had a personal connection through mutual acquaintances. They were respectable people temporarily without jobs or savings, but Joe regarded them all as bums. "Can you tell me anything about Dowling's son?" Joe writes to E.M. Kindle at the Geological Survey. "He is here in Toronto and claims he is unable to get any work so is borrowing money from anybody who will loan it to him. Can you give me any idea as to whether he is worth assisting or not? I do not want to be too hard on the son of an old friend of mine, but at the same time he looks to be an able-bodied man and should be able to earn his own living without any trouble, and it might do him more good to refuse to give him any assistance than to keep giving him money."

Did Joe not wonder why so many young, able-bodied men stood around his mine gates, hoping for work? Riding to his Toronto office in his chauffeured Cadillac, did he not see the soup kitchens, or homeless people crowded on the streets? *I am afraid that life off alone in the wilderness for half the year makes me entirely incapable of understanding the feelings of others, even those most dear.* Joe's wilderness remained, within.

On November 20, 1933, seventy-year-old James Tyrrell writes his brother Joe from Hamilton: "I am trying to rent my vacant apartment and to sell my lawn lot, but meanwhile I have no money to buy food or fuel, and am wondering if you can lend me $100.00 until I get a job or make a sale. I hate to ask you, but I do not know where else to get relief. My office is barely paying expenses."

James had made a good living as a surveyor, and had often worked on mining properties for Joe. An avid early motorist, James had drawn Ontario's first road map, and he had devoted years to scouting railway routes from Winnipeg to Hudson Bay. His memoir, *Across the Sub-Arctic of Canada*, an exciting yet authoritative narrative of the Tyrrell brothers' 1893 Barren Grounds expedition, had been published in 1897 to popular and critical acclaim. In 1900, James had led a Canadian government expedition by dog team and canoe across the Barrens from Great Slave Lake to Chesterfield Inlet, completing the map he and Joe had failed to finish in 1893. Following the Thelon, the mysterious, driftwood-laden river from the west that joined the Doobaunt before they flowed together towards Baker Lake, James discovered the earthly paradise Samuel Hearne had described in his *Journey*, a sheltered, timbered area rich in fish and game, home to the endangered musk oxen. In his report, James recommended, "For the preservation of the musk oxen – which may be so easily slaughtered – and are already rapidly diminishing in numbers, I would suggest that the territory between the Thelon and Back rivers be set apart by the Government as a game preserve." The Thelon Game Sanctuary became James's Barren Grounds legacy, but while James had prospected in the Porcupine and, later, Red Lake, Ontario, he had missed the gold that had made others rich.

On November 22, Joe replies: "I was sorry to learn from your letter that you say your office is barely paying expenses, but I am satisfied that if it will not support two, or three, it will support one and you are that one. . . . Besides, you told me two years ago that you had a good income from your houses. Perhaps the explanation of where the rents have gone is furnished by a visit which Hugh Brown made to my office during the summer to ask for money, and at the same time he intimated that he and your children were taking everything you had, but that was not enough for them. You must take your business back firmly into your own hands. Until you do, nobody can give you any real assistance. Your affectionate brother, Joe."

James replies the next day:

"My dear Joe,

"I wish to thank you for your prompt reply. It is well that I should understand my true situation.

"You were good enough to lend me $100 when I was in a tight pinch a year ago, and I paid you back out of the first money I received, and I thought perhaps you could accommodate me again, but I hope I have not caused you one unhappy moment by asking you. You seem to have a very strong impression about my children, or May in particular. I am sorry to say that I have not had a dollar to give to any of them for many months, and May has been scouring the city looking for some kind of employment to support herself and little children. I only mention this to correct your impression – not to change your refusal of the loan. Yours as ever, James."

James's family was suffering. May's husband had deserted her, and James's older daughter, Helen, had died, leaving a grieving husband, Hugh Brown, and a young son; James's sons, William and Douglas, both wounded in the First World War, were struggling to make ends meet. James, himself a widower – his wife, Belle, had died in 1928 – had taken May, Hugh, and their children into his own big house. But in 1932, he remarried, and his wife, Anne, a vivacious younger woman with brazenly dyed red hair, so offended his family that May, Hugh, and their children moved out.

Joe owed most of his early reputation as an explorer to James's modest, sympathetic portrait of him in *Across the Sub-Arctics of Canada*, but he had reason to be angry with James: in the past, he had more than once guaranteed thousands of dollars in bank loans for James's investments, including a poultry farm, that had failed. He now forgave a $7,000 mortgage he held on James's house, and helped him find work as a mine surveyor in northern Ontario. For the next two years, James and Anne lived in a log cabin near Geraldton, one of the coldest, most isolated places in Canada. On May 2, 1936, James writes Joe again, asking for "employment in any capacity that you may think suitable . . . there

J.B.T. and M.E.T., late in life. (TFRBL, J.B.T. papers, F3609)

is not now a living in my private practice." Joe's reply, missing from the record, has to be inferred from James's letter of May 5: "I confess that I had no idea that you are in the position you speak of. . . . I will plug along as best I can and trust in the Lord."

Joe helped James's sons cover their medical bills and university expenses, and James carried on until 1943, when, at the age of eighty, he was too disabled to work. "I have no income," he writes to Joe on April 14. "Would you have any place for me again at the mine?" Joe, still president of the Kirkland Lake Gold Mine at the age of eighty-five, found him a token position. The next year, James suffered a paralyzing stroke and died on January 16, 1945, in the village of Bartonville near Hamilton.

"James looked young, strong and resourceful, just as he had been with me many years ago," Joe writes in his diary on January 18 after viewing the body. In a letter to a mutual friend, Joe praises James as "a tireless and resourceful traveller, a cheerful and helpful companion," yet there is no expression of love or grief; Joe might have been describing one of a dozen old canoemen, or a sled dog. Joe clipped friends' and relatives' obituaries from newspapers and pasted them in his diary, or in scrapbooks, but wrote no comments. Dollie's sisters, Ellie and Alice, died within months of each other in 1942, and Joe's favourite sister, Lizzie, in December 1944.

Dollie, incoherent and confused, but cheerful, spent summers at the orchard, winters in her room. Joe, when he wasn't distracted by the myriad illnesses of old age, fumed about taxes, labour unrest – a strike briefly shut down the Kirkland Lake mines in 1941 – and gas rationing. He was as demanding and authoritarian towards his adult sons, George and Tom, as his father had been towards him. At first he had insisted that each, in turn, work in the office at the Kirkland Lake Gold Mine: when George, who had suffered lead poisoning at a mine smelter in Utah, resigned because of ill health, Joe made him manager of his expanding Agincourt apple orchard, an operation separate from Joe's own adjacent property. Joe invested a king's ransom buying

thousands of trees, but George, his wife Dora, and their two children, who lived year-round on the property, were responsible for
the arduous annual cycle of grafting and spraying, picking and
marketing the autumn harvest. While Joe hosted swank garden
parties for *le beau monde* at apple blossom time, George and his
family lived on apples, chickens from their henhouse, and the
produce of their garden.

Tom, a sensitive spirit, quit his job at his father's mine, and
made a career for himself in planning and development with the
Ontario government. During the Second World War, George
and Tom both served overseas as officers with the Canadian
Corps of Engineers, George with the rank of major, but to Joe
this war was as irritating an inconvenience as the First World War
had been. "I hope by the time this war is over," he writes dyspep-
tically to a friend, "that we shall have found some terrace between
autocratic tyranny and democratic waste and riot, on which civilization can have some chance of existing."

It was Dollie's turn now to be "away." She no longer knew
Joe, or anyone, but he'd sit by her chair, affectionately stroking
her hair. Later he said: "It was like a man standing on the shore
of a lake and seeing the person dearest to him drown, but could
do nothing to help." In August 1945, Dollie suffered a cerebral
thrombosis and slipped into a coma; she died, at seventy-five, on
October 14.

Like an explorer trudging ahead as his companions drop in
their tracks behind him, Joe expropriated Dollie's nurses, Ella
Parker and Mary Sinclair, as his own, and when his chauffeur, Fred
Wells, died, he assigned the additional job to Miss Sinclair. Her
most difficult task was to drive him periodically to Kirkland Lake,
a ten-hour trip, with meal stops, each way. Joe's visits gave the
mine executives fits, since, even after the age of ninety, and suffering from severe chronic chest pains, he insisted on descending
nearly two miles to the bottom of the shaft in his wheelchair. Joe
had nothing to do with running the mine, but he relished reading

his president's report to the annual shareholders' meeting, and spent every morning in his Toronto office dictating letters.

Most letters were to old colleagues in England and the United States, but Joe launched two concerted publicity blitzes to inflate his own reputation. First, he tried to persuade newspapers and politicians that he, not Prime Minister Sir Wilfrid Laurier, had created the famous phrase "the twentieth century belongs to Canada." Joe's evidence, lengthy, commonplace platitudes quoted by the Dawson *News* on January 1, 1901, was unanimously rejected. Then, he claimed credit for being the first to discover oil in Alberta. This too was absurd: the Athabasca oil sands had been well known for decades before Joe Tyrrell came on the scene, and Joe's cursory examination of tarry sand in a shallow pit north of Edmonton in 1893 did not make it an oil well.

Joe did admit, half jokingly, "Our country contains so many minerals that I often wonder how I missed so many." Indeed, he did. But then, so did his contemporaries: geology, as a science, had been as primitive as their tools. And in a letter to a geologist friend, Joe expressed regret over his bad temper: "When I was young I thought it was my duty to correct them [fallacies] but in that I was mistaken for it lead [*sic*] to personalities which were not intended."

This may have been a reference to a long quarrel over the Keewatin glacier with his old American friend and mentor, Warren Upham, and a school of geologists who contended that Keewatin was merely a "dome" within the larger Laurentide ice-sheet. Even more serious doubt was cast on the existence of Joe's Patrician glacier. An internecine squabble with few echoes out-side geological circles, it didn't stop the American Geographical Society from awarding Joe its highest honour, the Daly Medal, in 1930, and in 1947, Joe became the first Canadian since Sir William Logan to receive the London Geological Society's pres-tigious Wollaston Medal, an honour that elevated him to the exalted company of Sir Charles Lyell and Louis Agassiz. The

recognition was extraordinary in view of the fact that Joe's relatively brief, controversial career with the Geological Survey of
Canada had ended fifty years earlier. But Joe had cultivated friendships with the society's fellows on his frequent trips to London,
and he had rescued Sir William Logan's medals, including the
Wollaston, by buying them from a second-hand dealer and, some
years later, donating them to the Geological Survey of Canada.

Would Joe have been so celebrated had he been poor, and
out of the public eye? Millionaire mine owners, vilified by Socialists and Communists, especially among their own employees, were
regarded as fairy tale heroes by the public. Joe had built his own
reputation on the outstanding work of his colleagues: Dawson
and McConnell's discovery of coal and dinosaur fossils in Alberta;
Lawrence Lambe and Charles Sternberg's subsequent excavation
of an astonishing dinosaur graveyard in southeastern Alberta;
McConnell's research in the Klondike; Robert Bell's exploration
of Lake Athabasca and his encyclopedic knowledge of Hudson
Bay; D.B. Dowling's years of patient collaboration on Lake
Winnipeg and in northwestern Manitoba; Warren Upham's identification of Lake Agassiz . . . yet they were forgotten. Joe never
acknowledged them. Now they were all dead.

Joe Tyrrell seemed to be blessed with immortality. God
was dead, or at least confined to the churches, and by the 1940s
Darwin's theory of evolution, no longer atheistic heresy, was
taught in the schools. Joe's Keewatin glacier was prominently
marked on Canadian geological maps, along with Lake Agassiz,
and dinosaurs had caught the public's fancy: the skull of *Laelaps
incrassatus* that Joe had so ineptly excavated in 1884 had been
grandly christened *Albertosaurus* to commemorate the birth of the
province. Hollywood had made a popular movie, *The Trail of '98*,
of Robert Service's novel, and almost every Canadian, it seemed,
had seen Robert Flaherty's documentary film about the Hudson
Bay Inuit, *Nanook of the North*. In the early 1950s, Richard
Harrington's dramatic, heart-rending photographs and Farley

"Starving Padleimiut woman in camp at South Henik Lake, February, 1950." In the winter of 1950, Richard Harrington took dramatic portrait photographs of the destitute descendants of Ahyout and Kakkuk. The woman, Keenaq, rubs noses with a child, Keepseeyuk. (LAC, Richard Harrington fonds, PA-112083)

Mowat's passionate books, *People of the Deer* and *The Desperate People*, brought the Padleimiut (Caribou or Willow) Inuit international renown: the dying old woman, Arnalukjuak, in Harrington's photo may have danced by the Kazan River with Tyrrell and Ferguson in 1894. By 1954, Distant Early Warning radar stations had been strung across the Arctic for fear of a Soviet nuclear attack, and amateur canoeists were following Tyrrell's routes across the Barren Grounds; in 1955, an American, Arthur Moffatt, died running a rapid on the Dubawnt River, as the name is spelled today. Baker Lake was a permanent settlement, with an airport.

Joe Tyrrell became a cult figure. He never told a tale (or spelled a name) the same way twice, or let facts interfere with a good story, but, perhaps in deference to his age and fame, his charm, or his intimidating presence, everything he said was taken at face value: his long life had been so remarkable, it seemed mean-spirited to question his discrepancies, challenge his accuracy, or express a critical opinion. Canada's myth-makers wanted a living hero. Sir John A. Macdonald, Chief Crowfoot, Sam Steele of the Mounted Police, Sir William Mackenzie, Sir Harry Oakes – all had become legends, and Joe Tyrrell *had known them!*

Who else still alive had ridden the CPR tracks to the end of steel in 1883, crossed the Rockies on foot, and wandered the prairies before and after the 1885 Rebellion? This courtly, quiet old man in the expensive three-piece suits had driven dog teams, run rapids in birchbark canoes, camped in caribou-skin tents, and nearly died of starvation and exposure. As Harold Innis wrote to Joe, "Personally, I have felt that you have reached and surpassed the place held by your hero David Thompson as Canada's first geographer."

Showered with honorary doctorates, awards, and life memberships in a score of societies, Dr. Tyrrell, admiringly called the "Laird of Agincourt," or "The Father of Mining in Manitoba," was profiled in the press, interviewed on radio and television, and carried from banquet to banquet like an icon. Joe was too deaf to hear speeches, even with his hearing aid, and he could

"J.B. Tyrrell at ninety-five." From a bibliography compiled by his grand-daughter, Mary Edith Dalton. (CHP, James W. Tyrrell collection)

barely tell a person from a tree, but his smile was benevolent, his mind clear, and his physique splendid for a man in his nineties. As Conservative politicians revived Canada's northern vision, vaporous as the chimera that had enticed Martin Frobisher across the North Atlantic in the sixteenth century, a story in *The Beaver* history magazine in 1952 elevated Tyrrell of the North to "Tyrrell of Canada."

Privately, Joe was not treated with the deference he felt was his due. His middle-aged children and their families were attentive, and Joe was gentle and charming with women, but his sons never lived up to his expectations; the Laird of Agincourt did not include George, as strong-minded as his father, in interviews with reporters, or praise him publicly for having made the Tyrrell apple orchard a success. Then, in June 1954, Joe received an insulting letter from the lawyer for the Kirkland Lake Gold Mine, William Walton. Citing reduced income from the mine, and the cancellation of dividends, Walton suggested to the ninety-five-year-old president, "It would assist if you accept chair of the board at a reduced stipend." Kicked out as president of his own mine!

Thirty years had passed since Joe risked everything on his theory that a fabulous motherlode lay two thousand feet beneath the surface of the Kirkland Lake Gold Mine. He had been wrong, although he never publicly admitted it, but even so the mine, burrowing ever deeper, had found enough gold to produce an average of $1 million a year, and had paid out nearly $6 million in dividends. Chicken feed compared to Lake Shore and others, but nothing to be ashamed of. Yet as Joe became too physically incapacitated and professionally out of touch to fulfill his duties as president, he could not bring himself to relinquish at least nominal control. Why, he had a brand new RCA hearing aid, and Miss Parker could write for him!

Joe's title was not the issue: the mine executives were used to working around him. The key words in Walton's letter were *at a reduced stipend.* The mine was economizing, cutting costs, cancelling dividends. Was the gold petering out? Was the

Kirkland Lake Gold Mine washed up? A hole with nothing in it? Was he ruined?

The next year, new investors bought control. Joe was booted out as president, director, and chair of the board. He gleefully sold all his Kirkland Lake Gold Mine stock: INCO, Eldorado, Noranda, and Hudson Bay Mining & Smelting were much better investments. Increasingly housebound, Joe played the stock market and fiddled with his will. His assets as of December 1956 were $361,006.95. Almost all of it was in stocks, except for his farm, worth $60,000, adjacent to the Agincourt orchard. He'd given the orchard to George, who had run it for thirty years, and in his will Joe divided $200,000 equally between Mary and Tom. Small bequests went to grandchildren, friends, and loyal employees: his nurse and companion, Ella Parker, received six hundred shares in Noranda mines. Joe grew too blind to read, and reluctantly gave up going to his office, but he received callers and dictated long, chatty letters from his bed. In the spring of 1957, he was too weak to go to the orchard in apple blossom time; he gradually lost consciousness and died, at ninety-eight, on August 26.

Six weeks later, on October 4, the Soviet Union launched the world's first satellite, Sputnik 1, into outer space. Joe would have liked that.

NOTES AND SELECTED SOURCES

The primary source for this book is the extensive Tyrrell archive in the Thomas Fisher Rare Book Library at the University of Toronto (TFRBL). The collections of Joseph Burr Tyrrell, his brother, James Williams, and their father, William, include correspondence, published articles, field notes, newspaper clippings, scrapbooks, business and legal documents, photographs, maps, and unpublished manuscripts. The J.B. Tyrrell collection contains the letters of his wife, Mary Edith "Dollie" Carey Tyrrell. Additional material relating to the family is in the collections of the Community History Project Tyrrell Collection, Toronto, and Mrs. Katherine Stewart and John Tyrrell.

There are two published biographies of J.B. Tyrrell: *A Canadian Geologist*, by W.J. Loudon, Macmillan, 1930, and *Northern Vagabond*, by Alex Inglis, McClelland & Stewart, 1978. A brief biography of William Tyrrell, *William Tyrrell of Weston*, by Edith Morrison and J.E. Middleton, was published by J.B. Tyrrell in 1937. Written long after William's death, it is highly imaginative. *I Was There*, a memoir by Edith Tyrrell, was published by the Ryerson Press in 1938.

Incomplete early records of the Geological Survey of Canada (RG 45) are in Library and Archives Canada, Ottawa (LAC).

Basic sources for information on Canadian historical figures and events are *The Dictionary of Canadian Biography*, University of Toronto Press (prior to 1940), and *The Canadian Encyclopedia*, McClelland & Stewart, both available online.

INTRODUCTION

The quotes relating to Frobisher are from *The Three Voyages of Martin Frobisher*, a reprint of the first edition of *Hakluyt's Voyages*, with additional related documents, edited by Richard Collinson, Hakluyt Society, London, 1867.

Vivid accounts of the expeditions of both Sir John Franklin and James Knight are provided by two books by Owen Beattie and John Geiger, *Frozen in Time: Unlocking the Secrets of the Franklin Expedition*, Western Producer Prairie Books, Saskatoon, 1987, and *Dead Silence: The Greatest Mystery in Arctic Discovery*, Viking, 1993. Overviews of the history of Arctic exploration are found in *Discovery of the North*, by Daniel Francis, Hurtig, 1986, and *The Arctic Grail*, by Pierre Berton, McClelland & Stewart, 1988. An excellent anthology of early overland travel is *Canadian Exploration Literature*, edited by Germaine Warkentin, Oxford University Press, 1993.

Sir Charles Lyell describes Lake Ontario's beaches, as well as the formation of Niagara Falls, in his *Travels in North America*, published in New York in 1845. Lyell, the most respected geologist of the Victorian age, was an eloquent advocate for Earth's antiquity and mutability; his *Principles of Geology*, frequently revised, was a standard text. For basic terminology and geological history I consulted *The Geological Evolution of North America*, by Thomas H. Clark and Colin W. Stearn, Ronald Press, New York, 1968. Bruce Greenfield analyzes the "cult of expansion" in *Narrating Discovery: The Romantic Explorer in American Literature, 1790–1855*, Columbia University Press, NY, 1992.

CHAPTER ONE

Captain John Palliser, an Irish gentleman and big-game hunter, led the first British scientific expedition across the North-West to the Pacific Ocean between 1857 and 1860. The map was published by the British government in 1863 as part of *The Journals, Detailed Reports, and Observations Relative to the Exploration by Captain Palliser*.

Joe Tyrrell's field notes are in TFRBL. George M. Dawson's "Private Diary" for 1883 is in the Dawson collection, McGill University Archives, his field notes in the Geological Survey archives, LAC. *The Life of George Mercer Dawson*, a brief biography compiled by a niece, Lois Winslow-Spragge, was published in 1962. Stunted and malformed by a childhood illness, Dawson was a tireless traveller whose expertise included anthropology and botany. As a member of the United States–Canadian boundary commission, 1873–74, Dawson noted how glacial activity had shaped the landscape of the area. His *Report on the Geology and Resources of the Region in the Vicinity of the Forty-Ninth Parallel, from Lake of the Woods to the Rocky Mountains* (1875) formed the foundation for the Geological Survey's subsequent work in the North-West.

Pierre Berton tells the story of the building of the CPR in three books, *The National Dream* (1970), *The Last Spike* (1971), and *The Great Railway Illustrated* (1972), all published by McClelland & Stewart. '

A History of Alberta, by James Macgregor, Hurtig, 1972, gives a comprehensive overview of this period.

Two of Sir William Dawson's most influential and popular books were *The Origin of the World According to Revelation and Science*, Montreal, 1877, and *The Story of the Earth and Man*, London, 1883. Dawson gives a knowledgeable portrait of lush Devonian forests, Jurassic seas swarming with animals, and "gigantic pulsations in the thick hide of mother earth," while declaring that man, "a Son of God," was created in a post-glacial Garden of Eden about six to seven thousand years ago. Sir William Dawson died in 1899.

CHAPTER TWO

Reading the Rocks: The Story of the Geological Survey of Canada, 1842–1972, by Morris Zaslow, Macmillan, 1975, is an informative, entertaining official history that focuses on controversies and personalities. The *Life of Sir William Logan*, by Bernard J.

Harrington, was published in Montreal in 1883. Joe bought a copy immediately. Logan's self-description is in Suzanne Zeller's excellent *Inventing Canada: Early Victorian Science and the Idea of a Transcontinental Nation*, University of Toronto Press, 1987. Logan retired to Wales after leaving the Survey.

Rideau Hall: An Illustrated History of Government House, Ottawa, by R.H. Hubbard, McGill-Queen's, 1977, contains profiles of the Lansdownes and other governors general of Tyrrell's time. This period is also covered in *Ottawa, An Illustrated History*, by John H. Taylor, Lorimer, 1986. *Canadians on the Nile, 1882–98*, by Roy MacLaren, UBC Press, 1978, describes the impact of the Khartoum expedition on Canada.

The rivalry between E.D. Cope and O.C. Marsh is examined in *The Fossil Feud*, by Elizabeth Noble Shor, Exposition Press, NY, 1974. *The Life of a Fossil Hunter*, by Charles H. Sternberg, Jensen, 1931, describes the Sternberg family's methodology and field-work. *The Dinosaur Hunters*, by Deborah Cadbury, HarperCollins, 2000, tells how the scramble for fossils began in England, with equal venom, early in the nineteenth century.

James Hector's report is included in Palliser's *Journals, Detailed Reports and Observations . . .* Hector, later Sir James, went on to a distinguished geological career in New Zealand. Alexander Isbister, the British-educated Metis son of a Hudson's Bay Company fur trader, deserves credit for alerting Britain and Canada to the existence of "a vast coalfield, skirting the base of the Rocky Mountains for a great extent, and continued probably far into the Arctic Sea," in a lecture to the Geological Society of London in 1855.

Joe's dinosaur skull is in Canada's National Museum of Nature, Ottawa. Skeletons and replicas of *Albertosaurus* and numerous other dinosaurs subsequently unearthed in the bad-lands of the Red Deer River are on display at Alberta's world-renowned Royal Tyrrell Museum of Palaeontology and research centre in Drumheller, near the coal field Joe discovered. In 1936, Joe vaguely described the site of his dinosaur excavation as

Section 14, township 29, range 21, west of the 4th meridian. It has never been found.

CHAPTER THREE

"Dinosaurs and Coal in the Red Deer Country, Alberta, Canada," by J.B. Tyrrell, was published in the April 20, 1923, issue of *Science*. *Reminiscences Among the Rocks*, by Thomas C. Weston, Toronto, 1899, is a jolly, imaginative memoir. Dinosaur Provincial Park, a World Heritage Site, encompasses the dinosaur graveyard.

The Temptations of Big Bear, a novel by Rudy Wiebe, McClelland & Stewart, 1973, tells the story of Big Bear's Cree and the North-West Rebellion from their point of view; Major Charles Boulton gives the eastern Canadian homesteader's perspective, including an account of General Strange's column, in his *Reminiscences of the North-West Rebellions*, published in Toronto, 1886. It is tempting to imagine that at Morley, Joe Tyrrell met a young Stoney named George McLean, later the famous, picturesque chief Tatanga Mani, Walking Buffalo. A biography by Grant MacEwan, *Tatanga Mani*, Hurtig, 1969, gives a sympathetic portrait of the Stonies of this era.

Butler's visit to Rocky Mountain House is described in *The Great Lone Land*, Hurtig, 1968, Paul Kane's in his memoir *Wanderings of an Artist*, London, 1859. *Buffalo Days and Nights* was published by the Glenbow–Alberta Institute in 1976.

Senator Hardisty's Prairies, 1849–1889, by J.G. MacGregor, Western Producer Prairie Books, 1978, tells the dramatic story of the North-West during Hardisty's career. Hardisty was appointed to the Canadian Senate in 1888.

The historical spelling of Kootanie reflects the usage at the time.

"'To be fit for publication': The Editorial History of David Thompson's *Travels*, 1840–1916," by William E. Morrow, Papers of the Bibliographical Society of Canada, Fall 2001, is a definitive account of the manuscript's recovery and turbulent pre-publication history. Joe Tyrrell's files on his Thompson research, drafts, and letters are in both TFRBL and the National Archives of Canada (MG 30, D 49). Thompson's original manuscript is in TFRBL, his journals in the Archives of Ontario, Toronto. His large map is on display in the Archives' reception area.

CHAPTER FOUR

Louis Agassiz's quote is from an English translation of his speech, *Studies on Glaciers, Discourses of Neuchatel*, published by Hafner in 1967. Agassiz's subsequent career as a celebrity scientist in the United States is covered in *Louis Agassiz, A Life in Science*, by Edward Lurie, University of Chicago Press, 1960. Agassiz's expertise was in fossil fishes, and while his Ice Age theory created a sensation, the accuracy of his observations about boulders and moraines was undermined by his exaggeration and errors. He was wrong about the Alps, for one thing, and he later developed a theory that the Ice Age, a catastrophic act of God, had descended almost instantly, freezing animals in their tracks.

Sir William Dawson published his oft-repeated views in *The Canadian Ice Age* in 1893. The idea of an open polar sea predated Frobisher's voyages, and led to the obsessive search for the Northwest Passage. Warren Upham's seminal paper on Lake Agassiz, *The Geology of Central and Western Minnesota: A Preliminary Report*, was published by the Pioneer Press, St. Paul, Minnesota, in 1880.

Nationalist feelings were running high at the Geological Survey because the international boundary between Minnesota and Manitoba had not been marked until 1875, the result of a faulty map. After decades of bickering, the British and Americans compromised on the North-West Angle, a small thumb of American territory sticking up into Lake of the Woods between Manitoba and Ontario. The dispute, which involved David Thompson, is described in *A Good and Wise Measure*, by Francis Carroll, U of T Press, 2001, and in *Minnesota's Boundary with Canada*, by William Lass, Minnesota Historical Society Press, 1980.

Henry Youle Hind, a Toronto professor of chemistry and geology, published a two-volume *Narrative* of an exploring expedition he led to Red River and the Saskatchewan country, 1857–1858. This excerpt is from the Hurtig edition, 1975. Hind pointed out evidence of glaciation. *The Western Interior of Canada, A Record of Geographical Discovery, 1612–1917*, edited by John Warkentin, McClelland & Stewart, 1964, gives a comprehensive overview, including the contribution of Tyrrell and Upham. *Natural Heritage of Manitoba: Legacy of the Ice Age*, edited by James T. Teller, is a geological history.

Alexander Mackenzie's quote and an account of the wreck of the *Keewatin* are in an illustrated history of Lake Winnipeg, *Mistehay Sakahegan, The Great Lake*, by Frances Russell, Heartland, 2000. The newspaper clippings are in the J.B. Tyrrell papers, TFRBL.

CHAPTER FIVE

"Post-Tertiary Deposits of Manitoba and the Adjoining Territories of Northwestern Canada," by J.B. Tyrrell, was published in the *Bulletin of the Geological Society of America*, vol. 1, April 17, 1890. Warren Upham gave Joe full credit for his work in his definitive study, *Glacial Lake Agassiz*, United States Geological Survey, 1895.

Morris Zaslow discusses the feud at the Geological Survey in *Reading the Rocks*. Joe Tyrrell seems to have been no more scheming than most of his colleagues.

G.M. Dawson's speech, "On Some of the Larger Unexplored Regions of Canada," published as a pamphlet, set the course for a wave of exploration throughout the Arctic that established Canadian sovereignty over the land masses; the United States still claims that the Northwest Passage is an international waterway. William Gilder, the *Herald* reporter who accompanied Frederick Schwatka, published a book, *Schwatka's Search*, in 1882. It is one of several accounts, including Schwatka's own.

Thompson's account of his adventure on the Black River is from *David Thompson's Narrative of his Explorations in Western America*, edited by J.B. Tyrrell, Champlain Society, 1916.

CHAPTER SIX

Joe's optimistic view of the Barren Grounds reflected the enthusiasm of his old friend, Manitoba's Lieutenant-Governor John Christian Schultz. In 1888, while he was in the Senate, Schultz had chaired a committee to study the resources of the area, particularly the Peace and Mackenzie river basins. The entrepreneurial boosterism of the time is discussed in *The Opening of the Canadian North, 1870–1914*, by Morris Zaslow, McClelland & Stewart, 1967.

Sir John Richardson, a surgeon and naturalist, made three overland trips to the western Barren Lands, the first two, 1819–1822 and 1824–1826, with Sir John Franklin, the third, 1848–1849, in search of Franklin. His magnificently illustrated *Fauna Boreali-Americana* was published in four volumes between 1829 and 1837. In addition to his reports, Richardson published a history, *The Polar Regions*, Edinburgh, 1861.

James Tyrrell's role in the *Alert* expedition is described in "Report of the Hudson's Bay expedition of 1886 under the command of Lieut. A.R. Gordon, R.N." (TFRBL). *The Barren Ground of Northern Canada*, by Warburton Pike, Macmillan, New York, 1892, is Pike's account of his 1889 hunting trip towards Great Slave Lake. Pike's improvidence, stupidity, and contempt for the local people may have helped create a poisonous climate for the Tyrrells. Frank Russell's report, *Explorations in the Far North*, was published by the University of Iowa in 1898.

Samuel Hearne's epic *A Journey from Prince of Wales's Fort in Hudson's Bay to the Northern Ocean, 1769, 1770, 1771, & 1772*, was published in England in 1795, three years after Hearne's death. Excerpts in all chapters are from this source.

James Tyrrell's accounts are from his *Across the Sub-Arctics of Canada: A Journey of 3,200 miles by Canoe and Snowshoe*

Through the Hudson Bay Region, William Briggs, Toronto, 1897. An expanded edition was published in 1908.

Franklin's quote is from his *Narrative of a Journey to the Shores of the Polar Sea, in the years 1819–20–21–22*. Cannibalism is a theme in Canadian discovery literature; the *Voyages of Martin Frobisher* tells how afraid the sailors were that the Inuit would eat them.

Henry John Moberly published a memoir, *When Fur Was King*, J.M. Dent, Toronto, 1929. Born in 1835 in Penetanguishene, Ontario, on Lake Huron, Moberly had traded rum at Rocky Mountain House in 1854 and established Fort McMurray in 1870. He had been posted to Île-à-la-Crosse in 1889. Moberly spelled Ithingo's name Ethingo or Ethnigo.

CHAPTER SEVEN

Richardson's observation is from *The Polar Regions*. Hearne's is from his *Journey*.

F.W. Matheson's comments, with extensive observations about the weather and post routine, were written in the Fort Churchill post journal. It, and detailed post records, photographs, etc., are in the Hudson's Bay Company Archives, Provincial Archives of Manitoba, Winnipeg, Manitoba. Matheson was a temporary replacement for a post manager who had been invalided out to Winnipeg.

Joseph Lofthouse published a memoir, *A Thousand Miles from a Post Office*, in 1922. When Lofthouse encountered the Tyrrells, he was thirty-eight years old and had been a Church of England missionary in Churchill since 1883. He had met James Tyrrell in 1885 when the *Alert* docked at Churchill. Lofthouse built a small frame church and house, and he travelled extensively throughout his parish. He and his family left Churchill in 1898, "after years of suffering and privation." Lofthouse became Bishop of Keewatin with his headquarters in Kenora, Ontario. In 1900, he took part in James Tyrrell's expedition from Great Slave Lake along the Thelon River to Chesterfield Inlet.

The Canadian Journal of Lady Aberdeen, 1893–1898, was published by the Champlain Society, Toronto, 1960. An observant, opinionated reformer, Ishbel Aberdeen played an important, if socially radical, role as her husband's partner. Her Canadian legacy is the Victorian Order of Nurses.

Robert Munro Ferguson's handwritten diary is in TFRBL (MSS 3044). Ferguson left Canada with the Aberdeens in 1898. He died of tuberculosis in California in 1922. He was a better journalist and anthropologist than the public knew. Many pages from Joe Tyrrell's diary have been excised with a razor blade; a note in Joe's handwriting claims they were blank.

Samuel Hearne surrendered Fort Prince of Wales to Jean-François de Galaup, Comte de Laperouse, one of France's most brilliant and accomplished naval commanders. With no more than forty men, all civilians, Hearne faced three French ships, including a warship, and a force of nearly three hundred soldiers and gunners. There were no casualties. Laperouse later explored the Pacific Ocean, including the west coast of North America to the Arctic. Lost in a cyclone near Australia in 1788, he is a romantic figure in Jules Verne's *Twenty Thousand Leagues Under the Sea*. David Thompson, apprenticed to Hearne at Fort Churchill in 1784, was highly critical of his master's behaviour. In this case, Joe Tyrrell sided with Hearne.

CHAPTER EIGHT

Sir George Back's comments are from his *Narrative of the Arctic Land Expedition to the Mouth of the Great Fish River*, published in London in 1836. Fearless, intelligent, and efficient, Back was a talented artist and inexhaustible traveller. He is credited with saving Franklin's first overland expedition from annihilation by twice walking hundreds of miles on snowshoes for assistance. Back was criticized as vain and snobbish, perhaps because his expedition was a brilliant success.

Sleeping Island, The Story of One Man's Travels in the Great Barren Lands of the Canadian North, by P.G. Downes, was originally published in New York and Toronto in 1943. A new edition was published in 1988 by Western Producer Prairie Books, Saskatoon, Saskatchewan. Downes, a New England schoolteacher, made several trips to the North during the 1930s. Travelling with the bare minimum of equipment, Downes traced part of Joe's 1894 route, and encountered the Caribou Eskimo, rechristened the Padleimiut, or Willow People. *Sleeping Island* gives vivid, informed, and empathetic portraits of the landscape and the people.

Robert Peary achieved fame as a Greenland explorer more than a decade before his controversial expedition to the North Pole. Peary was a classic example of the megalomaniacal explorer. One of many biographies is *Peary: The Explorer and the Man*, by John Edward Weems, Boston, 1967.

A.P. Low's expeditions in Ungava and Labrador ranked with the Tyrrells' in extent, expense, and hardship. Later, Low was part of a Canadian expedition to assert authority over Ellesmere Island, and he served briefly as director of the Geological Survey.

CHAPTER NINE

Klondike: The Last Great Gold Rush, by Pierre Berton, McClelland & Stewart, 1958, is the classic history of the period from 1896 to 1899. *The White Pass*, by Roy Minter, McClelland & Stewart, 1987, portrays the pass Joe took in 1899. *Land of the Midnight Sun*, by Ken Coates and William Morrison, Hurtig, 1988, is an excellent general history of the Yukon. Lewis Green exposes the machinations around the concessions, including Treadgold's bizarre career and Joe Tyrrell's role with Bronson and Ray, in *The Gold Hustlers*, Alaska Northwest Publishing, 1977. *Lost Trail*, by Francis Cunynghame, Faber & Faber, London, 1953, portrays Treadgold as energetic, but stubborn, secretive, and an incompetent, dishonest businessmen. He died bankrupt.

Joe's letter to Robert Bell is from the R.A. Bell collection, LAC (MG 29B15). In Skagway, Joe seems to have run afoul of the legendary Soapy Smith gang, ruffians who preyed on the thousands of gold seekers until Smith was shot and killed in July 1898.

This edition of Martha Purdy Black's *My Ninety Years* was published by the Alaska Northwest Publishing Company, Anchorage, in 1976. An astute observer and active participant in Dawson's social, business, and political life, she gives a fair portrait of the "respectable" community. *Women of the Klondike*, by Frances Backhouse, Whitecap Books, 1995, is a comprehensive, realistic overview of women in Yukon society. Jill Downie tells Faith Fenton's remarkable story in *A Passionate Pen*, HarperCollins, 1996. *I Married the Klondike*, by Laura Berton, McClelland & Stewart, 1954, describes Dawson in its "indescribably drab" decline. Laura, a kindergarten teacher, arrived in 1907, after Joe Tyrrell had left. Dollie tells her Klondike stories in *I Was There*.

The Trail of '98 by Robert Service was published in Canada in 1910. Service was already world famous for his book of ballads, *Songs of a Sourdough*, published in Canada in 1907, which featured "The Shooting of Dan McGrew" and "The Cremation of Sam McGee." Service arrived in Whitehorse, Yukon, in 1904, and in Dawson in 1908. He left for good the following year.

CHAPTER TEN

The story of the mining discoveries is included in *Steam Into Wilderness*, the history of the Ontario Northland Railway (formerly the Timiskaming & Northern Ontario), by Albert Tucker, Fitzhenry & Whiteside, 1978. W.G. Trethewey's quote is from *Cobalt: A Pictorial History of the Development of Silver Mining*, by Doug Baldwin and John A. Dunn, Highway Bookshop, Cobalt, 1988. *Gold in the Porcupine!* (1976) and *The Town That Stands on Gold: Kirkland Lake* (1978), by Michael Barnes, Highway Book Shop, Cobalt, are informative popular histories of the area. Standard histories include *Free Gold*, by Arnold Hoffman, Rinehart, 1958; *Metals and Men*, by D.M. LeBourdais, McClelland & Stewart, 1957; *Three Miles of Gold*, by S.A. Pain, Ryerson, 1960. *The Railway King of Canada*, by R.B. Fleming, UBC Press, 1991, is a sympathetic biography of Sir William Mackenzie. The Canadian Northern Railway was incorporated into the Canadian National Railway.

Sunshine Sketches of a Little Town, by Stephen Leacock, was first published in 1912. The quotes are from a 1931 edition, McClelland & Stewart.

Joe's report, "Hudson Bay Exploring Expedition," was published in 1913 by the Ontario government.

"Mile Deep Through Gold," by Leslie Roberts, *The Canadian Magazine,* May 1932, tells the story of Joe's railway car encounter with William Sixt and their gamble on the mine. Readers likely didn't know that Joe paid Roberts $300 to $500, plus expenses, to write the story.

Blue Skies and Boiler Rooms: Buying and Selling Securities in Canada, 1870–1940, by Christopher Armstrong, U of T Press, 1997, deals in some detail with F.H. Deacon.

CHAPTER ELEVEN

Mr. Jackson was the celebrated Group of Seven painter, A.Y. Jackson. Joe took no interest in the fine arts, but Jackson mentions his encounter with Tyrrell, "the famous geologist," in his autobiography, *A Painter's Country,* Clarke Irwin, Toronto, 1958. May was Wilfrid "Wop" May, a celebrated pioneer bush pilot.

Joe's deafness is a bit of a mystery. Late in life, he claimed that scarlet fever had impaired his hearing at the age of five, but until he mentions a middle ear infection in 1925, there is no evidence in his notes or letters, including intimate discussions of hernias and hemorrhoids, to indicate any notable hearing disability.

The success of James Tyrrell's *Across the Sub-Arctic of Canada,* which went into three printings, may have created lasting tension between the two brothers. Dollie angrily denounced James for stealing the limelight from Joe; Joe did not contribute to the book, and declined to read the proofs. James's handwritten inscription on Joe's gift copy reads simply: *J.B. Tyrrell, from J.W. Tyrrell, Christmas, 1897.* Still, James spent a winter as Joe's partner in the Klondike, 1901–1902, and the brothers remained on friendly terms with each other and their oldest brother, Rob. The youngest Tyrrell, Henry Grattan, a prominent bridge engineer in the United States, became estranged from his brothers when he sued them, unsuccessfully, for a larger share of their father's estate. Joe took a generous, protective interest in Minnie's two daughters, Edith and Olive, and replied cordially to letters from their father, Lambert Lennox, but he never forgave his sister Annie for marrying him. Annie died in 1911, Rob in 1928, and Grattan in 1948. Their mother, Elizabeth, died in 1906.

Current geological maps confirm a glacial centre west of Hudson Bay within the Laurentide ice-sheet; the maps do not acknowledge Joe's Patrician glacier south of Hudson Bay. The newer maps extend the area once covered by glacial lakes or sea water, including a Tyrrell Sea, to include most of Ontario and the prairies. In *Sleeping Island*, P.G. Downes describes the area's post-glacial landscape from an aircraft:

> As we began to fly away from the lake and gain more altitude, we could see eskers of great length wiggling over the land in a south and southwesterly direction. They were very striking and intricate. Being of sand, and their embankment tops in many cases being exposed by the worn caribou trails, they stood out white and gleaming against the dark rock. . . . Though they were serpentine, they had a definite and pronounced trend. From the south and southwest they gradually began to swing more to the east and after an hour and a half of flight they were uniformly wiggling over the shell of the earth in an east-southeast direction.

In the North, Downes had heard of Ahyout, who died about 1895, and Kakkuk, who was still thriving in 1935, when Joe received this letter forwarded from the Hudson's Bay Post manager at Nuelton Lake:

We have also run into old Kakuk, Tyrrell's guide
down the Kazan and Ferguson rivers. He is still the
keenest and most energetic of his tribe although he
is now an old man. He knows what a corner on the
market is, and will buy up all the tea, tobacco, etc.
on hand if he thinks the Post cannot get any more
in for some time. Then he makes his fellow[s] pay.
His camp is still on the Kazan . . . where he has
quite an establishment – half a dozen outboard
motors, gramophones, accordions, two or three
wives and an organ which they say he plays well. He
claims to have been born in a church and that Jesus
Christ was his father. Certainly he knows and can
play many of the hymns.

In *People of the Deer*, Farley Mowat identifies a sorcerer he
calls Kakumee as Kakkuk's younger brother. According to
Mowat, the Padleimiut population had been tragically decimated
by epidemics, starvation, and relocation since Tyrrell and
Ferguson visited them in 1894, a judgment echoed by photographer Richard Harrington. Joe Tyrrell, however, was unsympa-
thetic to Mowat. Two recent illustrated books by David F. Pelly,
The Kazan (Outcrop, Yellowknife, NWT, 1991) and *Thelon: A
River Sanctuary* (Canadian Recreational Canoeing Association,
Merrickville, ON, 1996) bring the history and anthropology of
these areas up to date.

A Death in the Barrens, by George James Grinnell, Northern
Books, Toronto, 1996, tells the haunting story of Arthur Moffatt's
death in the context of Grinnell's own existential crisis as one of
the six men on Moffatt's expedition. Grinnell offers a rare insight
into the physical and psychological stresses that the Tyrrells and
their crews experienced, and overcame, with far fewer comforts.

Joe Tyrrell did have two detractors: historians A.S. Morton
and Richard Glover accused him of turning David Thompson, a

man of many shortcomings, into a plaster saint. Thompson's *Narrative*, however, spoke for itself, and Joe evaded the controversy that embroiled both Robert Peary, accused of lying about reaching the North Pole, and Vilhjalmur Stefansson, who repudiated his Canadian Inuit family and exploited everyone he met. Joe had also brought public attention to two of Thompson's contemporary surveyors, Peter Fidler and Philip Turnor. "Peter Fidler, trader and surveyor, 1769–1822," was published by the Royal Society in 1913, and the *Journals of Samuel Hearne and Philip Turnor* by the Champlain Society in 1934. Joe joked that he had "borrowed" Fidler's journal from York Factory in 1912, and remembered to return it to the Hudson's Bay Company in 1952.

Maplewood, the Tyrrell orchard, is now the Toronto Zoo. As a corporation, Kirkland Lake Gold is still in business, but its mine, originally called the Macassa, is adjacent to the one Joe owned. Joe's mine closed in 1960.

INDEX

Mackenzie, Alexander, 64–65, 92, 121, 150
Mackenzie, Sir William, 269–70, 274, 287
Mackenzie River valley, 64, 118
Mahdi (Muhammad Ahmad), 51, 67–68
Mah–Min (Stoney chief), 73
Mann, Donald, 269–70
Maple Creek, Saskatchewan, 15, *16*, 20
Marble Island, 167–70
Marsh, Othniel Charles, 53–54, 62
Matheson, F.W., *175*, 175–76, 327
Matonabbee (Chipewyan chief), 145
Maurice, François, 149, 174, 177
May, Wilfrid "Wop," 303, 331
McConnell, Richard G.: boards at Buchanan's, 105; children, 260; clothing burned in prairie fire, 44; finds bones of extinct mammals, 52–53, 62; his work builds Joe's reputation, 313; promotion at GSC, 236; surveys Klondike, 230–32
McDonnell (storekeeper), 67
McDougall, Dave, 33–34, 69, 76
McDougall, Elizabeth, 77
McDougall, James, 186–87
McDougall, John, 33–34, 69
McFarlane, Roderick, 186–87
McIntyre, Eunice, 286, 293
McKay, Alexander, 65
McKay, Angus, 96–98, 101
McKay, Henry, 95
McKay, William, 147
McKinley, James, 267
McLean, Donald, 114
McLeod, Roderick, 144
M'Clintock, Leopold, 4
McMartin, Duncan, 265–66
McMartin, John, 265–66
Mercredi, Joe, 127, 153
Meskinsot, James, 99
Meta Incognita (Baffin Island), 1–2, 8
Metis: as guides for Joe, 9, 120, 174; North–West Rebellion, 65–66, 103; Red River Rebellion, 51
Michel (Iroquois voyageur), 152
Michel Creek, B.C., 24
Middleton, Frederick, 66
Milk River, 10, 14–15

Miller, Willet, 272
Mississippi River, 79, 87
Moberly, Henry John (HBC trader), 120, 177, 219, 327
Moberly, H.J. (Chipewyan guide), 9, 152–53, 155, 219
Moffatt, Arthur, 315, 333
Moose Factory, Ontario, 299
Morley, Alberta, 56, *69*, 69
Morphy, Harry, 101
Morton, A.S., 333
Mount Nelson, 75
Mowat, Farley, 313, 315, 333
Mulligan (survey assistant), 57
Mulroney, Belinda, 237, 248, 259, 263
Munck, Jens, 4
Murchison Medal, 296

Nahathaway people. *See* Cree people
National Geographical Society, 294
Nelson, Robert, 4, 279
Nelson River, 4, 176, 278–80
New Liskeard, Ontario, 268
Nome, Alaska, 239
North American Trading Company, 242
North Kootenay Pass, 26–27
North Saskatchewan River, 55
North West Company, 79–80, 88, 295
North West Mounted Police: four officers freeze en route to Dawson, 299; harass Indians to stick to reserves, 13; and North–West Rebellion, 65–66; protect Indians from whisky smugglers, 19, 66; strict in Dawson City, 242
North–West Canada: Canada's claim to, 120; free or cheap land to settlers, 35, 68; increasing white population, 68, 77–78; Indian populations in 1870s, 6; purchased from HBC, 6
Northwest Passage, 4, 7, 9, 152, 298, 324, 325
North–West Rebellion, 65–66, 103
Norton, Mary, 199–200
Norton, Moses, 198–99
Norway House, Manitoba, 95, 176–77, 201, 214, 279